EXPLOSIVES FOR ENGINEERS

Fourth Edition

Other books published within the
Series on Mining Engineering

M.L. Jeremic:
Elements of Hydraulic Coal Mine Design
1982
(ISBN 0-87849-040-X)

Donald A. Trotter:
The Lighting of Underground Mines
1982
(ISBN 0-87849-041-8)

C.E. Gregory:
Rudiments of Mining Practice
1983
(ISBN 0-87849-042-6)

S. von Wahl:
**Investment Appraisal and Economic
Evaluation of Mining Enterprises**
1983
(ISBN 0-87849-048-5)

Mining – Science & Technology
1987
(ISBN 0-87849-059-0)

W. Durst & W. Vogt:
Bucket Wheel Excavator
1988
(ISBN 0-87849-075-2)

E.A. Wright:
Open Pit Mine Design Models
1990
(ISBN 0-87849-083-3)

A.-Z.M. Abouzeid:
Mineral Processing Laboratory Manual
1990
(ISBN 0-87849-082-5)

Series on Mining Engineering
Vol. 10 (1993)

EXPLOSIVES FOR ENGINEERS

Fourth Edition

by
Cedric E. GREGORY

BE, BA (*Adel*), BEcon, ME, PhD (*Qld*)
Chartered Engineer

Registered Professional Engineer

Professor Emeritus of Mining Engineering
in the University of Idaho, USA

Visiting Professor,
Virginia Polytechnic Institute and State University, USA

Visiting Professor,
King Abdulaziz University, Jeddah, Saudi Arabia

1993

TRANS TECH PUBLICATIONS

Explosives for Engineers
Fourth Edition

Distributed worldwide by

TRANS TECH S.A.

Trans Tech House
CH-4714 Aedermannsdorf
Switzerland

by

TRANS TECH PUBLICATIONS

P.O. Box 1254
D-38670 Clausthal-Zellerfeld
Germany

ISBN 0-87849-084-1

PRINTED AND BOUND IN MALAYSIA

Inscribed to the Memory of my son Paul:
Too young
and too good
to die

Acknowledgement of Photographs

Grateful acknowledgement is also made to the following who have given permission to reproduce photographs:
Austin Powder Co. (Figs. 28, 35, 48)
Canadian Industries Ltd. (Figs. 1, 4, 7–10, 12–16, 18, 19, 21, 24, 25, 32–34, 36)
DuPont de Nemours & Co. (Figs. 2, 3)
Hercules Inc. (Figs. 5, 6, 23, 27, 29, 30)
Jet Research Center, Inc. (Figs. 65, 66)
Vibration Measurement Engineers, Inc. (Fig. 20)

Preface to Fourth Edition

The need for a fourth edition has become starkly evident mainly because of the rapid development of emulsion explosives, the further expansion in precise forms of electric detonators, and of non-electric initiating systems, all in the interests of improved safety levels and blasting efficiency.

Furthermore, the spread of manufacturers' marketing interests into other countries and continents has become a complex international matter; and the pace of multi-national and intra-national take-overs has accelerated.

For this reason, I have decided to drop the regional titles (Australasia and North America) and to target this fourth edition to worldwide readers; and thereby to include technical information on blasting methods that have become of general interest to the blasting fraternity of the world as a whole.

The rapid growth of bulk emulsion blends has now predicated the need to revert to the distinction between capsensitive and non-capsensitive types; and this feature has been incorporated in this edition.

The international approach to this new edition has also underlined the need to express units of measure in SI units, although in practice I have retained Imperial units for minor aspects and for quoted passages. There should be no difficulty in converting these units with the aid of the table provided.

Again I invite members of the trade to comment or correct any misconception about their products; and for manufacturers in any country that are not cited in the book to contact me. Language and postal address problems have defied my attempts to present a more widespread coverage at this time.

I wish to thank the IME and those members who have provided recent information on their (North American) products; the Australian Standards Association for permission to reproduce their material expressed in Appendix D; and especially the ICI Australia Operations Pty. Ltd. on whose support and interest the First Edition was based.

30 Wiangaree Drive   C. E. Gregory
Toowoomba
Queensland 4350
Australia

Preface to Third Edition

With the passage of time and the contemporary development of some new techniques in rock blasting, it now seems expedient to up-date this book in the shape of a third edition.

This means that opportunity can now be taken to inject some of the recent approaches to improved safety and efficiency that are having a wide impact on some sections of the explosives industry. These are mainly associated with new initiation methods: new styles of electric detonators, and both electric and non-electric delay systems. Otherwise, opportunity occurs to bring other features up to date.

I have also now dropped the (somewhat theoretical) distinction I drew in the second edition between slurry blasting agents and slurry explosives. I find it difficult to maintain this slender distinction because AN/FO, slurries and emulsions are (from a convenient and expedient pragmatic viewpoint) so essentially similar in character, even though some appear to be rather more cap-sensitive than the current definition would allow.

Unfortunately, I still feel thwarted in being unable to change to **Système International** units of weights and measures. I had hoped to do so, but although Canada is ready, I find that the United States have not yet made any perceptible practical move in achieving metrication. So the best I can do at this stage is to offer a conversion table.

If any member of the trade wishes to correct or up-date any of the statements I have made about its products, I would welcome such help if sent to my address below.

My thanks are again due to the IME and its members for their continuing support; to Mr. *B. P. McHugh*, Chief Inspector of Explosives in Ottawa; and to Mr. *Richard A. Dick* of the U.S. Bureau of Mines.

C. E. Gregory

Preface to Second Edition

This new edition provides an opportunity to revise the original, to bring it up to date, and to give due emphasis to new techniques that have developed over the last five years. Unfortunately, I have been unable to predict the final outcome of new regulations currently under consideration by the U.S. Department of Transportation. However, I have dropped the term "Nitrocarbonitrate (NCN)" because it is meaningless, if not misleading.

I have always held that loose expressions and confusion in usage of terms are dangerous in this safety-conscious industry, especially among new trainees and neophytes generally. For this reason, I have made a conscious effort to crystallize some of these terms in the hope that manufacturers will be gracious enough to follow my example. For instance, I now use the term:

- **Detonating cord**, because 'detonating fuse' is liable to be con-fused with 'safety fuse'.

- **Boosters**, for the cast explosive units as supplied by the factories. They should not be called 'primers'. They do not become primers until armed with a detonator.

- **Slim boosters**, (for want of a better name), to distinguish these slip-on sheath type boosters from ordinary boosters.

- **Boostering charges**, for the free-flowing explosive material used to supplement cartridged charges in a quarry hole.

- **Minimum initiator**, to replace the term 'minimum booster'.

- **Capped fuse**, instead of 'fuse primer', which is an abomination.

It is recognized that the NFPA definition of blasting agent, based upon cap-sensitivity, has been a great advantage to the explosives industry. This definition seems to have been justified over about twenty years of experience, except that recent rapid developments in slurries have produced a grey area in the definition. To overcome this problem, it appears logical to include cap-insensitive slurries under the heading of blasting agents (SBA); and to regard cap-sensitive slurries (or those containing an explosive ingredient) as slurry explosives (SE). I have therefore taken the liberty to make this distinction in the book. Accordingly, slurry explosives are now dealt with, among other high explosives, in Chapter 3; and slurry blasting agents, as usual, in Chapter 4. There seems no other practical choice than to split slurries in this way, even though other properties of slurries are uniquely similar in character.

I had planned to switch to *Système International* (SI) units of weights and measures in this edition. Although Canada has moved in this direction, there has been no evident similar approach in the United States. Accordingly, I have been obliged to retain the use of English units.

In my classes over recent years I have been encouraged by the warm response to this book, not only by mining students, but also by civil engineering students. Otherwise, it is sad to note that so many civil engineering curricula of universities in the United States are devoid of courses in rock blasting, quarrying or tunnelling – subjects so vital to the civil engineering contractor.

As before, I am indebted to the Institute of Makers of Explosives and to their constituent members for providing trade literature. Where any of these members are not represented in the text, it is perhaps for lack of a sufficient postal address. They are encouraged to contact me for future reference.

C. E. Gregory

Preface to First Edition

North American professional engineers at graduation have had little opportunity to embrace much of the rudimentary lore and practice of explosives. Many of them gain little more knowledge throughout their professional careers. Yet, to my mind, the intelligent use of explosives represents an important tool in many fields of engineering endeavor.

Although a sound knowledge of explosives principles is basic to the mining engineer, and very important to the civil engineer, I find, as a university teacher (in three American Universities), that the competition for lecture hours in our already congested curricula precludes the opportunity to cover the ground, even superficially, in regular classes.

It thus becomes necessary to deflect too large a part of the work to private reading by students. This again is a pious hope in view of the aforesaid crammed curricula and the meagre hours available for reading. But it would be significantly easier if there were available some publication dealing with the elementary principles and practices of those particular explosives marketed in North America and used under American and Canadian conditions.

It is too difficult and confusing for students in the time available to sift and screen separate disconnected items of trade literature to gain a firm conception of modern explosives practice in terms of the particular brands of explosives materials available; and the trade hand books available are too voluminous and confusing, quite unsuitable for teaching purposes, and restricted to the particular manufacturer's range of products.

Hence, I have been inspired to write this "primer" (pronounced with a short "i") or elementary monograph on the basic principles, types available, and methods applicable to the North American scene.

I make no claim to have covered the subject exhaustively either in breadth or depth. On the other hand, I have had great difficulty in confining the material to basic principles and generalities.

Moreover, I admit that I am out of fashion in this present-day world in aiming to prepare a textbook that is both readable and understandable: by presenting the subject matter clearly and omitting the more sophisticated though worthy analytical material. But in this way the book should also be of substantial benefit to operators in the field, and to their trainees at various levels. Otherwise, for those who would wish to delve deeper, an extensive reference list is provided at the end of each chapter.

As a necessary aid in clarification, I have condensed and classified the bewildering multitudinous array of explosives products available (some quite anachronistic and obsolete), along with their trade names. Naturally, even the trade names themselves may become outdated in time; this is one of the perils of publishing "useful" material.

This book is written in terms of Canadian spelling; however, as a concession, the words ending in *-our* have been translated into American *-or* forms.

The title is perhaps a misnomer, unless one is prepared to add *English text*. Apologies are therefore offered to my French-, Dutch-, Spanish-speaking friends in Canada, Mexico, Central America and the Caribbean zone. The preparation of a Latin-American edition in Spanish and Portuguese is presently under consideration.

A glossary is provided in case certain technological terms are not well understood by the reader.

Although I have drawn largely upon my own observations and experience over many years as a miner, as a mining engineer, as a mine manager, and as a mining professor, I desire to acknowledge my indebtedness to Nobel (Australasia) Pty. Ltd., upon whose technical material the Australasian editions (and a good deal of this edition, where applicable) have been based.

My personal thanks are also due to Mr. *Harry Hampton Jr.*, Secretary of the Institute of Makers of Explosives, and to his Technical Committee, who have responded so magnificently in providing trade information from constituent members; to Mr. *W. B. Morrey* of Canadian Industries Ltd., to Mr. *B. P. McHugh*, Assistant Chief Inspector of Explosives of the Canadian Department of Energy, Mines and Resources, who reviewed the manuscript and proposed many helpful improvements; to Mr. *Clyde W. Eilo* (Hercules Incorporated) and to Dr. *J. J. Yancik* (U.S. Bureau of Mines) for reviewing my rough draft of Chapters 3 and 4 respectively; to Mr. *Richard A. Dick* (U.S. Bureau of Mines), upon whose excellent publications I have heavily drawn; to the National Fire Protection Association for the use of their material; to Austin Powder Company, Canadian Industries Ltd., E. I. DuPont de Nemours & Co. Inc., Hercules Incorporated, Jet Research Center Inc., and Vibration Measurement Engineers Inc., for provision of photographic and other material, not otherwise acknowledged; to Mr. *Albert E. Teller*, President of the International Society of Explosives Specialists; and to many others for their kind assistance and support.

Finally, I am indebted to the University of Queensland Press for permission to use certain material and diagrams appearing in my second Australasian edition.

C. E. Gregory

CONTENTS

PART I: EXPLOSIVES AND ACCESSORIES

CHAPTER 1   Introduction

CHAPTER 2   Rationale of Explosives Usage

CHAPTER 3   High Explosives

CHAPTER 4   Blasting Agents

CHAPTER 5   Initiating Devices

CHAPTER 6   Firing with Conventional Safety Fuse

CHAPTER 7   Electric Shotfiring

CHAPTER 8   Shotfiring with Detonating Cord

CHAPTER 9   Sequential Firing

CHAPTER 10   Special Forms of Explosives

CHAPTER 11   Practical Usage of Explosives

PART II   BREAKING GROUND WITH EXPLOSIVES

CHAPTER 12   Introduction

CHAPTER 13   Blasting Theory

CHAPTER 14   Special Techniques

CHAPTER 19   Blasting in Stoping Operations

CHAPTER 20   Blasting in Coal Mines

CHAPTER 21   Explosives in Agriculture

CHAPTER 22   Laws Relating to Explosives

Appendices

Glossary of Terms

Index

PART I

EXPLOSIVES AND ACCESSORIES

ABBREVIATIONS

AWG	American Wire Gauge
FGAN	Fertilizer grade ammonium nitrate
ft	foot, feet
ft^3	cubic foot (feet)
ft^3/lb	cubic feet per pound
ft/sec	feet per second
ft^3/ton	cubic feet per short ton
g	gram(s)
g/cm^3	grams per cubic centimetre
gr/ft	grains per foot
in	inch(es)
lb	pound(s)
lb/ft^3	pounds per cubic foot
lb/in^2	pounds per square inch
lb/ton	pounds per ton
min	minute(s)
mm	millimetre(s)
msec	millisecond(s)
mWs/ohm	firing energy (milliwatt-seconds per ohm)
sec/ft	seconds per foot
USSS	United States Standard Sieve

CONVERSION TABLE

(To be read in conjunction with the list of Abbreviations on the previous page)

To convert from	to SI units	Multiply by
British Thermal Units (BTU)	kJ	1.055
BTU/lb	kJ/kg	2.326
Degrees Fahrenheit (°F)	°C	$°C = (°F - 32)/1.8$
Feet (ft)	m	0.3048
ft^2	m^2	0.0929
ft^3	m^3	0.0283
ft^3/lb	m^3/kg	0.0624
ft^3/sh ton	m^3/t	0.0312
ft/sec	m/sec	0.3048
Grains (gr)	g	0.0648
gr/ft	g/m	0.2126
Inches (in)	mm	25.40
in^2	mm^2	645.16
in^3	mm^3	16387.06
in/sec	mm/sec	25.40
Miles	km	1.609
Pounds (lb)	kg	0.4536
lb/ft	kg/m	1.488
lb/ft^3	kg/m^3	16.02
lb/sh ton	kg/t	0.500
lb/in^2	kPa	6.8947
Seconds (sec)	sec	1.000
sec/ft	sec/m	3.281
Tons, short (sh ton) 2000 lb	(tonnes) t	0.907
Tons, long (1 ton) 2240 lb	t	1.016
sh ton/yd^3	t/m^3	1.186
Yards (yd)	m	0.9144
yd^2	m^2	0.836
yd^3	m^3	0.7645

CHAPTER 1

Introduction

Definition

The most generally accepted definition of an explosive is expressed in the following terms:

> A solid or liquid substance or mixture of substances which, on the application of a suitable stimulus to a small portion of the mass, is converted *in a very short interval of time* into other more stable substances, largely or entirely gaseous, with the development of heat and high pressure.

The explosive material derives its disrupting force, when confined in a borehole in a rock mass, mainly from the strain energy (SE) creating radial cracking in the rock, and from the "bubble energy" (BE) representing the high pressure gases in expanding these cracks to the point of brittle fracture (see Chapter 2). These hot gases occupy many times the original volume and thereby exert high pressure on the surrounding rock.

The stimulus in the above definition may be provided accidentally by friction, impact, or heat; but under controlled conditions by the shock wave produced by a detonator incorporated in the explosive charge (see Chapter 5).

Historical

Gunpowder, or blasting powder (BP), was first used in the thirteenth century. Its first recorded use in mines was in Slovakia in 1627 [1]. Blasting powder was introduced into Cornwall in 1689, but its use did not become general until a safe method of ignition (by safety fuse) was invented by *William Bickford* in 1831.

Nitroglycerine (NG) and nitrocellulose (NC) were developed in 1846, but not used as explosives until *Nobel* introduced the fulminate detonator in 1867. In the same year *Nobel* made nitroglycerine safe to handle by absorbing it in kieselguhr, forming a plastic mass containing 75 per cent of NG. This was known as "Guhr Dynamite".

In 1875, *Nobel* followed the invention of dynamite by that of blasting gelatine (BG). This was a gelatinous mixture, formed by incorporating 92 per cent of NG with 8 per cent of NC. It is still one of the most powerful of the industrial explosives.

This important development was followed in 1879 by his invention of lower strength explosives by the admixture of sodium nitrate (SN) and other materials to NG and NC. A wide range of explosives based upon these substances has since been developed.

Other important developments include (a) low-freezing types of nitroglycerine explosive; (b) permitted (permissible) explosives for use in underground coal mines; (c) electric instantaneous and delay detonators; (d) detonating cord; (e) liquid oxygen explosives; (f) shaped charges (first propounded by *Munroe* over one hundred years ago); (g) binary (high energy) explosives, and (h) integral delay blasting systems.

In 1935, a canned variety of factory-mixed blasting agents, mainly consisting of ammonium nitrate in varying densities, was introduced in the United States; later, the development of "Akremite" in 1954–1955 gave an impetus to the "on-site" mixing of various types of blasting agents. Since then, there has been a phenomenal growth in the usage of this family of ammonium nitrate carbonaceous mixtures (generally known by the most popular type, AN/FO), giving rise to the recent development of slurries (water gels), and emulsion explosives.

Experiments conducted in Nevada and New Mexico since 1957 by the Project Plowshare team have successfully demonstrated the applicability of underground nuclear blasting for peaceful purposes.

Applications

Explosives are now employed in the following ways:

1. Military purposes:

For propellants in gun ammunition.

For rocket propulsion.

As a destructive agent in bombs, torpedoes, and grenades.

For demolition purposes.

For pseudo-civil purposes such as excavating, quarrying, road-making, etc.

2. Industrial purposes:

(a) *Mining*

By far the largest consumption of industrial explosives is involved in mining for the following specific applications:

For excavation of shafts, tunnels, headings, galleries, and general mine workings.

For recovery of minerals from mines and collieries.

For winning of non-metallic material such as limestone, ironstone, road metal, etc., from quarries.

For geophysical shotfiring (seismic blasting).

(b) *Civil Engineering*

For excavation of railway, highway and hydro-electric diversion tunnels.

For building and machinery foundations.

For road and railway formations in hilly country.

For general earthworks.

For submarine harbour development.

(c) *Agriculture*

For well sinking.

For excavating irrigation and drainage ditches.

For removal of tree stumps.

For forestry applications.

For sinking post-holes for fencing.

For boulder blasting.

For orchard management.

(d) *Mechanical-electrical*

For preparing machinery foundations.

For demolishing or adjusting foundations in an existing power station.

For breaking up heavy machinery in an existing power station.

For blasting transmission line pole-holes.

(e) *Petroleum Engineering*

For seismic prospecting.

For perforation of oil wells.

For stimulating oil flow.

(f) *General*

For avalanche and lava control.

To precipitate rainfall.

For rare medical applications.

The use of explosives has contributed largely to our present high standard of living by minimizing the arduous nature of rock excavation work and by increasing the productivity of such operations. Indeed, many operations now regularly carried out with ease would not be possible without the use of industrial explosives.

Furthermore, certain major classes of excavation work (of extreme importance in national development programmes), now considered economically impracticable with the use of conventional explosives, may possibly be effected in the future by nuclear blasting.

Manufacture

In the various countries, industrial explosives and/or components are currently being manufactured by the following major suppliers. For convenience, they are referred to later in this book by the code name appearing in brackets.

In the United States, they include the following:

Appalachian Explosives, Inc.	(APE)
AN/GEL International	(ANGEL)
Apache Powder Company	(Apache)
Atlas Wireline Services#	(AWS)
Austin International Inc.	(AustInt)
Austin Powder Company*	(Austin)
Baker Sand Control#	(BAKER)
H.L. & A.G. Balsinger, Inc.*	(Balgr)
Amos L. Dobly Company#	(Dobly)
El Dorado Chemical Company*	(EDC)
Douglas Explosives Inc.#	(DEX)
ECONEX Incorporated	(ECONEX)
EIT Corporation	(EIT)
The Ensign-Bickford Company*	(EBCO)
Explosives Supply Company, Inc.	(ESC)
Explosives Technologies International Inc.*	(ETI)
GOEX Incorporated*	(GOEX)
GOEX International Inc.#	(GINC)
D.C. Guelich Explosive Company#	(GLEC)
Hercules Incorporated#	(Hercules)
ICI Explosives USA Inc.*	(Atlas)
Independent Explosives Co. of Penna	(Indpt)
IRECO Incorporated*	(IRECO)

Jet Research Center, Inc.	(JRC)
Kinepak Inc.	(KPI)
Maynes Explosives Company#	(Mayex)
Mining Services International*	(MSI)
Mt State Bit Service Inc.#	(MSBS)
W.A. Murphy Inc.#	(Murphy)
Nelson Brothers Inc.*	(Nelson)
Nitrochem Inc.*	(NIT)
North American Explosives	(NAX)
Owen Oil Tools, Inc.#	(OWEN)
Pacific Powder Company	(Pacific)
E.I. DuPont de Nemours & Co. Inc.#	(DuPont)
St Lawrence Explosives Corp.*	(STLEX)
Schlumberger Perforating Center#	(SCHLM)
A.E. Sibley, Inc.	(Sibley)
Sierra Chemical Company*	(Sierra)
Slurry Explosives Corporation	(SLEX)
Southeastern Energy, Inc.	(SEN)
Southern Explosives Corporation	(SEC)
Talley Defense Systems Inc.#	(Talley)
Thermex Energy Corporation	(Thermex)
Trojan Corporation#	(Trojan)
Universal Tech Corporation	(UTC)
Viking Explosives & Supply Inc.*	(Viking)
Woodard Companies Inc.#	(Wood)
WYCON Chemical Company	(WYCON)

In Canada:

Austin Powder Canada	(AUSCAN)
Canex Explosives Inc.	(CANEX)
CXA Ltd	(CXA)
Explosives Technologies International Inc.	(ETCAN)
ICI Explosives Canada# (formerly Canadian Industries Ltd)	(CIL)
IRECO Canada	(Irecan)
Nitrochem Inc.	(Nitchem)
Titan Explosives Ltd	(TITAN)

In Europe:

Dynamit Nobel AG, Germany	(DYNAG)
Dyno Industrier AS, Norway	(DYNO)
East Bohemian Chemical Works, Czechoslovakia	(EBCW)
Eszakmagyarországi Vegyimüvek, Hungary	(EV)
Explosives & Chemical Products Ltd, U.K.	(ECP)
Explosives Developments Ltd, U.K.	(EDL)
Explosivos Rio Tinto SA, Spain	(ERT)
ICI Explosives International, U.K.	(ICIXI)
Irish Industrial Explosives Ltd, Ireland	(IIE)
Italesplosivi, Italy	(ITPL)
Kemira Oy, Finland	(Kemira)
Kimit AB, Sweden	(KIMIT)
KOPEX Export-Import Co., Poland	(KOPEX)
Kösponti Banyaszati Fejlesztési Intézet, Hungary	(KBFI)
Mechanikai Müvek, Hungary	(MECH)
Nitro Bickford, France	(NBK)
Nitrokémisi Ipartelepek, Hungary	(NKI)
Nitro Nobel AB, Sweden	(Nitro)
Nobel Explosifs, France	(NEF)
Nobel's Explosives Company, U.K.	(Nobex)
Norsk Hydro Research Centre, Norway	(NHRC)
Peremartoni Vegyipari Vallalat, Hungary	(PVV)
Schaffler & Co., Austria	(SCH)
SEI Societa Esplosivi, Italy	(SEI)
Société des Explosifs Titanite, France	(Titanite)
Société Suisse des Explosifs, Switzerland	(SSE)
Syndicat des Fabricants d'Explosifs, France	(SFE)
Vitezit, Yugoslavia	(VTZ)
Wasagchemie Sythen GmbH, Germany	(WASAG)
Westspreng GmbH, Germany	(WEST)

In Australia:

CBS Explosives Pty Ltd	(CBS)
Dyno Wesfarmers Pty Ltd	(DPW)

ERT Explosives Australia Pty Ltd	(ERTEA)
ICI Australia Operations Pty Ltd	(ICIA)
Initiating Explosive Systems Pty Ltd	(IES)

In Africa:

African Explosives & Chemicals Ltd, South Africa	(AECI)
CADEX, Morocco	(CADEX)
Dantex Explosives (Pty) Ltd, South Africa	(DANTEX)
Expert Explosives, South Africa	(EXPERT)
Liberia Emirates Explosives Private Ltd, Liberia	(LEE)
Nitro Atlasco Nigeria Ltd, Nigeria	(NAN)
SMX Explosives Ltd, South Africa	(SMX)
West African Explosives & Chemicals, Liberia	(EXCHEM)

In Latin America:

Atlas de Mexico, Mexico	(ATM)
Britanite Industrias Quimicas, Brazil	(BIQ)
Cia Mexicana de Mecha para Minas SA, Mexico	(CMMPM)
ENAEX SA, Chile	(ENAEX)
Explo Industrias Quimicas e Explosivos SA, Brazil	(EXPLO)
Explobel Explosivos Ltda, Brazil	(EXBEL)
Explosivos SA, Peru	(EXSA)
Explosivos Cardoen Ltda, Chile	(ECL)
Explosivos Mejillones SA, Chile	(EXMESA)
Explosivos Mineros SA, Chile	(EXPLOMIN)
Explosivos Nacionales SA, Panama	(EXPLONSA)
Fabrica de Mechas SA, Peru	(FAMESA)
Ind Paulista de Explosivos, Brazil	(IPEL)
Lodos Industriales SA, Costa Rica	(LISA)
Química Sol SA, Peru	(QSSA)

In Asia:

Anil Chemicals Ltd, India	(ANIL)
Asahi Chemical Industry Co., Ltd, Japan	(ACI)
Atlas Taiwan Corp, Taiwan	(ATC)
Dahana Public Corp, Indonesia	(DPC)
Dyno Hutchinson Explosives, Hong Kong	(DHEX)

IBP Co. Ltd, India	(IBP)
IDL Chemicals Ltd, India	(IDL)
Indian Explosives Ltd, India	(IEL)
Japan Industrial Explosives, Japan	(JIE)
Makina Kimya – Nitro Nobel, Turkey	(MKNN)
Narendra & Co., India	(NACO)
Nippon Kayaku Co. Ltd, Japan	(NKC)
Nippon Koki Co. Ltd, Japan	(KOKI)
Nippon Oil & Fats Co. Ltd, Japan	(NOF)
Philippine Explosives Corp, Philippines	(PEX)
Saudi Chemical Company, Saudi Arabia	(SCC)
Tamilnadu Industrial Explosives Ltd, India	(TEL)
Wah Nobel Ltd, Pakistan	(WAHNL)

There may also be manufacturers in various other countries.

The names of firms appearing above with an asterisk (*) are Regular Members of the Institute of Makers of Explosives (1120 Nineteenth Street NW, Washington DC 20036, USA), a trade association formed in 1913 to promote better safety practices within the industry – hereinafter cited as the IME. Associate Members are denoted by #.

Apart from the manufacturers of explosive materials listed above, others supply a wide range of accessories to service the explosives industry, such as blasthole drills and appurtenances; blasthole dewatering systems; transport, mixing and loading equipment; charging machines and vehicles; blasting machines; blasting instruments; AN prills and nitroparaffins; seismographs; storage magazines; aluminium granules and powders; microspheres; blasting wire; and general blasting supplies.

The field of industrial explosives and blasting has spread across the world, with many international ramifications.

For instance, the ICI Explosives Group now embraces Nobel's Explosives Co. Ltd (Scotland), ICI Australia Operations Pty Ltd (Australia), ICI Canada Inc., ICI Explosives USA Inc., CXA Ltd (Canada), Atlas Powder Company (USA), African Explosives & Chemical Industries Ltd (South Africa), ICI India Ltd, IEL Ltd (India); and has interests in EXPLO (Brazil), PEX (Philippines), ATC (Taiwan), EMEX (Dubai), Atlas de Mexico, and Explosivos Mineros SA (Chile).

ICI is also connected with explosives plants in Oman, Liberia, Saudi Arabia (SCC), New Zealand and Zambia. It is now regarded as the largest explosives group in the western world.

Within this group, ICI Australia Operations Pty Ltd has also developed its local interests, with the formation of subsidiaries such as Incitec Ltd (to expand ammonium nitrate production), Techmaster Well Services Australia Pty Ltd (to extend its services to the petroleum industry), Initiating Explosives Systems Pty Ltd (IES), and the ICI Mining Services Technology Park at Cessnock, NSW.

The Dyno Explosives Group is a part of Dyno Industrier AS, a joint venture with Norsk Hydro. It now consists of four divisions (Norway, Sweden, IRECO and Asia Pacific); is closely associated with IDL Chemicals Ltd (India), Nobel Explochem Ltd (India), Oy Forcit (Finland) and SPEL (Portugal); and has joint ventures with Nitro Nobel Zimbabwe Ltd and Dyno Wesfarmers Pty. Ltd. (Australia).

Division Sweden covers the activities of Nitro Nobel AB, Dyno Nitrogen AB and Nitro Consult AB (now incorporated with Dyno Konsulent AS).

Nitro Nobel also holds a majority interest in a new joint venture company with the Yakutugol Combine and the Skochinsky Mining Institute, within the Russian coal industry. This new JV company is known as Nitro Sibir.

Division Asia Pacific comprises Nobel Philippines Inc., Tenega Kimia BHD (Malaysia), Nitro Nobel Pty Ltd (Australia), Nitro Nobel Johnson Bulk Explosives Pty Ltd (Australia) and Nitro Nobel (South East Asia).

DuPont has spread its activities into Central and South America, Asia, Australia and Africa; but DuPont itself has now become Explosives Technologies International (ETI). Except in Hong Kong, Mexico and Australia, DuPont's interests have recently been absorbed by IRECO.

IRECO has also absorbed the Hercules and ECONEX companies' explosives interests and now operates 35 production facilities in a wide international field, and licenses its patents and technology to thirty other major producers. IRECO has also recently acquired a range of independent explosives companies in the USA, including Independent Explosives Co. of Penna. IRECO itself is now part of Dyno Industrier AS.

ETI has licensed the SMX Explosives Division of SASOL Ltd, who can now manufacture and market ETI's Tovex MMAN-sensitized water gels throughout southern Africa.

Austin International Ltd has purchased Thermex Canada which will now trade as 'Austin Powder Canada'.

ERT Explosivos has six manufacturing centres in Spain, and has associate companies in other countries, viz. Compagnie Madacasse Commerciale (Madagascar); ERT Explosives Australia Pty Ltd (Australia); Explosivos de Trafaria (Portugal); Industrias Quimicas Altas Explosivos de Seguridad SAIC (Argentina); Mechas del Sur SA (Peru); Nigerian Explosives & Plastics Co. Ltd (Nigeria); Union Peruana de Explosivos SA (Peru).

The Ensign-Bickford Company and the Royal Ordnance (of British Aerospace) have formed a joint venture partnership under the name of North American Explosives (NAX).

Thermex Energy Corporation of Texas has recently acquired Gulf Oil Explosives and Nitrate Services Corporation; but its midwestern operations have recently been absorbed by Slurry Explosive Corporation (SLEX). SLEX manufactures a full line of Detagel and Slurran 900 series high explosives, Slurran 800 series blasting agents, Detagel Pre-split explosives and T100 2-component explosives, now under licence from Universal Tech Corporation (UTC).

Technical Service

All production operations are closely controlled, and rigorous tests are made at each stage of manufacture. The results of research into newer methods, better performances, greater safety, and more durable packaging media are constantly being applied.

Most manufacturers maintain a field technical sales service for their customers and industrial users generally. These representatives perform an excellent service and are readily available to help with technical recommendations, trouble-shooting, sales problems and the like. However, the mining, quarrying and construction industries should not lose sight of the fact that improved costs would be realized if their own engineers were better trained in the use of explosives.

A large number of blasting contractors and consulting companies offer their services to the explosives industry. Some of these specialize in demolition work and in ground vibration analysis.

In addition, a number of associations with a central interest in the explosives industry have been founded. Among these are:

In North America:
American Blasting Association
Center for Explosives Technology Research (New Mexico Tech)
Franklin Research Center, Philadelphia
Institute of Makers of Explosives (IME)
International Society of Explosives Engineers
International Society of Explosives Specialists
Montana Tech Blasting Laboratory
Soc d'Energie Explosives du Quebec.

Elsewhere:
Australasian Association of Manufacturers and Users of Explosives
Australasian Society of Explosives Engineering
Chinese Society of Engineering Blasting (CSTAM)
Chinese Society of Explosives Engineers
Committee for Industrial Blasting Technique, Hungary
Danish Federation of Explosives Engineers
Deutscher Spreng-Verband, Germany
Dutch Federation of Explosives Engineers
European Federation of Explosives Engineers (EFEE)
Explosives Society of Korea
Federation of European Explosives Manufacturers
Institute of Explosives Engineers, U.K.
Japan Industrial Explosives Association
Julius Kruttschnitt Mineral Research Centre, Australia

Norwegian Rock Blasting Society

Physics Research Laboratory (of Nitro Nobel AB)

Soc Nat des Poudres et Explosifs, France

South African National Institute of Explosives Technology (NIXT)

Swedish Detonic Research Foundation

Verband der Sprengbefugten Österreichs, Austria.

Conferences, seminars, field-oriented training programmes and blasters' certification courses are also conducted by various bodies, institutes, government departments and universities at intervals throughout the world.

DuPont Explosives Management Services has been formed to provide a consulting service offering comprehensive advice for mine and quarry operators. They include computer-aided blast design, noise and vibration control, project planning and management, and safety training.

Also, the ICI Explosives Group has developed a new spreadsheet-based microcomputer software programme to assist mine managements to compare various explosive products and to develop optimal blast results in open cut mines. Such a programme is designed to overcome tedious repetitive calculations to achieve optimal drilling patterns consistent with good fragmentation and other parameters. It is referred to as ICI Computer Blast Modelling, specifically a "Scientific Approach to Breaking Rock with Explosives" (SABREX). For more irregular blasting scenarios, SABREX 3 is used.

Precision Blasting Services of Montville, Ohio, USA and other firms provide computer software services to optimize the entire or major elements of the blasting operation.

The Julius Kruttschnitt Mineral Research Centre (JKMRC) at the University Experimental Mine of the Queensland's Sir James Foots School of Mineral Resources conducts an Advanced Blasting Technology project. The JKMRC has developed its '3 x 30 Software Program' for the rapid design and analysis of open pit blasts; coupled with its '8 Channel Blast Event Timer', which provides an easy determination of the actual in-situ performance of explosives and detonators. It has been awarded continuing grants from the Australian Mineral Industry Research Association (AMIRA) in support of the project. Sponsors include many Australian and international (mainly Chilean) mining companies.

The Noka Software Systems Inc. of Canada has also produced a line of Blast Computer Software, called 'BlastCalc'; as has Blast Dynamics Inc. (a subsidiary of Vibra-Tech), with its 'ProBlast System'.

Safety

In the interests of safety, various entities such as explosives manufacturers, government organizations, universities and other bodies conduct Safety Training courses, developed to meet the needs of all personnel in the explosives industry. Their courses are generally of a practical nature, and significant educational pre-requisites are not necessary. Many such courses are designed to provide Blasters' Certificate requirements.

In the United States, the Safety Alliance for Explosives (SAFE) has been formed to assure that the laws governing the manufacture, distribution, use and handling of industrial explosives are uniform, technically sound, and reasonable to provide safety to employees, users, the public and the environment, while at the same time maintaining the viability of the mining, construction, petroleum, agricultural and other essential industries that must rely on explosives for their day-to-day operations.

References

[1] Italesplosivi, *Gli Esplosivi* (History of Explosives) (Milan, 1982)

CHAPTER 2

Rationale of Explosives Usage

Characteristics

In order to fulfil the requirements of everyday modern industrial usage, an explosive should have the following characteristics:

1. It should contain a substance, or mixture of substances, which is sufficiently insensitive to be safe under all conditions of handling and storage, but is sensitive enough to initiate readily when required.

2. Upon initiation it must rapidly undergo chemical change, yielding gaseous products whose volume under normal pressure and at the high temperature resulting from the exothermic reaction is much greater than that of the original substance.

3. The reaction must be exothermic in order to increase the pressure.

4. The substance should be simple and inexpensive to produce from readily available raw materials.

5. It should have:

    (a) Adequate strength or power for the purpose required.

    (b) A high inherent velocity of detonation (except where excessive shattering is to be avoided).

    (c) A density suited to its particular application.

    (d) Good water resistance (or be specially wrapped and dipped to promote water-resistance).

    (e) Good fume characteristics.

    (f) No propensity to freeze or dissociate (e.g., by exudation of nitroglycerine) at the working temperature.

    (g) Suitable physical characteristics, depending upon the inclination of the borehole.

    (h) Good storage qualities.

Properties

The properties discussed below are weight strength, cartridge strength, velocity of detonation (VOD), sensitivity, density, detonation pressure, water resistance, and fume characteristics. These properties vary with different types and formulations of explosives as prepared by manufacturers.

The **Strength** of an explosive is related to its energy content and is therefore regarded as a measure of its ability to do useful work. However, it is not a good yardstick.

In the past, the strength of a particular dynamite type explosive was determined by comparing its capacity to deflect a ballistic mortar with that of Blasting Gelatine or TNT (see Glossary). In the trade, two ratings of strength are used, both related to the nitroglycerine (NG) content of various grades of "straight dynamites" (see later) as a standard.

For instance, equivalent **Weight Strengths** (lb for lb) of ammonia gelatines and ammonia dynamites are given the same percentage ratings (gradings) as those corresponding to the NG content of a straight dynamite. A 50% ammonia dynamite has the same strength as a 50% straight dynamite even though it contains much less than 50% NG. Actually, it contains ammonium nitrate (AN) in addition.

In the same way, the **Cartridge Strength** of a 50% ammonia dynamite has the same cartridge strength as that of a 50% straight dynamite. Since the specific gravity of straight dynamite is 1.4, the weight strength and cartridge strength of a given explosive are equal when its density is also 1.4; otherwise the relationship depends upon its density (see later).

In any case, *Dick* [1] has pointed out that the field performances of two different dynamites of the same weight strength may differ because of a difference in VOD. This shows that "strength" is not a useful parameter for the rating of explosive performance.

Some manufacturers rate their explosives on weight strength and others on a cartridge strength basis. Some do not even rate them at all in their literature, but refer to them under a trade name. Naturally, all manufacturers use trade names for their products, but many of these have little or no logical significance or consistency.

With bulk explosives such as blasting agents, the use of a ballistic mortar to determine strength (or available energy) is inapplicable.

Most manufacturers now use the Underwater Test Method, where a measured quantity of explosive is detonated at a specific depth in a pond of water of known dimensions. The explosive energy released by such an explosive charge in an underwater test can be recorded in two forms: Shock Energy (detonation pressure) and Bubble Energy (borehole pressure).

The strength of explosives is now also expressed on a different basis, relative to "Standard AN/FO", which has an assigned RWS and RBS value of 100. Standard AN/FO is defined as a mixture of prilled AN having a 1% inert coating and 5.7% diesel fuel, resulting in a product whose density is 0.84 and which has a deficient oxygen balance of 0.5%.

Another way of referring to the strength rating for bulk explosives is termed Relative Effective Energy (REE). This refers to the effective energy of a particular explosive related to that of Standard AN/FO. When compared on a mass basis, it is termed Relative Effective Energy Weight Strength (REEWS); or by volume, the REEBS.

The **Velocity of Detonation** (VOD) refers to the speed at which a one-dimensional detonation wave (see later) representing a shock front, travels through a charge of explosives confined in a borehole.

The VOD of an explosive depends upon various other factors, such as the density, the constituents, their particle size, the diameter of the hole (or charge), the degree of confinement, the coupling ratio and the size of primer.

Some manufacturers test under unconfined conditions, in which case the unconfined value is only about 75 per cent of the confined VOD. Values are best expressed in ft per second (or metres per second) when tested confined in a pipe of a specified diameter at 40 °F (4.4 °C). In general, the VOD increases with the diameter, but not linearly. With commercial explosives, the VOD ranges from 1,500 to 7,500 m/sec.

A new electronic instrument, the VODR-1, is a Velocity of Detonation Recorder that has recently been developed to record a range of parameters associated with the confined VOD of explosives in holes ranging from 20 to 445 mm in diameter.

Two areas of **Sensitivity** are recognized in respect of explosive properties. One of these is termed **Hazard Sensitivity** and relates to the "relative hazards involved in the formulation, handling, storing, and transportation of the explosive" [2].

The other is generally referred to as **Performance Sensitivity** since it measures three different aspects of reliability of performance of explosives under certain specified conditions.

One of these is termed **Initiation Sensitivity** – the ease with which an explosive charge can be detonated. Most cartridged high explosive charges (dynamites and gelatines) can be detonated when primed with a single No. 6 detonator (see Glossary). It is in the category of (insensitive) blasting agents that initiation sensitivity becomes critical. The threshold value of initiation sensitivity for a particular charge (under certain specified conditions) is expressed as the **minimum initiator** (or the minimum number of No. 6 caps) needed to detonate the charge.

The second aspect of performance sensitivity is usually distinguished by the name of **Propagation Sensitivity**, which is a measure of the ability of an explosive to support or reinforce a detonation that has already been created [3, 4]. Since the tendency for the detonation wave to fail or fade increases as the hole diameter is reduced, it has become customary to measure propagation sensitivity by the (minimum) **critical diameter** of a charge at least six diameters long that will support the detonation process once created [3, 4]. At a point below this value, a detonation wave cannot be consistently propagated, and a misfire (see Glossary) may occur; or otherwise the reaction may be incomplete, resulting in a poor blast effect and significant fume.

The third aspect of performance sensitivity is known as **Gap Sensitivity**, determined by the comparative length of air gap or discontinuity between two cartridges in a single charge [2]. It also relates to the distance between two adjacent blastholes in cases where *sympathetic detonation* could be a problem, or in a certain type of ditch blasting (by the propagation method), where it is an advantage. This phenomenon is peculiar only to (sensitive) high explosives such as dynamites and gelatines.

The **Density** of a particular explosive is expressed either in terms of specific gravity, or by cartridge count. Since the standard case (box or carton) in the United States contains 50 lb weight of explosives, it is conventional to quote the cartridge count as the number of $1^{1}/_{4}$ x 8-inch cartridges in a case; but in Canada and other countries, a 25 kg standard case is now used.

Explosives presently available range in specific gravity from 0.6 to 1.7, and with cartridge counts from 232 to 83 in the United States.

With free-running blasting agents, it is the loading density that is significant: the weight of material per ft of charged borehole of a given diameter; or otherwise in grams per cm^3. This measure will depend upon the degree of compaction achieved when loading. With wet holes, it needs to be sufficient to displace the water (see Appendix G).

The **Detonation Pressure** is a measure of the pressure in the detonation wave front. It is a function of the VOD and the density of an explosive, and is therefore a very important property, especially in hard rock. At the point where the detonation wave has just completed its passage through the column of explosive and the gases have expanded to fill the borehole and are available to commence their work, the borehole pressure is at its peak value [5].

Water Resistance, for dry boreholes, is not required; but for prolonged exposure to water, as in wet holes, an explosive needs to have very good water resistance to avoid deterioration or loss of sensitivity. The more gelatinous types of explosive have the better resistance to water. These are especially suitable for underwater blasting.

The **Fume Characteristics** of an explosive are of extreme importance when used in confined spaces as in underground mines.

Ideally, industrial explosives should be designed to produce gaseous products such as nitrogen, carbon dioxide and water vapour. In practice, some toxic gases such as mixed oxides of nitrogen and carbon monoxide (known collectively as "fumes") may be formed. These are extremely dangerous to inhale in certain concentrations [6].

The IME has established a Fume Classification Standard based upon the volume of poisonous gases emitted by a $1^{1}/_{4}$ x 8-inch cartridge when detonated under standardized conditions. High explosives may be classified under this standard as follows:

Class 1: 0 to 0.16 ft^3 per 200 g cartridge

Class 2: 0.16 to 0.33 ft^3 per 200 g cartridge

Class 3: 0.33 to 0.67 ft^3 per 200 g cartridge

Only those explosives meeting the requirements of Class 1 may be used in underground mines. For coal mines, the MSHA has determined that the volume of poisonous gases produced must not exceed 71 litres per 454 gm of permissible explosive (2.5 ft^3/lb). In any event, good ventilation is a necessary requirement; and the need to disperse the fumes from a blasted heading before miners return to work is a vital precaution.

Explosives in many countries are formulated with a low freezing point component to prevent *freezing* under the coldest weather conditions. Heated storage magazines are therefore unnecessary, even for slurries. Without this component, dissociation and exudation of NG and deterioration of the explosive would be likely to occur.

Testing of Explosives

A number of methods of testing or checking the various properties of explosives have been proposed or recognized in the past. The development of more sophisticated methods is constantly being applied as improved instruments and procedures become available. However, since testing is considered to be primarily a phase of the manufacturing process, details will not be offered in this book. A review of methods currently used by the U.S. Bureau of Mines has been prepared by *Mason* and *Aiken* [7].

Types of Explosives

The exothermic decomposition of an explosive produces exceedingly high gas pressures at the prevailing high temperature of the reaction.

Therefore the effectiveness of an explosive depends upon the amount of heat liberated.

Although the explosive energy is equi-directional, its rupturing effect is greatest in the path of least resistance.

If the explosive decomposition reaction moves through the charge faster than the speed of sound, it is termed *detonation*. If slower, then we have *deflagration*.

All high explosives and blasting agents detonate when properly initiated, whereas low explosives (black powder) deflagrate.

There are five main types of modern commercial explosive. One of these is the class of initiating explosives used only as a loading medium in detonators and detonating cord.

The selection of an explosive for a given engineering duty such as rock breakage may be made from the four other main types, viz.

  a)   high explosives (TNT, dynamite, etc., or others similarly sensitized/fuelled). All are cap-sensitive.

  (b) low explosives (blasting powder).

  (c) blasting agents (dry, slurries or emulsion types), or

  (d) binary, or two-component explosives.

1.   **Initiating explosives**, because of their high cost, are suitable only for *initiating* high explosive charges as detonating agents in small quantities. Upon initiation, they produce an intense shock capable of initiating a detonating wave in a charge of high explosives. These explosives are loaded as small pressed charges into copper or aluminium tubes to form detonators (q.v.), or as a core load in detonating cord.

2. **High explosives**, according to their composition, *detonate* at velocities of 1,600 – 7,500 m per second and produce large volumes of gases and considerable heat at extremely high pressure. The performance of such an explosive depends chiefly on the volume and temperature of the gases produced and on the velocity of detonation.

High explosives usually contain chemical components with a more or less unstable molecular structure, capable, on detonation, of molecular rearrangement into more stable forms of potential energy. Thus, the compound is capable, within its own volume, of being converted into gases at very high temperature and pressure. The entire products of the explosion should be gaseous. (Solid products would tend to produce smoke.)

As an example, the chemical change that takes place when nitroglycerine explodes is shown by the following equation:

$$4C_3H_5(NO_3)_3 \rightarrow 12CO_2 + 10H_2O + 6N_2 + O_2$$

Similarly, the typical chemical reaction which takes place when a mixture of nitroglycerine and ammonium nitrate is exploded is:

$$2C_3H_5(NO_3)_3 + NH_4NO_3 \rightarrow 6CO_2 + 7H_2O + 4N_2 + O_2$$

It will be noted that in each case, at the temperature of the reaction, all the products are gaseous.

3. **Deflagrating or low explosives** were the earliest type developed. This type of explosion is really a rapid form of combustion in which the particles *burn* at their surfaces and expose more and more of the bulk until all has been consumed.

Typical of these low explosives is Blasting Powder or gunpowder which is a mixture of substances having an affinity for oxygen with others which are rich in oxygen. The common form is black blasting powder which is a mechanical mixture of potassium or sodium nitrate with sulphur and finely ground charcoal.

In action, they are characterized by a *push*, rather than a *blow*, or a *lift* rather than a *shatter*.

Propellants in ammunition are low explosives. The slow gradual development of pressure in the chamber of a gun allows the projectile to issue with a high muzzle velocity without shattering the gun barrel. Since about one-half the products of combustion are solids, much smoke is formed.

$$20NaNO_3 + 30C + 10S \rightarrow 6Na_2CO_3 + Na_2SO_4 + 3Na_2 S_3 + 14CO_2 + 10CO + 10N_2$$

4. **Blasting agents** are mixtures "consisting of a fuel and an oxidizer, intended for blasting, not otherwise classified as an explosive, provided that the finished product, as mixed and packaged for shipment, cannot be detonated by a No. 8 blasting cap in a specific test prescribed by the Bureau of Mines" [8].

They are classified as "oxidizing materials" under the U.S. Department of Transportation (DOT) regulations (see Chapter 22), and are thereby exempted from the restrictive regulations necessarily applying to the transport of high (cap-sensitive) explosives. In

Canada, they are classified as "Explosives Class 2", and transport and mixing procedures are more closely controlled.

A blasting agent consists primarily of inorganic nitrates and carbonaceous fuels, and may contain additional nonexplosive substances such as powdered aluminium or ferro-silicon [1].

Blasting agents (of which the more generally known is AN/FO) are now extensively used for both surface and underground blasts. The relatively inactive AN, in a suitable physical form, can be mixed with fuel oil (in the proportion of 94:6 by weight), or other carbonaceous fuel. It will detonate at a velocity of 3,300 to 4,500 m per second (generally at a total rock breakage cost of about one-third to one-quarter of that of NG-based high explosives) according to the following general reaction:

$$3NH_4NO_3 + CH_2(X) \rightarrow 7H_2O + CO_2 + 3N_2$$

Apart from AN/FO, there are **slurry blasting agents** (SBA) and **blasting emulsions** which are of greater density, higher detonation velocity, and of very much greater water resistance. See Chapter 4 for further details.

5.   **Binary Explosives** are those consisting of two separate components, each intrinsically safe, but which can develop a high explosive power when mixed, placed and detonated. For details, see Chapter 10.

Classification of Explosives

Blasting agents are classified as "oxidizing materials" under the U.S. Department of Transportation (DOT) regulations and are therefore exempted from the restrictive regulations necessarily applying to the transport of high (capsensitive) explosives. In Canada, they are classified as "Explosives Class 2", and transport and mixing procedures are more closely controlled. But as from 1994, explosive materials will be classified in accordance with the rules laid down in Appendix H.

Mechanics of Detonation

Under the heading of "Deflagration and Detonation" *Clark* [9] states:

> "Explosives either react slowly, or deflagrate, or they may detonate. A distinguishing characteristic of a high explosive is that it detonates when it is properly primed and an explosion is initiated in it. **Detonation** is the description of the process of the propagation of a shock wave through an explosive, which is accompanied by a chemical reaction that furnishes energy to maintain the explosion in a stable manner. Black powder is a good illustration of deflagrating explosives while [high explosives] are representative of detonating explosives."

Although **high explosives** will burn or deflagrate if small amounts are thermally ignited, large masses (above the *critical mass* for any given explosive) will deflagrate progressively more fiercely until detonation takes place (without the actual presence of a detonator).

However, for proper and effective control, a charge of high explosive confined in a borehole is usually *initiated* by some type of **initiating explosive**, in the form of a **detonator** (see Chapter 5). The detonator is usually incorporated in a cartridge of high explosive to form a **primer**. The detonator itself is thermally ignited, if plain, by **safety fuse** (see Chapter 6); or if electric, by an electrical impulse.

The thermal ignition of the initiating explosive in the detonator is referred to as **detonation.** This is a reactive shock, caused by instantaneous exothermic decomposition of the initiating explosive, accompanied by rapid expansion of the reactive products, thereby producing a high pressure shock, or detonation, wave.

This shock wave proceeds along the high explosive charge with a *transient* velocity of detonation for some finite distance corresponding to a very minute interval of time until the main charge is initiated (by the high pressure and temperature of the gaseous products of the detonation reaction) at the *Chapman-Jouget* Plane [10] (see Glossary).

At this C-J Plane, the detonation wave is reinforced and propagated throughout the charge by the rapid exothermic decomposition of the main charge, at what is known as the *steady-state* velocity of detonation (usually a constant speed varying from 1,600 to 7,500 m/sec, depending upon the performance parameters of the particular charge).

The **explosive coupling** [3, 11] (or **coupling ratio**) relates to the efficiency with which the chemical energy of the explosive is transferred to the enclosing rock of the borehole. With good coupling, there is little energy lost (e.g., through air space between the charge and the wall of the borehole).

Rock may be broken by an explosive charge according to the **Reflection Theory** propounded by *Hino* [2] and elaborated by *Duvall* and *Atchison* as follows [13]:

> "The detonation of the explosive charge creates a high gas pressure in the charge hole, which in turn generates a compressive strain pulse in the surrounding rock. This compressive strain pulse travels outward in all directions from the charge hole. Near the charge hole the amplitude of the strain pulse is sufficient to cause crushing of the rock. However, as the strain pulse travels outwards, its amplitude decays rapidly until no further crushing of the rock is possible. The compressive strain pulse continues to travel outward until it is reflected by a free surface. Upon reflection, the compressive strain pulse becomes a tensile strain pulse. As the strength of the rock in tension is much less than in compression, the reflected tensile pulse is able to break the rock in tension, progressing from the free surface back towards the shot point. In other words, the rock is pulled apart, not pushed apart.... The high gas pressure generated by the detonation of the charge produces the stress waves, but the expanding gases are not directly responsible for much of the fracturing that occurs."

Since most hard tenacious rocks are characterized by high compressive, lower shear and much lower tensile strength, it is, of course, logical to aim to break the rock in tension.

However, the phenomenon of spalling, as characterized by the reflection theory, is not now regarded as the only cause of rock failure. Several other factors contribute. The peak strain energy (SE) developed at the wall of the blast hole by high detonation pressure is designed to overcome the dynamic compressive strength of the rock. This compressive strain wave causes crushing and cracking around the blast hole. If a free face occurs within its zone of influence, a reflected tension wave will generate external spalling from the free face. The high borehole pressure (bubble energy, BE) developed by the expanding gases then extends the cracks to the point of flexural rupture of the rock, aided by the external spalling [14].

According to *Hagan* [15], the relative values of strain and bubble energy are more reliable indicators of explosive effectiveness than strength data. Strain energy is more effective in hard brittle rocks; and bubble energy in rocks of lower degrees of elasticity. Different explosive formulations provide varying SE:BE ratios.

A study of the respective contribution made in breaking rock (a) by the stress waves reflected from the free face; and (b) by the expanding gases has been conducted by *Clark* and *Saluja* [16], who infer that the latter cause preponderates where lower velocity explosives are used.

However, no generally acceptable quantitative theory has yet been developed to explain the rock failure process [17].

It should also be noted that, since lower velocity explosives are more effective in breaking rock material exhibiting significant plasticity (see Chapter 14), the relative elasticity of the rock to be broken is a contributing factor.

The above discussion dealing with the mechanics of detonation refers to high explosives and blasting agents.

On the other hand, **low explosives** may be thermally ignited directly by means of a safety fuse without the interposition of a detonator. This means that they burn or deflagrate, yielding gases and solids more slowly and at lower but sustained pressures, thereby developing a heaving action, more applicable to the blasting of soft plastic rock and coal (where lump size is to be retained, and where firedamp conditions allow).

Black powder is now used mainly in the blasting of dimension stone and slate, where a minimum amount of shattering can be tolerated. Otherwise, in finer gradings, it is used as a core load in the manufacture of safety fuse.

Comparison of Basic Prime Costs

Comparative prime costs of different explosive materials are given below, based upon information published by *Dick* [18] and using bulk AN prills as a base range of 100 – 200.

Bulk AN prills	100	–	200
Bulk AN/FO	150	–	300
Bagged AN/FO	200	–	500
Cartridged AN/FO	300	–	600

Bulk or bagged AN slurries	400 –	1250
Bulk emulsions	300 –	900
Dynamites	750 –	1600
Gelatine dynamites	850 –	1700

Nevertheless, when total costs per ton of ore or rock are considered, the differences may become subject to modification.

Explosives Consumption

Based on figures supplied for consumption in the United States in 1989, the following estimates of annual explosives usage is offered.

AN prills and AN/FO (all types)	89%
AN slurries and emulsions	8%
Dynamites and gelatines	2%
Permissible explosives	1%

Figures available show a total annual consumption in the United States of about two million tons of explosives, represented in the following categories of industry:

Coal mining	65%
Metalliferous mining	10%
Quarrying etc.	15%
Construction work	6 – 7%
All other purposes	3 – 4%

Blasting agents accounted for 97 per cent of the total consumption.

References

[1]   R. A. Dick, "Factors in Selecting and Applying Commercial Explosives and Blasting Agents", *U.S.B.M., I.C.* 8405 (1968)

[2]   M. A. Cook, *The Science of Industrial Explosives* (IRECO Chemicals, Salt Lake City, 1974)

[3]   J. J. Yancik, "ANFO Manual" (St. Louis: Monsanto Company, 1969)

[4]   J. J. Yancik, R. F. Bruzewski, and G. B. Clark, "Some Detonation Properties of Ammonium Nitrate", Fifth Annual Symposium on Mining Research, *University of Missouri School of Mines and Metallurgy, Bulletin,* No. 98 (1960)

[5]   A. Bauer, "Current Drilling and Blasting Practices in Open Pit Mines on a World Basis", Paper presented at the 1971 Mining Show of the American Mining Congress (Las Vegas, October 11-14, 1971)

[6] B. D. Rossi, (ed), "Control of Noxious Gases in Blasting Works, and Methods of Testing Industrial Explosives", VZRYVNOE DELO Collection No. 68/25 (Translated from Russian)

[7] C. M. Mason and E. G. Aiken, "Methods for Evaluation Explosives and Hazardous Materials", *U.S. Bureau of Mines I.C.* 8541 (1972)

[8] R. A. Dick, *Private communication*, 15 October, 1981

[9] G. B. Clark, "Mathematics of Explosives Calculations", Fourth Annual Symposium on Mining Research, *University of Missouri School of Mines and Metallurgy, Bulletin,* No. 97 (1959)

[10] C. H. Johansson and P. A. Persson, *Detonics of High Explosives* (London: Academic Press, 1970)

[11] T. C. Atchison, "The Effect of Coupling on Explosive Performance", *Quarterly of Colorado School of Mines*, Vol. 56, No. 1 (1961)

[12] K. Hino, *Theory and Practice of Blasting* (Asa, Japan: Nippon Kayaku Co., 1959)

[13] W. I. Duvall and T. C. Atchison, "Rock Breakage by Explosives", *U.S. Bureau of Mines, R.I.* 5356 (1957)

[14] R. L. Ash, "Improving Productivity through Better Blasting Control", Paper presented to AIME Annual Meeting (New York, February 1975)

[15] T. N. Hagan, "Rock Breaking by Explosives", *Australian Geomechanics Society*, National Symposium on Rock Fragmentation (Adelaide, February 1973)

[16] L. D. Clark and S. S. Saluja, "Blasting Mechanics", Trans, AIME, Vol. 229 (March 1964)

[17] G. D. Just, "The Mechanics of Rock Breakage by Explosives", (University of Queensland, Rock Breaking Seminar, February 1971)

[18] R. A. Dick, "Current and Future Trends in Explosives and Blasting – Part I", *Pit & Quarry*, July 1971

CHAPTER 3

High Explosives

Introduction

Most high explosives consist of mechanical mixtures of two or more explosive bases and other additives (see Table 1) [1].

In formulating explosive mixtures, it is necessary to achieve an *oxygen balance* in order (a) to maximize the explosive energy of the reaction by aiming at complete combustion, and (b) to avoid the presence of toxic gases in the combustion products.

This is generally achieved by using (a) combustibles/fuels (Table 1) to react with the excess oxygen and thereby prevent the formation of toxic oxides of nitrogen; or (b) oxidizing agents (oxygen carriers) to promote full oxidation of the carbon to carbon dioxide, thereby inhibiting the formation of toxic carbon monoxide.

An absorbent (Table 1) such as kieselguhr has been used (since 1867) to absorb liquid explosives such as nitroglycerine. Antacids promote stability in storage. Low freezing point compounds reduce the propensity of the mixture to freeze in cold weather. Gelatinizing agents promote water resistance (as for the gelatine dynamites). Flame depressants or coolants reduce the size, duration and temperature of the flame during the explosive reaction to avoid methane/coal dust explosions in coal mines (Chap. 20).

In the category of high explosives, the chief explosive bases are nitroglycerine (NG), and ammonium nitrate (AN).

Other explosive bases listed in Table 1 are used predominantly as gelatinizing agents, low freezing compounds, initiating explosives (for use in detonators or detonating cord), black powder (the typical low explosive), and trinitrotoluene (TNT) which has a limited application in the industrial explosive area.

Among the high explosives, each has differing physical characteristics and chemical composition; but all have comparable values as explosives in blasting rock. All are ranked as "Explosives Class A or B" and must be transported, stored, handled and used in compliance with all applicable U.S. federal, state, and local laws and regulations.

Table 1:   Ingredients used in explosives

Ingredient	Chemical Formula	Function
Ethylene glycol dinitrate (nitroglycol)	$C_2H_4(NO_3)_2$	Explosive base; lowers freezing point
Nitrocellulose (NC) (guncotton)	$C_6H_7(NO_3)_3O_2$	Explosive base; gelatinizing agent
Nitroglycerine (NG)	$C_3H_5(NO_3)_3$	Explosive base
Nitrostarch (NS)		Explosive base; "nonheadache" explosive
Trinitrotoluene (TNT)	$C_7H_5N_3O_6$	Explosive base
Metallic powder	Al	Fuel-sensitizer
Black powder (BP)	$NaNO_3 + C + S$	Explosive base; deflagrates
Pentaerythritoltetranitrate (PETN)	$C_5H_8N_4O_{12}$	Explosive base; caps, detonating cord
Lead azide	$Pb(N_3)_2$	Explosive base; used in blasting caps
Mercury fulminate	$Hg(ONC)_2$	Explosive base; used in blasting caps
Ammonium nitrate (AN)	NH_4NO_3	Explosive base; oxygen carrier
Liquid oxygen (LOX)	O_2	Oxygen carrier
Sodium nitrate (SN)	$NaNO_3$	Oxygen carrier; reduces freezing point
Potassium nitrate	KNO_3	Oxygen carrier
Ground coal	C	Combustible, or fuel
Charcoal	C	Combustible, or fuel
Paraffin	C_nH_{2n+2}	Combustible, or fuel
Sulphur	S	Combustible, or fuel
Fuel oil	$(CH_3)_2(CH_2)_n$	Combustible, or fuel
Wood pulp	$(C_6H_{10}O_5)_n$	Combustible; absorbent
Lampblack	C	Combustible
Kieselguhr	SiO_2	Absorbent; prevents caking
Chalk	$CaCO_3$	Antacid
Calcium carbonate	$CaCO_3$	Antacid
Zinc oxide	ZnO	Antacid
Sodium chloride	NaCl	Flame depressant (permissible explosives)

In Canada, the corresponding high explosive types include NG, NC, AN, PETN and TNT (and cover any of the so-called blasting agent mixtures that contain any of these elements, and thereby render them sensitive to initiation). These explosives ("nitro-compounds") are classified as Class 3 explosives, and are subject to stringent federal and provincial regulations, in respect of manufacture, storage, transportation, sale, possession and usage.

The above American and Canadian classifications, as described above, are now due to be phased out (by 1996) in order to conform to the United Nations Recommendations (see Appendix H).

Trinitrotoluene

Trinitrotoluene (TNT) is a high density explosive of excellent water resistance. Although of considerable importance in the field of military explosives, it is manufactured commercially in North America only by CIL, in the form of pellets, flakes or grains. It combines the important advantages of a high strength explosive base with that of low hazard sensitivity.

Pelleted TNT is produced as smooth pellets about one-eighth of an inch in diameter by CIL under the trade name of 'Nitropel'. They perform as well as 60 per cent ammonia gelatines, with a blasthole loading density of 0.94 g/cm^3.

Individual pellets have a density of 1.5 and therefore they sink readily in water.

Nitropel is used in a variety of ways:

(a) As a supplement to rigid dynamite or blasting agent cartridges in large diameter quarry holes, to improve loading density and coupling ratio;

(b) as a sensitizer in the formulation of certain slurry explosives; and

(c) in seismic prospecting applications.

Nitropel can be poured direct into wet and dry quarry holes either as the main charge, or to fill the annular space around rigid cartridges as a supplement. In the latter case, it is primed by the surrounding charge. When used as a main charge, it calls for a high strength primer. When detonated, much fume is produced; therefore TNT cannot be used underground.

Crystalline TNT (flaked and grained) is used in the manufacture of cast Pentolite boosters (see Glossary), in certain slurry explosives, and in some blasting accessories.

Most forms of TNT are packed and shipped in woven polypropylene 25 kg bags, but special packs are used for seismic exploration applications.

Dynamites and Gelatines

Most dynamites employ nitroglycerine (NG Table 2), with some nitroglycol, as the explosive base. Gelatines also contain nitrocellulose (NC). Some manufacturers (Trojan) use nitrostarch as the base.

Nitroglycerine (NG) is the most basic of all industrial explosives, although ammonium nitrate (AN), as the oxidizing element in blasting agents, has recently gained tremendous significance.

Nitroglycerine is a yellow oily transparent liquid made by the action of nitric acid on glycerine. In this (liquid) form it is too sensitive to be handled safely; it is therefore converted into a more convenient gelatinous (plastic) solid by the addition of 8 per cent guncotton (NC) to form Blasting Gelatine (in accordance with *Nobel*'s patent of 1875); or by admixtures with other explosive agents and additives (to form lower strength dynamites and gelatines) in line with *Nobel*'s invention of 1879.

Nitroglycerine explosives require careful handling. They are rated among the most powerful of the industrial explosives. They are easily ignited, in which case they will burn slowly in small quantities but may detonate if burned in a mass.

Nitroglycerine freezes at 55 °F (13 °C) as a crystal. In thawing out of this phase, it is sensitive to shock. In order to reduce this hazard, all NG-based high explosives in the North American cold climate incorporate in their formulation a proportion of explosive compounds which lower the freezing point.

Nitroglycerine (and most other nitro-compounds) are poisonous if taken internally. Contact with the skin or inhalation of the vapours (except nitrostarch) will give rise to "powder headache". The hands should be washed after handling explosives.

Dynamites in North America are manufactured in the following classifications:

Straight Dynamites
Ammonia Dynamites
Straight Gelatine Dynamites
Ammonia Gelatine Dynamites
Semi-gelatines.

Practically all dynamites contain NG in their formulations. All are detonating explosives; and for proper and safe control, must be initiated by some form of blasting cap (detonator) or detonating cord (see Glossary).

Straight NG dynamites

Guhr Dynamite, as originally formulated by *Nobel* in 1867, by absorbing liquid NG in kieselguhr to form a plastic mass, was the fore-runner of the straight dynamites. As such, it contained about 75% NG.

Present-day straight dynamites have various proportions of active constituents substituted for much of the kieselguhr with resulting higher performance. They also use low freezing explosive compounds as replacements for much of the NG. (It will therefore be seen that the term "Straight Nitroglycerine Dynamite" is no longer straight). Table 2 gives a range of compositions and properties derived from *Dick* [1], representing average formulations of high explosives marketed by various manufacturers in North America.

As will be seen from this table, straight dynamites achieve a high VOD and therefore give fast shattering results. They generally have fair water resistance, but poor fuming characteristics, which disqualifies them for underground applications.

Because of their high cost, their sensitivity to friction and shock, and their high inflammability properties, their industrial use and importance is declining and giving way to ammonia dynamites. Their main usage is for ditch blasting by the propagation method (see Chapter 21).

Ammonia dynamites

Ammonia Dynamites (also known as "Extra Dynamites") have largely replaced straight dynamites in the commercial field and are in fact one of the most commonly used dynamites in present-day operations.

Although similar in composition to straight dynamites, a portion of the NG and SN is replaced by AN. This means that the ammonia dynamites generally are of lower VOD, lower density, higher shock resistance, and better fume characteristics.

They are used for rock of medium hardness and average water conditions in quarrying, stripping and some underground mines, in small diameter holes. They are also used for small blasting operations and agricultural purposes.

Some manufacturers produce both high- and low-density ammonia dynamites, and high- and low-VOD versions of the low density product. Low-density ammonia dynamites are generally the lowest cost rigid cartridged explosives available. They contain rather less NG and more AN than a typical high-density ammonia dynamite. Since they have poor to fair water resistance, they appear to have less to commend their use than blasting agents (see later).

Straight gelatine dynamites

The most distinguished member of this class of high explosives is Blasting Gelatine, invented by *Alfred Nobel* in 1875 by incorporating 92 per cent of liquid NG with 8 per cent of nitrocellulose.

With a weight strength of 100 per cent (comparable with TNT) and a specific gravity of 1.3 (cartridge count, 110), it has a cartridge strength of 90 per cent.

Although it detonates at a very high velocity (8,300 m/sec) and has excellent water resistance, it has very poor fume characteristics and cannot be used underground. Its chief industrial use (despite its high cost) is in high pressure underwater operations.

Lower strengths of straight gelatine dynamites contain NG gelatinized with nitrocellulose (guncotton) as the explosive base; they therefore have excellent water resistance and a high VOD and density.

Formerly, straight gelatines were used in extremely hard rock or in under-water and oil well shooting. They are now used for the latter purpose and for seismic blasting.

However, it is important to note that straight gelatines may not develop their fully rated VOD if the degree of confinement and the initiation energy are inadequate; or in cases where high hydrostatic pressure exists. In order to avoid this problem, a high-VOD series of straight gelatines has been developed. These are more sensitive to detonation shock, and always achieve their rated VOD, even under high water pressure.

Table 2: Compositions and properties of dynamites in North America

Item	Unit	Dynamites		Gelatines		Semi-gelatines
		Straight	Ammonia (high density*)	Straight	Ammonia	
Compositions						
Nitroglycerine (NG)		20–57	12–22	20–50	23–35	
Sodium nitrate (SN)		59–23	57–15	60–39	55–33	
Ammonium nitrate (AN)	%	–	12–50	–	4–20	see
Nitrocellulose (NC)	by	–	–	0.4–1.2	0.3–0.7	later
Carbonaceous fuel	weight	15.4–18.2	10.2–8.6	8.5–8.3	8.3–7.9	
Sulphur		2.9–0	6.7–1.6	8.2–0	7.2–0	
Antacid		1.3–1.2	1.2–1.1	1.5–1.1	0.7–0.8	
Properties						
Weight strength	%	30–60	20–65	20–90	30–80	62–70
Cartridge strength	%	20–60	36–50	30–80	35–75	30–60
Cartridge count	per 50 lb case	100–108	105–118	85–105	92–115	100–152
Specific gravity	–	1.3–1.4	1.2–1.35	1.3–1.7	1.3–1.6	0.9–1.4
Confined VOD	ft/sec	9000–19000	8000–15300	11000–23000	14000–20000	10500–17500
Water resistance	–	poor–good	fair	excellent	excellent	fair to very good
Fume class	–	2–3	1	1–3	1–3	1

* Low density ammonia dynamites have a weight strength of 65%, cartridge strengths of 20–50%, cartridge counts of 174–120, specific gravities of 0.8–1.2, and two velocity ranges 63–8100 and 8300–11000 ft/sec. Water resistance is poor-fair, with fume class of 1.

Ammonia gelatine dynamites

An ammonia gelatine (or "gelatine extra") bears the same relationship to straight gelatines as ammonia dynamites bear to straight dynamites, in that part of the NG and SN has been replaced by AN.

Ammonia gelatines have generally a lower VOD, lower water resistance, better fume characteristics, and lower cost than comparable grades of straight gelatines (see Table 2).

Semi-gelatines

This type of "hybrid" explosive is designed to bridge the gap between high-density ammonia dynamites and ammonia (or extra) gelatines. It is a good general-purpose cartridged high explosive with considerable economic advantages, suitable for use underground. Its properties are listed in Table 2.

Further background information on the rationale of semi-gelatines is given by *Fordham* [2]:

"The true [NG] powder explosives contain no nitrocellulose and, therefore, can only be made at relatively low densities and are also susceptible to the action of water. The true gelatine explosives, on the other hand, have a continuous phase of gelled nitro-glycerine and, therefore, have a high density and are relatively unaffected by water for an appreciable length of time. Semi-gelatine explosives can be made with properties which range over the extreme limits between powders and gelatines."

"The choice of composition of a semi-gelatine depends ultimately on two requirements, namely, the strength required and the resistance to water needed for the particular application. For economic reasons the lowest nitroglycerine content which satisfies both these requirements is always chosen."

Other High Explosives

Apart from TNT and the dynamites/gelatines, there are other formulations classified as high explosives [4, 5]. These are cap-sensitive slurries (water gels) and emulsions; and certain high explosives adapted for particular applications, such as:

Coal mining (see Chapter 20)

Overbreak control (see Chapter 14)

Secondary blasting (see Chapter 14)

Seismic exploration (see Chapter 14)

Shaped charges (see Chapter 10)

Trenching (see Chapter 17)

Underwater blasting (see Chapter 17).

1. Cap-sensitive (CS) Slurries

For details, see Slurry Type Blasting Agents, in Chapter 4.

Cap-sensitive slurries are generally those in which some form of high explosive is incorporated as a fuel. With the recent development of emulsions, slurry explosives are now being superseded. Typical brands of CS slurry explosives are given below, in respect of different manufacturers:

Atlas	Powermax Apex 1000
BIQ	Tovex 100, 200, 220, 300, 320, 700, 800 Britanite AL
DANTEX	Tovex 130, 200, 220, 240, 800

Table 3:   Some typical trade names of high explosives listed by manufacturers

Manufacturer (for code, see Chap. 1)	Powder type	Gelatinous type	Semi-gelatinous type
AECI		Ammon Gelignite	Dynagel
Atlas	Extra Dynamite	Giant Gelatin	Gelmax
	Powerditch	Powerfrac	Geldyne
Austin [3]	Extra Dynamite	Helix	Apcogel B
	Ditching Dynamite	Extra Gelatin	
BIQ	Britamon	Gelatel	
		Britagel	
CIL		Forcite 75	Geldyne
		Powerditch 1000	Xactex
		Powerfrac	
DNAG	Donarit	Ammon-Gelit	
		Special gelatine	
DNW	Pelonit D	Gelatine Donarit 1, 2	
	Katamerit		
	Donarit 1,2		
DYNO	Glynit	Dynamit	
	Koronit	Extra Dynamit	
	Minit		
EBCW	Permon 10	Perunit 20, 22, 28, 44. 48	
	Permonex V19		
ECP	Quarrex	Fortex	ECP 2
		Gelamex	
		Opencast Gelignite	
ERT	Amonita	Goma	
	Ligamita		
ETCAN		Dynamite B, C	Dynamit A
ETI		Dynamite B, C	Gelex II
EXSA	Exadit	Gelatine Especial	Semexca
	Amonex	Gelignita	
IEL	Hectorite	Special Gelatine	
		Opencast Gelignite	
		Gomia Gelatine	
IIE	Frangex	Quarigel	Quarrex
		Opencast Gelignite	
		Gelamex	
IRECO	IRECON	Extra Gelatin	Gelamite
	Extra dynamite	Powergel A, D	Unigel
		UNIMAX	
		Gelaprime	
ITPL	Vulcan	Blg Gelatine	
	Cava	Spl Gelatin	
Kemira	Aniitti	Dynamite	
KIMIT			Kimulux 42, 82
NEF	F 16, 19 GUM		
NKC		Sakura	Akatsuki
		Kiri	
		Enoki	
NOBEX	Ammon Dynamite	Blasting Gelatine	Belex
	Trimonite	Gelatine	
	Belex	Special Gelatine 80%	
		Tunnel Gelatine	
		Opencast Gelignite	
SFE	Sofranex	Gomme B A M	Minex F
	Gomme F 15	Titadyn 40	
	Titadyn 25		
SSE		Gamsit A	
TEL		TELGEX	
		TELPOW LD	
WAHNL		Wabox 40, 60, 80	Wabofite

DuPont/ETI	Drivex
	Tovex 90–800
	Tovex SDX
	Tovex Hi-drive
ECP	Cosminex
ETCAN	Tovex Blastrite 1, 2, 3
	Tovex Minerite 1, 2, 3
EXSA	Lurigel
ICIA	Powergel 1500
	Molanite
IDL	Superdyne
	Aquadyne
	Toeblast
NEF	Iremite 110
	Gelsurite 2000, 3000
NOBEX	Powergel 800, 900
SFE	Sigma 5, 505, 512
	Titagel 200, 1000
	Gelsurite 2000, 3000
SLEX	Slurran 605, 606, 600 SLX
SMX	Explogel 130, 200, 220, 225, 250, 800, 825
TEL	TELGEL
	TELBASE
Titanite	Titagel 1000, 3000

2. Cap-sensitive (CS) Emulsions

In water-in-oil emulsions, the internal phase is a super-saturated solution of AN in the form of extremely fine droplets dispersed through a fuel oil medium. An emulsifying agent is added to stabilize the emulsion. A special calcium nitrate formulation from Norsk Hydro can be used to extend stability, improve solubility and rheology, and increase the energy content. Air bubbles are introduced as sensitizers to increase the bulk from a density of 0.80 to 1.35 g/cm^3, yielding a corresponding range of sensitivity (see also Chapter 4). Artificial air bubbles in the form of glass microspheres are commonly used. In this way, the sensitivity can be controlled to produce emulsions that are explosives (cap-sensitive) or blasting agents that need a primer for initiation (see Chapter 4).

Typical types of cap-sensitive emulsions available from different manufacturers are given below:

Atlas	Powermax 120, 140, 420, 440, 460
	Apex 1000
	Superfrac

CIL	Magnafrac 1000, 3000, 5000
	Superfrac 4000, 7000
DNW	Lambrex 1, 2
DuPont/ETI	Tovex
	Tovan
	ANFO Extra
DYNO [6]	Dynex
	Emulite 100
ICIA	Powergel 3000
	Powergel Magnum
	Powergel Pulsar
IRECO	Iremite 42, 62, 82, 102
	Powermite
NEF	Iremite 1000, 2500, 4000
Nitro Nobel	Emulite 100
NKC	Kayamite
SSE	Sempionite
WAHNL	Emulite 100
WEST	Emulgit 22, TX, 42G, 42GP, 82GP.

General

Descriptions of packaging methods for general and specific purposes are dealt with in Chapter 11; as are methods of loading charges.

References

[1] R. A. Dick, "Factors in Selecting and Applying Commercial Explosives and Blasting Agents", *U.S.B.M, I.C.* 8405, 1968

[2] S. Fordham, *High Explosives and Propellants* (Oxford, Pergamon, 1966)

[3] Austin Powder Co., "Apcogel Semi-Gelatin", Bulletin SG851

[4] R. A. Dick, *et al.* "Explosives and Blasting Procedures Manual", *U.S.B.M, I.C.* 8925, 1983

[5] J. J. Manon, "Explosives: Their Classification and Characteristics", *E & MJ*, 1977

[6] "Emulite", Nitro Nobel AB, Gyttorp, Sweden

CHAPTER 4

Blasting Agents

History and Development

Although originally patented in 1867 by two Swedish scientists (*Ohlsson* and *Norrbein*) as an explosive mixture, the use of ammonium nitrate, sensitized with a carbonaceous additive, did not develop commercially until 1955. Meanwhile, AN itself had been used extensively as a component of NG explosives to provide lower-strength types at lower costs; and in about 1935, a pre-packaged form of AN blasting agent was developed and marketed by DuPont [1] under the name of "Nitramon". It was sealed in metal cans to render it waterproof. A high explosive primer containing TNT was necessary for initiation. Other associated derivatives were developed later.

After the Second World War (when the need for military explosives had been greatly reduced), the United States Government encouraged the development of a non-caking grade of ammonium nitrate (FGAN) for fertilizer purposes in order to absorb the excess capacity.

Following disastrous explosions of shiploads of FGAN (unwittingly sensitized with a wax coating as an anti-caking agent) in Texas City, in Brest (France), and in the Black Sea in 1947, it became obvious that a new explosive of tremendous power was available to be developed. Various field experimenters followed up this lead in an effort to effect economies in their mining operations [2, 3].

By 1955, *R. I. Akre*, drilling superintendent at Maumee Collieries Co., Terre Haute, Indiana, and *Hugh Lee* had patented the use of this low-cost FGAN (mixed with carbon black) as "Akremite". Others had been experimenting with fuel oil as a sensitizer for FGAN. By 1956, Professor *Cook* was able to show that a 94/6 mixture of AN and fuel oil was an approximately correct composition on an oxygen-balanced basis to yield a maximum of energy from the explosive reaction [3]. A worldwide revolution in explosives usage (for nonmilitary purposes) has been developing since then.

However, AN/FO, as a dry mixture had one major disadvantage. It had no water resistance. Although its use in industry had gained tremendous momentum because of its safety and economic advantages, it could not be used satisfactorily under wet conditions. *Cook* and others were inspired to experiment further to overcome this problem. By 1960, they had dissolved the AN in just enough water to form a soupy mixture or "slurry". By adding TNT and aluminium powder as sensitizers, they developed a detonable mixture which, when used with a thickening agent, had great water resistance. Since then, slurry blasting agents have been further developed and have become of major significance in the explosives industry [3, 4].

During the 1970s the development of emulsions added a new perspective to industrial blasting (see below).

General Composition

Although TNT and the dynamites develop their explosive power on detonation from a basic decomposition reaction, resulting in a transformation of their molecules, the explosive power developed by blasting agents is based upon a different type of action.

The main explosive base of blasting agents is ammonium nitrate (in one form or another), acting as an oxidizer. But it obviously depends on the complementary action of a reducing agent to provide or support the chemical (explosive) reaction.

Such reducing agents are termed *fuels.* They generally comprise a range of carbonaceous combustibles (such as carbon black, powdered coal, sugar, molasses; or more generally, No. 2 diesel fuel oil), but may also take the form of smokeless powder, finely divided weak metals (such as aluminium) or certain organic compounds, like nitropropane or methanol, or even encapsulated air bubbles.

By definition, blasting agents are cap-insensitive; but some of the fuels used can produce cap-sensitive mixtures and should therefore be regarded as explosives.

In Canada, blasting agents are classified as Class 2 explosives (nitrate mixtures) so long as they are insensitive to cap initiation.

Even though not classified as explosives in the United States, it is convenient to regard blasting agents as 'explosives' in the broad general sense of the term.

Advantages of a Blasting Agent

The chief advantages in its use are related to economy, efficiency, and safety. In certain applications, an overall cost saving of up to 75 per cent over conventional NG explosives has been reported. Where used under well-controlled conditions, it is reported to perform as well as, or better than, the dynamites, and, by virtue of its greater gas production, may even give better fragmentation. It is safer to handle and use because its hazard sensitivity is low, and misfires are easily and safely resolved.

One of its important virtues is that it is not classified as an explosive; but, when mixed in the correct stoichiometric proportions under preferred physical conditions with adequate primage, the mixture becomes a powerful low-cost explosive.

Disadvantages

Ammonium nitrate, being soluble, is not resistant to water – hence, there is a loss of efficiency or failure when AN/FO (see later) is used under wet conditions. (On the other hand, specially designed AN-slurry mixtures and AN-emulsions have been developed for blasting in wet holes [2].)

Because of the widely varying conditions and equipment available at different mining sites, non-standardized mixing methods may give rise to loss of control and low efficiency. As with all "do-it-yourself" systems, the results are only as good as the methods used.

The commonest carbonaceous fuel in general use is about 6 per cent by weight of fuel oil; but an intimate degree of mechanical mixing is required in order to effect an efficient reaction; otherwise reddish-brown fumes of oxides of nitrogen and poor blasting performance result.

Unfortunately, AN particles collect moisture and tend to cake. For this reason, FGAN particles were formerly protected with wax coatings, until several ship-loads "blew up" with disastrous results. They were later coated with inert diatomaceous earth (kieselguhr).

Whereas granular particles of AN would not readily or evenly absorb oil, AN is now manufactured in porous "prilled" forms by spraying a concentrated solution through coarse spray nozzles into a stream of cool air. Prilled AN, coated with kieselguhr, readily absorbs by a sort of capillary diffusion process about 6 per cent of fuel oil. However, the kieselguhr coating is inclined to inhibit initiation sensitivity. Some suppliers overcome this problem by using surface-active agents instead of kieselguhr in the production of prilled AN.

The difficulty in securing an intimate mixture of AN and fuel oil is perhaps because they are mutually repulsive. *Hino* and *Yokogawa* [5] have shown that this problem can be ameliorated by the use of surface-active agents.

Coxon [6, 7] has shown by practical trials that the physico-chemical bond between AN and fuel oil can be substantially improved by use of surfactants and water which produces emulsions of fuel oil in water, resulting in greater sensitivity and better explosive properties.

These tests have been followed by the development by Atlas of *blasting agent emulsions,* where the AN oxidizer is encapsulated by the fuel in a water-in-oil emulsion (see later).

For dry holes, 94/6 AN/FO seems to be the best mixture yet developed. Where wet conditions prevail, a series of AN-slurry mixtures has been developed by Professor *Cook* [2, 3] and others. These consist generally of AN-TNT-water or AN-molasses-water. Metallized slurries and emulsions have also been developed (see later).

Performance Parameters

Basically, the performance of blasting agents depends on the intimacy of the mixing process of the two main components. This, in turn, depends on the physical character-istics of the AN in respect of such features as size, shape, grading, hardness, porosity, and moisture-resistance of particles, and whether they have been treated with inert coating agents or surfactants.

Suppliers of AN blasting agents now aim to incorporate the best of the above features into their (prilled) products under competitive marketing conditions. Prills give a lower charge density and better oil absorption, thus improving initiation sensitivity and blasting performance. For effective performance, the mixture should release a maximum amount of available energy. This infers a high performance sensitivity (for both initiation and propagation), high borehole pressure, and a high VOD (both transient and steady-state) [2, 3, 4].

Other important parameters are (a) the diameter of the charge or borehole, (b) the load-ing density of the charge (which for AN/FO should not exceed about 1.1 g/cm^3), (c) the degree of confinement of the charge, (d) the correct stoichiometric addition of fuel, (e) the absence of excess moisture, and (f) strength, shape, and position of primer or booster [8].

As with all blasting agents, adequate primage with high-VOD primers is essential. Inad-equate priming does not allow a blasting agent to develop its rated VOD. The reaction tends to fade, part of the charge may misfire, and noxious fumes may occur.

Types of Blasting Agents

In further describing the broad spectrum of blasting agents in this chapter, it will be convenient to make three separate classifications, as set out below.

1. Dry free-running blasting agents

These are basically prilled AN or a mixture of AN prills and fuel oil (AN/FO). They may be purchased separately or ready mixed, in 50 or 80 lb polyethylene or multi-wall bags, or in bulk.

For relatively dry holes they have a great advantage over cartridged or canned explo-sives in that better coupling is obtained. For quarry applications, the holes can be load-ed by gravity (simple pouring) or by bulk trucks; or by pneumatic loaders for under-ground work (even for long "up" holes). See Chapter 11 for further details.

The most distinguished member of this family is AN/FO. Proper mixing of the AN and the oil is essential. When gravity loaded into holes, the density varies between 0.75 and 0.95 g/cm^3 for best results. AN/FO has poor water resistance. To overcome this prob-lem, some quarry operators line the hole with a plastic sleeve and load the AN/FO into the sleeve (Fig. 1).

The confined VOD of AN/FO depends upon the diameter of the hole, even with ade-quate primage. Table 4, derived from *Dick* [9], demonstrates this feature.

Yancik [10] has shown that at least 25 variables affect the blasting performance of

Table 4: Variation of confined detonation velocity and borehole loading density of AN/FO with borehole diameter (assuming density of AN/FO = 0.84 g/cm^3)

Borehole diameter (mm)	Average confined VOD (m/sec)	Average loading density (kg/m of borehole)
38	2620	0.96
51	3020	1.74
76	3410	3.86
102	3740	6.95
127	3930	10.77
152	4060	15.42
178	4160	20.65
203	4230	27.51
229	4300	35.01

Fig. 1: Auger-loading dry AN/FO into sleeve-lined hole from a mix truck

AN/FO. But for a loading density of 0.85 g/cm^3 and under other controlled conditions, he shows that:

1. The theoretical energy released (heat of explosion) and the VOD are both at a maximum at the point of oxygen balance (i.e., at 5.7% fuel oil). The values of both factors fall off more gradually with an over- than with an under-supply of oil.

2. Initiation sensitivity maximizes at a two per cent fuel oil content but falls off rapidly above six per cent.

3. Both the initiation sensitivity and the VOD increase with the degree of confinement and borehole diameter (up to 6 and 11 inches diameter respectively).

4. The VOD increases and the initiation sensitivity decreases markedly when the loading density exceeds 0.9 g/cm^3. This depends partly on the particle size range. Ejector type pneumatic loading machines may sometimes compress the charge to a density of 1.2 g/cm^3 at which point the detonation may not be sustained, even though adequately primed. To avoid this problem, ejectors should be operated at lower air pressures (see Chapter 11).

5. With finer particle sizing than −8 / +20 USSS, the initiation sensitivity increases markedly. However, other physical problems then arise.

6. The length of exposure time to water is more effective in reducing VOD and initiation sensitivity than the actual water content. The blasting performance of AN/FO is not reliable in the presence of water.

7. The critical diameter of holes charged with AN/FO depends upon the degree of confinement and the loading density. With good confinement, AN/FO can be successfully fired in boreholes as small as 1 inch in diameter. As the loading density increases, so does the critical diameter. At a packed (limiting) density of 1.25, the charge may not detonate, even though the borehole diameter may be six inches or greater. With pneumatic placement in small diameter holes, high densities should be avoided.

8. The VOD decreases as the coupling ratio (or degree of coupling) falls off. This becomes more pronounced in the field of overbreak control, a procedure that capitalizes on this relationship.

9. Standard 50 gr/ft detonating cord should not be used with AN/FO in blastholes less than six inches in diameter. Such a practice promotes low order detonations laterally and tends to nullify the effect of the primers in the column.

10. High energy primers are essential for use with all blasting agents.

11. The diameter of the primer should approximate the hole diameter for maximum detonating effect in most blasting agents.

12. The use of AN/FO in small diameter underground blastholes ensures better coupling through pneumatic placement than with cartridged explosives. However, care should be taken to limit density to 1.1 g/cm^3.

The classification of these mixtures as blasting agents by the Department of Transportation means that the components can be delivered separately to the blast site (without incurring excessively costly and restrictive transport and storage conditions) and mixed locally as and when required. Alternatively, they can similarly be supplied premixed (at the factory), usually in 50 or 80 lb polyethylene or multiwall paper bags.

With the availability of AN prills and AN/FO mixtures, most open cut mines and quarries have discontinued using cartridged NG explosives (except for special purposes); many underground mines are gradually following this practice, with consequent significant improvement in operating costs.

Under wet conditions and for special purposes, however, some operators prefer to retain the use of conventional explosives. Slurries are now being adapted for general underground usage where wet conditions prevail; as also are emulsions.

In other cases, where densification is necessary to allow cartridges to sink in wet holes, a portion of the prills is pulverized, mixed with the remainder, and vibrated (compressed) into rigid cartridges or burlap bags.

2.   Slurry type blasting agents (non-capsensitive)

The lower costs and desirable safety aspects achieved by the development of AN-based blasting agents inspired researchers to solve their notorious disadvantages of low water resistance [3, 11, 12, 13].

This work has led with signal success to the development of *Slurry Blasting Agents* (SBA) in which the combustible fuel is mixed with granular AN (and sometimes SN) and dispersed with just enough of an aqueous solution of AN to give a thick soup mixture. Hence the term *slurry* (also known as *water gel*). They contain up to 20 per cent water.

Several types of combustible fuel have been used, such as molasses, sugar, sawdust, sulphur, nitrostarch, or a heat-producing metal (magnesium or aluminium).

In using such a slurry the mixture is thickened with gelling agents immediately before loading in such proportions that it can be timed to form a thick gel immediately after charging into the borehole. This has the effect of immobilizing the aqueous solution and shielding the mixture from external moisture, thereby ensuring almost complete water resistance.

This virtue (of promoting water resistance) is sufficient to justify the use of slurries where wet holes are encountered. However, slurries have other distinctive advantages over AN/FO, particularly where extremely hard tenacious rock formations are to be blasted.

Slurries have a higher density than AN/FO, ranging from 1.05 to 1.6 g/cm^3. This enables the charge to sink readily (even without pumping) in boreholes containing water.

The VOD of slurries is also much higher, ranging from 3,500 to 6,000 m/sec, depending upon composition, charge diameter, degree of confinement, and density.

Slurries have similar coupling advantages to AN/FO, are less dependent upon borehole diameter, may even be more insensitive (requiring high VOD primers), but yield much higher detonation pressures (by virtue of their higher density and VOD). For this reason, borehole geometry can in some cases be expanded, and drilling costs thereby significantly lowered.

Most formulations of SBA contain from 15 to 20 per cent water. However, by using their patented organic monomethylamine nitrate (MMAN) sensitizer in their Tovex products, DuPont claims that less than 10 per cent water is required, thereby increasing the available energy.

When metallic fuels (as high as 35%) are used, the heat of the explosion is significantly increased. Metallized slurries are therefore indicated where extremely hard rock (such as taconite) is to be blasted [13].

Slurries are used mainly in surface blasting, and chiefly in the larger scale operations. For this reason, bulk transport, bulk loading, and the use of mobile "mix trucks" of ingredients or mixtures are usually employed. Details of bulk loading procedures are given in Chapter 11.

Slurries that are sensitive to a No. 8 cap are regarded as "explosives", even though less sensitive than dynamites. They must be treated as *slurry explosives* during handling and storage. Those fuelled with explosives or aluminium are generally more dense and develop more energy under wet conditions or when blasting in hard dense rock.

Slurries generally depend on entrapped air for their sensitivity and respond well to the recent availability of encapsulated air bubbles (microspheres).

3.   Emulsions (non-capsensitive)

Following earlier work by *Coxon* and others, the development of water-based blasting agent emulsions during the 1970s has added a new perspective to industrial blasting.

Emulsions consist of small droplets of AN solution tightly packed in a mixture of oil and wax (the fuel), and stabilized with an emulsifying agent. This gives a very intimate contact between the fuel and the oxidizer, providing rapid and complete combustion in a water-resistant setting, and giving increased VOD and energy output.

Emulsions differ from slurries in that the components (fuel and oxidizer) are both in a liquid state and are mixed at a higher temperature. They contain no gelling agents. The water level of the oxidizer is reduced by using a super-saturated AN solution in the form of minute droplets, tightly compacted within the continuous fuel phase [14].

Emulsions do not normally contain a chemical sensitizer, but depend on the presence of voids for initiation and propagation. Sensitivity and VOD depend on the amount of voids present, related to density. Therefore adjustments to density provide differences in the other properties. This is particularly evident when used in small diameter holes.

The energy is released faster, yielding superior rock-breaking characteristics. In practice, emulsions may be used alone as a surface charge, or along with dry slurry charges, blended in differing proportions to suit various conditions.

Certain emulsion formulations are of such physical conditions and consistency that they can be pumped into storage and re-pumped into blast holes when required, after blending with AN/FO or dynamites or otherwise. These are known as 'Repumpable Emulsions'.

Blasting agent emulsions (NCS) are extremely safe to handle. They do not produce "fracteur headaches".

Because of their many superior advantages, emulsions are preferred to slurries in a variety of blasting situations.

Compounding of Blasting Agents

In very hard rock that does not readily respond to the low loading density of AN/FO charges, the use of aluminized AN/FO products may be indicated. In these formulations, either powdered or granular aluminium is added to increase the density and available energy of the charge. Where extra power is required under dry conditions, aluminium granules, 4 to 10% by weight, may be added to AN/FO.

AN/FO and SBA formulations and emulsions may be enhanced in terms of explosive power by 'metallizing' with aluminium powder. An addition of 6 to 15 per cent of aluminium granules or powders can be used to advantage in AN/FO mixtures; up to 35 per cent in slurries. When so metallized (aluminized), the density and available energy are significantly increased, the latter due to the high heat of formation of Al_2O_3 in the reaction.

Aluminium granules and powders are specially prepared for these applications by the Aluminum Company of America (ALCOA), and by Aluminum Metallurgical Granules, of Kansas City.

However, where rock of lower tenacity is encountered under relatively dry conditions, AN/FO (or metallized AN/FO) is in many cases a logical choice rather than slurries or emulsions, because of its superior cost advantage under these conditions. Each has its preferred field of use. Sometimes they may be used in conjunction (in the same borehole), where slurry or emulsion is placed at the bottom of the hole (to counter the effects of water, or to break or adequately fragment a hard 'toe'), with a top load of AN/FO.

When AN/FO is mixed with bulk emulsion, extra energy [14], improved water resistance and higher densities can be achieved. Variations in the proportions used can yield improved properties up to a density of 1.3 g/cm^3. These mixes are referred to as **Heavy AN/FO**, as an *emulsion blend*.

Based on an intensive study of ultra-high speed blast photography, Blast Dynamics Pty Ltd, of Southport, Queensland 4216, has demonstrated that considerable advantages can ensue from the use of special blends of patented **Lite AN/FO** in wet blastholes.

Extra energy, good water resistance and higher density can be achieved by using a blend of 5% to 95% emulsion with AN/FO. Emulsified AN/FO is also supplied in many formulations by Atlas and others.

Microspheres

As has long been realized [15], the sensitivity of blasting agents under normal conditions is enhanced by the presence of entrapped air; so this fact has led to the development of artificial air bubbles as a component of a charge, particularly apt for emulsions and slurries. These sensitizers are now variously described in the trade as Q-CEL hollow microspheres (PQ); Scotchlite glass bubbles (3M); hollow glass microspheres (Dicaperl); DSG Extendospheres (P.A. Industries); and Sensilite microspheres (Fillite).

Packaging of Blasting Agents

Where bulk supplies or bulk mixing and delivery plants are not available or cannot be justified, AN prills, AN/FO, and some slurry and emulsion products can be supplied in 30, 50, and 60 lb plastic bags, or plastic-lined multi-wall paper bags, as shipped from the factory.

The early forms of blasting agents, such as DuPont "Nitramon" and the later "Nitramex 2H" were packed in metal cans to ensure unlimited water resistance. The same applies to CIL "Nitrone", "Nitrox" and"Amite" .

These were originally designed for bottom loading in wet quarry holes, but the coupling qualities (see Glossary) were poor unless complemented with Pelletol or Nitropel. Their chief application at the present time is in coyote blasting (see Chapter 14); and for marine offshore seismic work (see Fig. 2).

For less severe conditions in quarry holes, a number of blasting agents are available packed in fibre drums/tubes; or in heavy asphalt laminated paper shells with metal ends; or with 23G long tapered crimp on one end and fibre insert closure on the other (see Fig. 3).

Most dry (free-running) blasting agents are packed in 12.5, 15 or 25 kg bags, shipped on pallets, or in bulk containers.

Whereas dynamites and gelatines have traditionally been supplied in rigid waxed paper cartridges of various diameters and lengths, the physical nature of AN/FO, emulsions and slurries and the development of plastic films have provided an opportunity to cartridge some of these (in a range of diameters) in plastic tubing, packed in a 50 or 60 lb fibreboard carton. Such plastic shells allow for an improved coupling ratio in the blasthole.

A logical development of these plastic cartridges has recently been provided in the form of a continuous cartridge of slurry of a hose-like nature, for loading directly from a coiled tube packed in a box.

For smaller operators, slurry mixtures are available in polyethylene bags that may be slit before dropping into holes in order to achieve good coupling conditions. Also **Pourable Slurries** have recently been developed to allow smaller operators to use SBA without the need or expense of a mobile mix truck. These mixtures are designed to be poured easily into a hole as small as 8 cm in diameter.

Further details on packaging are given in Chapter 11.

Fig. 2: Blasting agent in sealed threaded can units for seismic blasting

Fig. 3: Large diameter 23G tapered-crimp-ended cartridges for quarry blasting

Seismic Blasting Agents

Slurry blasting agents have been developed for particular aspects of seismic prospecting, in addition to the seismic high explosives mentioned in Chapter 3.

Products Available

Representative trade names of AN prills, dry blasting agents, slurry blasting agents and seismic types marketed by various manufacturers are set out in Table 5.

Prices

Typical comparative average prices for blasting agents in carload lots are given below, based on AN prills = 100.

AN prills	100	AN/FO mixtures	150		
Slurries	185 – 500	Emulsions	300 – 900	Seismic types	1000 – 1500.

Table 5:   Representative trade names of products

Manufacturer	AN prills	AN/FO	Slurries (NCS)	Emulsions (NCS)
AECI	Nitropril			
Apache	FGAN	Carbamite Carbagel		
Atlas		Pellite HD		Powermax Apex Plus Power AN
Austin		Austinite	Hydromite	Hydromite Heet #
CIL		Anfomet * Amex II Lomex II	Aquamex	
DANTEX			Tovex 620, 650	
DNW		Ammonit C		
DYNAG		Andex 1 #		Nobelit
DYNO		Anolit	Trialit Slurrit	Emulite Emulan
EBCW	PERMON 10	PERMON DAP	PERMON Extra 11	EMSIT EMSITAN #
ECP	Prillex D7	Ammospex Ammoblast	Delta	
ERT		Nagolita AN-FOS Alnafo	Riogel Riogur	Riomex

Table 5 (continued): Representative trade names of products

Manufacturer	AN prills	AN/FO	Slurries (NCS)	Emulsions (NCS)
ETCAN		FRAGMAX FRAGPAK Nilite FR Nilite FRM-5 * Nilite WR	Tovex P Tovan Super Pourvex	
ETI		ANFO-P Nilite ANFO Extra#	Tovex Tovex Extra Tovex Extra A * Tovan Tovan WR % Pourvex Extra Pourvan 100	ANFO Extra # Tovex E #
EXSA		Examon	Primoflo Slurrex	
ICIA	Nitropril	ANFO AMEX Energan #	IREGEL * Powergel 1500 Aquapour Molanite	Pulsar Powergel 3131 Energan#
IDL		Energel Supergel *	Emulking Supermix #	
IEL		GN/1	Powerflo GMX Slurry	Powergel
IIE		Ammogex Aldinex		
IRECO	Super prills	ANFO IREMEX #	IREGEL SMS Blast Gel	IREGEL Blastex
Kemira		Anfo		Kemiiti500
KIMIT		Kimanol		Kimulux
NEF		ANFO NF4		
NKC		ANFO		
NOBEX	Anopril	Nobelite Anobel	Powergel	Powergel
SFE		Anfotite	Sigma 89 Hydrolite	
SLEX			Slurran 600 SLX	
SSE		Anolit	Tovex S,A,T	
Titanite		Anfotite Ferrolite		
WAHNL		Wapril		Emulite
WEST				HANAL 1, 1U HANAL 3 *

* Aluminized # ANFO/Emulsion blend % ANFO/Slurry blend

References

[1]   E. I. DuPont de Nemours & Co., *Blasters' Handbook,* 175th Anniv. ed. (Wilmington, DuPont, 1977)

[2]   M. A. Cook, "Modern Blasting Agents", *Science,* Vol. 132, No. 3434 (21 October 1969)

[3]   M. A. Cook, *The Science of Industrial Explosives* (Salt Lake City, IRECO Chemicals, 1974)

[4]   R. A. Dick, "Explosives and Borehole Loading", ed. I. A. Given, *SME Mining Engineering Handbook,* (New York, AIME, 1973)

[5]   K. Hino and M. Yokogawa, *Ammonium Nitrate-Fuel-Surfactant Explosives. Their Fundamentals and Performance,* ed. G. B. Clark, International Symposium on Mining Research, University of Missouri School of Mines & Metallurgy (London, Pergamon, 1962)

[6]   R. W. Coxon, "Ammonium Nitrate Explosives – Some Experimental Mixes", paper delivered to AusIMM Annual Conference, Port Pirie, South Australia, 1963

[7]   R. W. Coxon, "The Use of Surface Active Agents to Sensitize ANFO Mixtures", paper delivered to AusIMM Annual Conference, Kalgoorlie, West Australia, 1964

[8]   W. C. Maurer, "Detonation of Ammonium Nitrate in Small Drill Holes", *Quarterly of the Colorado School of Mines,* Vol. 58, No. 2 (April 1963)

[9]   R. A. Dick, "Factors in Selecting and Applying Commercial Explosives and Blasting Agents", *U S Bureau of Mines, I.C.* 8405,1968

[10] J. J. Yancik, "ANFO Manual" (St. Louis, Monsanto Company, 1969)

[11] B. G. Fish, "Ammonium Nitrate as a Bulk Blasting Agent", *The Quarry Managers' Journal,* June, July, August, 1961

[12] B. G. Fish, "Slurry Explosives and Their Application", *The Quarry Managers' Journal,* Feb. 1972

[13] R. A. Dick, "The Impact of Blasting Agents and Slurries on Explosives Technology", *U.S. Bureau of Mines, I.C.* 8560, 1972

[14] Atlas Blasting Data Sheets, 706, 715 (1987)

[15] P. Brett *et al.*, "Explosive Sensitization: Microsphere Effect", *J. of Explosives Engineering*, Vol. 2, Nos. 2, 3 (1984)

CHAPTER 5

Initiating Devices

General

High explosives (and blasting agents) are designed to be relatively stable for safe handling, transport, and storage. They cannot readily be initiated by the application of heat by burning (as is the case with low explosives) because, although they will burn, their explosive power cannot be adequately developed or controlled by this method.

In order to initiate high explosives (and blasting agents), a powerful localized shock or detonation is required. This is accomplished by means of a *detonator* incorporated in a cartridge of dynamite or gelatine to form a *primer,* or, in a prefabricated initiating unit, sometimes termed a *booster.* Alternatively, *detonating cord* may be used.

All detonators consist of a metal tube or shell (of copper or aluminium) which is closed at one end and into which is pressed a base charge of PETN (penta-erythritol-tetra-nitrate) or of other initiating explosive. On this is superimposed a mixture of sensitive explosives to prime the base charge. This mixture usually contains lead azide and lead styphnate with a little aluminium powder and is referred to as the priming charge.

Plain Detonators (Blasting Caps)

This type of detonator is the simplest and is used for all general purposes under relatively dry non-gassy conditions and particularly where single independent charges are fired.

The detonator is ignited by means of a safety fuse, which is inserted into the open end as far as it will go and fixed in position by "crimping" the mouth of the tube to the fuse (see Chapter 6).

The No. 6 strength of plain detonators is in general use. Tubes are approximately $1/4$ in diameter and $1^3/8$ in long. They are packed in lots of 100 in a small cardboard box in case lots of 5,000 (see Fig. 4). No. 8 plain detonators are used in cases where a more powerful detonating effect is required. They are longer than, but of the same diameter as, the No. 6, and have twice the strength. Both types are supplied in aluminium shells.

Plain detonators store well for long periods. However, they are readily susceptible to desensitization under damp or wet conditions. In order to prevent this they should be waterproofed after crimping.

Fig. 4:   No. 6 plain detonators

Conventional (Standard) Electric Detonators (Instantaneous)

These are of the same general construction as plain detonators except that an electric bridge wire is provided, and the mouth of the detonator tube is sealed with a plastic plug through which pass the plastic covered leg / lead wires (see Fig. 5).

On the passage of a suitable electric current, the bridge wire of the fusehead "fuses", becomes incandescent and ignites the priming charge. For all practical purposes, the detonator is fired *instantaneously,* i.e., at the same time as the current is applied.

The leg wires are usually supplied in plastic covered 22 AWG tinned copper for normal applications; or with tinned iron wires for coal or salt mines; or aluminium wires for talc and white clay mining.

Cap shells are usually of copper or bronze for most applications (necessarily so for coal mining), but aluminium shells are also available. Electric detonators (EB caps) are sold with leg wires in a number of standard lengths ranging from 4 to 60 ft in steps for copper; but because of its lower conductivity, seldom more than 16 ft for iron wires. Leg wires are folded or bundled in a special way to minimize kinking when being extended during the charging process. Each bundle is plainly labelled or banded with the length of leg/lead wire (Fig. 5).

As a safety precaution against premature explosion due to possible stray currents, the wire ends of all EB caps are completely shielded with a metal foil or plastic *shunt* which is designed to remain in place until the final act of connecting the blasting circuits is in process. Such *shunt* protection also serves to keep wire ends clean and bright until connections are actually made.

Fig. 5: Instantaneous electric detonator

Instantaneous EB caps are supplied in copper, bronze or aluminium shells in both No. 6 and No. 8 strengths. For seismic applications, No. 8 caps are prepared in copper or bronze shells only.

Trade names of electric detonators supplied by various manufacturers are set in Table 6. Electric delay detonators are dealt with in Chapter 9.

Special Electric Detonators

The above paragraph refers to conventional electric detonators. But in recent years, some special types of electric detonators have been developed. They are generally not compatible with conventional (standard) electric detonators as described above.

Special electric detonators are manufactured and supplied by Schaffler & Co. and France Explosifs for use in central Europe.

Schaffler produces three basic types of detonator: the normal type A, and two other types of lower sensitivity for special purposes, as outlined in Table 7. All three types can be supplied as instantaneous or delay detonators. Specifications are given in the table.

Other manufacturers in Europe, such as ERT, DNAG and Italesplosivi produce detonators of similarly differing degrees of sensitivity. Operators should check the properties with the particular manufacturer concerned.

In Germany and Switzerland, the equivalent of FIDUZ and POLEX detonators are referred to as U and HU types, respectively.

Some manufacturers supply detonators designed to withstand high water pressures (for underwater blasting applications); and for high temperatures.

For further details on Special electric detonators, see Chapter 9.

Detonating Cord

Another initiating device is *detonating cord* which consists of a core of initiating explosive (usually PETN) contained within a plastic sheath and wrapped in various combinations of textile, wire and plastic coverings.

Although safe to handle, detonating cord (DC) can be regarded as a continuous detonator with a VOD of 6,500 m/sec, when initiated with a detonator (plain or electric) strapped or otherwise connected to the free end. To enable a network or trunkline of detonating cord to initiate each of several charges in a blast, the DC downlines are laced through a cartridge, or threaded through a cast booster (for blasting agents) to form the primer. See Chapter 8 for further details.

Primers and Boosters

The *primer* is the key element in a charge of explosives. It is a high-density explosive unit designed to provide a high velocity and a high detonation pressure for adequate

Table 6:   Trade names of instantaneous electric detonators as supplied by various manufacturers

Manufacturer (for code see Chapter 1)	Normal	Seismic
AECI	IED No. 6	IED No. 8 Star
Atlas	SF No. 6	Staticmaster No. 8
Austin		Seismic Star
DNAG	Delay No. 0 (U type) Momentzünder	Seismic U-S
DuPont/DPW	No. 8 instantaneous	Seismodet SSS SSS Seismograph No. 8
DNW	Instantaneous No. 8, 10	
DYNO	Instantaneous	Seismic
ECP	Instantaneous No. 6/8	
ERT	Instantáneo S	Sismicos SS
FAMESA	Fulmelec Inst	Fulmelec SSS
ICIA	Inst No. 6 Inst No. 8	Seismic No. 8 star
IDL	Instantaneous No. 6, 8	
IEL	Instantaneous	
IIE	Inst No. 8	
IRECO	Instadet No. 8	Vibrodet No. 8
Italesplosivi	Instantaneous No. 8	Seismic
Kemira	Vihtavuori inst	
NEF	Z series (S, V Range)	
NKC	Inst No. 6	Seismic No. 8
SCH	Schaffler Inst type A Schaffler Inst type F	Type SA Type SF
Titanite	Davey-Bickford DEI	Davey-Bickford DESTP

Table 7:   Three basic types of detonator produced by Schaffler

Schaffler	Units	Normal A type (sensitive)	FIDUZ (insensitive)	POLEX (highly insensitive)
Bridge wire resistance	ohms*	1.5	0.6	0.06
Firing impulse (energy)	mWs/ohm	1.8	14	1900
Approx. ratio of firing impulse	–	1	10	1000
Assured firing impulse (to be supplied by exploder)	mWs/ohm	4	20	3300
Lowest limit for initiation	amp	0.2	0.6	4.0
Current required for safe firing of 5 dets in series	amp	0.8	1.8	25

* Mean values.
  Exceptionally well-insulated leading wires are required for firing POLEX detonators.
  Seismic detonators (type SA) have same characteristics as A type detonators, and type SF correspond to FIDUZ detonators. They have a high degree of firing uniformity and a reaction time of less than one msec.

Fig. 6:   Various sizes and shapes of cast boosters

Fig. 7:   Detonating cord threaded through (and looped
          around) a cast booster

initiation of the main charge. It also provides a reliable base for locating the detonator in a firm position in the charge.

For small underground holes where cartridged dynamites or gelatines are used, the charge can be adequately "primed" for initiation with a primer made from one of the cartridges and a detonator.

With blasting agents, however, the initiation sensitivity is so low that a high velocity primer is required. For small diameter holes, up to 62 mm, a cartridge of high velocity gelatine is sufficient. But for larger diameter holes on the surface, the shape of the unit becomes an important consideration. For a given weight of the unit, the diameter is usually considered more important than its length, because it should correspond proportionately with blasthole diameter in order to project a detonation wave axially rather than laterally. Because a large diameter cartridge of gelatine would give an unnecessary length dimension, it became obvious that such priming units should be specially designed and manufactured for priming blasting agents loaded in bulk.

This provided an opportunity to prepare special factory-made cast boosters* of high velocity, and of a useful range of shapes, along with a pre-formed well to accommodate a detonator, or a small diameter hollow core through which to thread detonating cord (see Figs. 6 and 7). However, only those boosters that have cap wells are recommended for use with detonators.

Many of these cast boosters are made of pentolite, a mixture of TNT and PETN, and are therefore not readily detonable by shock, heat or friction. Procore (protected core) boosters consist of TNT cast around a pentolite core.

A new style of primer is the Magna Primer, a plastic unit incorporating a cast pentolite charge containing two in-built Magnadets, as designed and manufactured by the ICI Explosives Group; and by REO in the USA.

When blasting agents are cartridged in flexible plastic tubing, it is not always practicable to use cast boosters. For these purposes, a new type of booster has been developed. These may be logically termed *slim boosters* because they are prepared as a thin sheath to accommodate the detonator, which can then be entered into a plastic cartridge to form a primer after cutting a small opening at one end. Otherwise, they can be used in small diameter holes (less than 50 mm) pneumatically loaded with AN/FO.

For seismic blasting using a string of interlocking screwed cans of blasting agents, one such special can of the string contains a seismic booster, which has provision for arming with a seismic detonator, or detonating cord.

Trade names of various boosters marketed by different manufacturers are given in Table 8 overleaf.

Particular *Slider primer* assemblies (armed with special detonators) are supplied by some manufacturers. They are designed for specific types of downlines, detonators and delay mechanisms to match the main and/or deck charges. Some of these are also listed in this table.

---

* It should be noted that, strictly speaking, a primer is an explosive unit already armed with detonator. Therefore, a booster unit, as it comes from the factory, should not be termed a "primer" until it is so armed. In the interests of safety, such loose terminology should be avoided.

Table 8:   Trade names of various boosters

Manufacturer (for code see Ch. 1)	Cast or cartridged boosters	Slider primers	Slim boosters	Seismic boosters
Atlas	Power Primer Atlas G Hi-prime Pentex	Deckmaster sliding delay primer		Seisprime
Austin	ACP	ADP	Silver Nuggets Gold Nuggets	Austimon
BIQ	Britanite Britex			
CIL	Pentex 16, 12, 8 Magna	CIL Slider		
DANTEX	Tovex Primer			
DPW	HDP Detadrive	Detaslide ADP slider	Detaprime	
DuPont	HDP Detadrive	Detaslide	Detaprime	HDS Nitramon S
ERT	Multiplicador			
ETCAN	Boostrite		Detaprime	
ETI	Cor-det 3 SD Primer			
FAMESA	Booster	Fame Master		Sismic X
GOEX	Go Blast			
ICIA	Anzomex	Anzomex slider		Anzomex Miniseis
IDL	Pentolite			
IRECO	Titan G Extra Gelatin Ireprime		Anfodet	
NAX	Cast booster		Slip-on booster	
NEF	Boostex 65			
Sierra	Cast booster			
Trojan	Super Prime		Trojan	Hydratol S

CHAPTER 6

Firing with Conventional Safety Fuse

General

This method involves the initiation of a high explosive charge by a plain detonator which has been ignited by *safety fuse.*

The basic rationale of safety fuse is the built-in safety feature provided. It is a device that burns at a closely controlled regulated rate, so that a given length represents an equivalent interval of time. In other words, a fuse of a certain length can be selected to provide adequate time for the shotfirer to retreat to a place of safety. It is of course paramount that the length of the shortest fuse used in any particular firing should provide ample time with a wide margin for safety.

Safety fuse was invented by *William Bickford* in 1831, as a safe means of initiating black powder charges. It is still used today for this purpose. It is mainly used, when "capped" with a plain detonator, for initiating high explosives.

Safety fuse consists of a central core of specially formulated black powder formed around a centre strand of cotton, supported by and enclosed in various textile wrappings and waterproofing materials to protect it from mechanical damage and from external oil or moisture.

Some fuses incorporate a plastic sleeve in their construction. This aims to provide better resistance to water and AN/FO oil; and to mechanical damage and static electricity. Storage qualities are also enhanced.

In order that safety fuse may be readily distinguished in grey rock, black coal or in light-coloured mineral headings, it is available in orange, white or black outer coverings with a heavy wax finish to provide a good crimping surface.

Safety fuse should be stored in a cool dry well-ventilated storage area, separated from contact with oils, paints, kerosene or similar solvents, which could cause deterioration by penetrating the outer covering. Fuse should be stored at temperatures between 10 and 38 °C (50 and 100 °F), and at low relative humidity. Older stocks should be used first.

Trade names of safety fuse marketed by various manufacturers are given in Table 9.

Table 9:   Trade names of safety fuse

Manufacturer (for code see Ch. 1)	Brand	Standard burning speed
AECI	Safety fuse	99–121 sec/m
CIL	Black Clover	110 sec/yd ± 10%
Coast	Sequioa	120 sec/yd ± 10%
DNW	Safety fuse	120 sec/m ± 10%
DYNO	Safety fuse	105–130 sec/m
EBCO/CMMPM	Sword	120 sec/yd ± 10%*
ERT	Mecha lenta	120 sec/m
FAMESA	Mecha de Seguridad	145 sec/m
IEL	Blue Sump / OCPS / Blue Plastic	100–120 sec/m
ITPL	Safety fuse	110 sec/m ± 10%
NEF	UniKord	120 sec/m
NKC	No. 2 cotton safety fuse	110–140 sec/m
NOBEX	White safety fuse Orange safety fuse	100–125 sec/m 135–160 sec/m
WAHNL	Safety fuse	90–110 sec/m

* subject to test

Safety fuse and igniter cord cannot be used in underground coal mines.

Fig. 8:   Typical packages of safety fuse

As a service to their customers, all explosives manufacturers handle orders for safety fuse and other components.

With the use of safety fuse, it is of course paramount that the length of the shortest fuse used in any particular firing should provide ample time for the shotfirer to withdraw to a place of safety.

Local regulations in some cases provide that the minimum length of fuse shall be 2 m for general blasting and 130 cm for "blockholing". Longer minimum lengths are prescribed for shaft sinking. The breaching of such regulations is regarded by all concerned as a very serious matter.

Preparation of Capped Fuse

The crimping of safety fuse to a plain detonator (i.e., the "capping of fuse") can be performed either with a bench-mounted Detonator Crimper (Fig. 9) or with an approved type of hand crimping pliers (Fig. 10). Both incorporate a fuse-cutter and crimping jaws.

The Detonator Crimper is universally used where large numbers of capped fuses (incorrectly termed "fuse primers") are made each day in central capping stations on surface or on underground levels.

The hand crimping pliers (Fig. 10) are used for isolated *ad hoc* capping by prospectors, farmers, road gangers, and small quarry and mine operators, where a few charges are fired infrequently.

The prescribed safe series of operations for hand crimping is as follows:

1. Cut squarely across the fuse to the standard length required.
2. Remove detonator carefully from cardboard box (Fig. 4).
3. Insert freshly and squarely cut end of fuse into detonator as far as possible without using force; avoid using a twisting action.
4. Crimp mouth of detonator over fuse evenly.
5. Dip in waterproofing compound so that the whole of the detonator and about one inch of the fuse is submerged.
6. Avoid squeezing or pressing (or applying heat to) the closed end of the detonator.

It is very important to cut the end of the fuse squarely so that the end of the powder train is in close contact with the surface of the priming charge in the detonator, as in Fig. 11(a). If the fuse end is cut on the slant, as in Fig. 11(b), the "end spit" (see later) may not ignite the priming charge and a misfire will occur.

The procedure with the detonator crimper is similar except that the detonator is inserted into the machine, the fuse is entered until it meets the charge, and the lever operating the crimping jaws is depressed. An escape chamber is usually embodied in the detonator crimper to localize safely an accidental explosion.

Where igniter cord (IC) is used, the metal IC connector can also be crimped to the free end of the capped fuse (see later).

Fig. 9: Bench-mounted detonator crimper for cutting and capping safety fuse

Fig. 10: Method of cutting safety fuse and crimping plain detonator to fuse with hand crimping pliers

Methods of Igniting Safety Fuse

By lighting the safety fuse (with a hot flame, see later) a jet of flame known as "ignition spit" is observed by the shotfirer, giving him positive evidence that the fuse is alight and functioning normally. The burning powder then travels slowly along the length of the fuse (while the shotfirer retires to a place of safety) until it reaches the other end, which has been "crimped" into the detonator, as in Fig. 11. Here a jet of flame (referred to as "end spit") ignites the priming charge (and then the base charge) in the detonator, and the main explosive charge is thereby safely initiated.

Fig. 11: Correct and incorrect methods of cutting safety fuse before crimping to a detonator

Types of fuse lighters in use are:

1. **Hot wire fuse lighter**: This is a stiff wire (7, 9 or 12 inches long) coated with an incendiary composition that burns slowly with an intensely hot fire zone. This flare is held against the freshly cut end of fuse to be lighted. This type of lighter must not be used as a timing device.

2. **Pull wire fuse lighter**: The freshly cut fuse end is inserted in the open end of the lighter until it touches the end of the wire, which is then deliberately pulled, setting off a mechanical lighting arrangement.

3. **Lead spitter**: A thin lead tube filled with black powder, coiled in a 8 m length on a spool, is lighted at the free end and held against the freshly cut fuse end. The spitter gives an intensely hot flame which progressively burns the tube away. The lead tube is paid out as required and finally cut off behind the flame as the lighting operation is completed.

4. **Match, match-head, cigarette lighter**: This practice is not recommended where more than one fuse is to be lighted.

5. **Fuse Igniter**: A 15 cm long hollow tube of about 6 mm diameter, filled with pyrotechnic material. When lit, it produces an intensely hot flame for lighting individual fuses. It burns for about two minutes.

6. **Multiple Fuse Igniter**: A cylindrical cardboard tube, closed at one end (like a sporting cartridge), at the bottom of which a small quantity of gunpowder is adhered. The tube will hold eight safety fuses (as receptors) and a short master fuse, the free end of which is lit. This burns down to the gunpowder which then fires the eight active fuses.

7. **Igniter Cord (IC)**: see below

Igniter Cord (IC) System

Igniter cord (IC) is an automatic device for lighting any number of safety fuses in the desired sequence. It is a cord-like fuse burning with an intense flame progressively along its length at a fairly uniform rate. At certain points along its length it is connected to the safety fuses for the individual holes by a special metal connector, loaded with an incendiary composition. As the flame reaches each connector, it automatically lights each safety fuse in turn (Fig. 12).

Joints in the IC trunkline may be made by doubling the ends and tying a square knot.

Since IC gives a certain amount of time delay and may be operated from a remote point, fuses may be of shorter length; but never shorter than one metre.

The metal connectors are usually pre-crimped to the capped fuses; the IC trunkline is conveniently attached to the connectors by locating it in a special slot and closing it with moderate thumb pressure (Fig. 12).

Fig. 12: Igniter cord located by thumb presure in slotted end of metal connector which has previously been crimped to free end of capped fuse. When the flame of the burning IC reaches the connector, the fuse will be lit automatically.

Current trends show that the purchase of **Fuse Assemblies** from manufacturers will increase in future. They are factory-assembled capped fuses of various standard lengths equipped with metal IC connectors. These units are safer to handle and more reliable than field-assembled units. As this practice develops, the use of central capping stations (see below) will no doubt correspondingly wane.

Igniter cord is made in three colour types with different burning rates, for particular applications:

(a) **Fast** type: The cord burns rapidly enough to be clear of holes already exploding, such as in narrow longwall faces, in other than coal mines.

(b) **Medium speed** type: It burns rapidly enough to ignite all the fuses before the first shot explodes; and yet gives enough lead time between holes to fire in sequence (see Chapter 9). The distance between fuse connections should be two inches for every foot of fuse in a hole. Used typically in stope blasting.

(c) **Slow speed** type: It is designed for heading blasts in which many holes are to be fired in long sequences in a restricted area. Fuse connections should be spaced at a distance of one inch per ft of fuse in a hole. Sufficient time is thereby allowed to have each fuse lit before the first explodes; and yet with adequate lead time between sequential holes.

With any type of igniter cord, there is no need to trim fuses (see Chapter 9) because the firing sequence is adequately provided for in the IC circuit. On the other hand, the cord needs to be ignited at one point only, thus providing an excellent safety feature (Fig. 13).

Fig. 13: Lighting one end of an IC circuit which progressively lights all the safety fuses in turn as the IC flame reaches the particular connector

Fig. 14: Igniter cord packed a) in 33 ft pull-out spools, and b) on 100 ft plastic reels

It is important that all other fuses in the round are alight and burning before the first hole detonates. This means that the length of igniter cord between the first and the last fuses should represent a time interval shorter than that of the first fuse between ignition and detonation. This particular length of igniter cord is known as the *limiting cord distance.* It obviously depends upon the speed of the type of igniter cord used.

Fig. 15: Igniter cord connectors

All three types are marked clearly at intervals to enable distance gauging to be readily made. Each type is supplied on 100 ft plastic reels with 50 spools (5000 ft) to a box; or alternatively, in 33 ft pull-out spool packs (Fig. 14). The cord has a finished diameter of about 2 mm, and is fabricated with a core of thermite powder within wirebound textile wrappings. It is especially designed as a safe reliable method of firing a large number of holes sequentially with safety fuse in underground blasting applications other than in coal mines (Fig. 13).

Connectors are packed in boxes of 100, with 50 boxes (5000 connectors) per carton (Fig. 15).

Igniter cord is rather perishable and should not be stored for long periods, especially in a humid atmosphere. *It should never be used as a substitute for safety fuse.*

Igniter cords supplied by various manufacturers are given in Table 10.

Table 10: Igniter cords

Manufacturer (for code see Ch. 1)	Trade name	Fast	Medium	Slow
AECI	Slow Igniter Cord	–	–	30–45 sec/m
CIL	Thermalite	4 sec/ft	8 sec/ft	16 sec/ft
EBCO	Ignitacord	3–5 sec/ft	8–10 sec/ft	15–25 sec/ft
FAMESA	Ignitacord	26 sec/m	35 sec/m	59 sec/m
ICIA	Igniter Cord	1 sec/ft	–	10 sec/ft
NOBEX	Plastic Igniter Cord	5 sec/m	–	33 sec/m 50 sec/m

Preparation of a Primer Assembly

For large diameter holes on surface, and particularly where blasting agents are used, prefabricated cast boosters and slider primers are employed (see Chapter 5).

These are designed and manufactured with either a cap well (to accommodate a detonator) or an axial tunnel (through which detonating cord may be threaded) or both. There is therefore no problem in activating these boosters with the necessary detonating device.

However, for the small diameter holes employed in underground blasting (and for small scale surface blasts), it is customary to form a primer from a stick of high explosive (dynamite or gelatine) of the same grade as used for charging the round; or where AN/FO is used, from the standard grade utilized on the mine (but preferably, a gelatine).

Such a primer assembly would consist of a cartridge of high explosive into which a detonator has been placed. It can be an electric detonator or a capped fuse assembly (incorrectly referred to sometimes as a "fuse primer", even though it does not become a primer until it is incorporated in a plug of explosive or a booster).

The following describes two alternative methods of assembling a primer with a cartridge of dynamite or gelatine and a capped fuse.

Electric primers are dealt with in Chapter 7.

First method

1. Take a whole cartridge of high explosive; do not break it in halves; do not remove paper wrapping.
2. Form an opening about 5 cm deep axially in the end of the cartridge with a wooden skewer or with a brass or copper "pricker".
3. Insert the detonator end of the capped fuse into the hole so formed until the detonator is completely buried in the explosive cartridge.

A variation of this method is first to open the wrapping on the end of the cartridge and (after the detonator has been placed) to restore the wrapping and, if desired, to tie it round the fuse with twine.

Second method

1. Take a full cartridge of explosive; do not remove wrapping.
2. With a wooden or copper "pricker" form a diagonal opening about 5 cm deep in the side of and near one end of the cartridge.
3. Insert the detonator end of the capped fuse into the hole so that the detonator is completely buried.
4. Fasten the capped fuse to the cartridge with string. (For this purpose hemp twine is supplied with the capped fuse, hitched around the fuse about 15 mm from the crimp).

The advantage of the second method is that the fuse is not disturbed or deformed by the tamping pole when charging the hole, but the detonator cannot be placed in a truly axial position.

The main essentials of a primer are that:

1. The detonator should not become dislodged from the cartridge.
2. The detonator should be in the safest position in the cartridge.
3. The primer should be capable of being loaded safely and easily into its desired position in the hole without damage to the fuse.
4. The detonator should be inserted deeply into the cartridge (i.e., buried) and should lie as far as possible with its long axis along the centre line of the cartridge.
5. The closed end of the detonator should point towards the larger bulk of the cartridge. In other words, the mouth of the detonator should be next to the nearer end of the cartridge.

Central Capping Stations

Central capping stations are set up on medium and large mines and quarries where a large volume of capped fuse is used per day.

By centralizing these activities, the benefits of specialization are achieved. Skilled operators, and well-designed measuring, cutting, crimping, waterproofing, and coiling equipment are thus available under conditions of efficiency and safety. Routine tests can also be made of the output.

A special fireproof room, well-ventilated and secure, is constructed specially for the purpose. It embraces a receiving annexe for cases of reeled fuse, detonators, and waterproofing compounds. It also includes a storage annexe for the storage of different categories of standard lengths of capped fuse ready for issue.

The main section contains a working bench. Over the feed end is a bracket to hold a 1,000 m reel of fuse as supplied by the manufacturer, an automatic machine for measuring and cutting the desired standard length of fuse, a Detonator Crimper on which the fuse is crimped to the detonator, and a waterproofing dip tank. Automatic fuse-cutting machines at present in use have a capacity of 900 fuses per hour.

The chief advantages of a central capping station are:

1. Production of more uniformly accurate lengths of capped fuse.
2. Proper cutting of fuses.
3. More effective crimping.
4. Better waterproofing.
5. The opportunity to test.
6. Fewer misfires.
7. More efficient blasting.
8. Better supervision.
9. Improved conditions of safety.
10. IC connectors may be crimped to the free end of the capped fuse in a more efficient manner than by hand at the face.

BIQ produces capped fuse in various lengths, in two styles, for either dry or wet conditions, under the trade name of Britaprim.

CHAPTER 7

Electric Shotfiring

General

Interest was first aroused in electric blasting procedures over a century ago when *Siegfried Markus* [1] built an electric blasting machine for "spark-detonators". In 1876, *H. Julius Smith* invented the first electric detonator as we know it today. Electric shotfiring was introduced into the United States about twenty years later [2].

Blasting by electrical means has great technical and economic advantages over fuse firing. For many reasons, firing by safety fuse and plain detonators was restricted in the past to a limited number of shots and to other than underground coal mines. With electric firing, an almost unlimited array of charges can be fired, all with a single act (of pressing a button or actuating a switch), in a safe place (remote from the blast site) and in a deliberate manner. There are other advantages, mainly in the promotion of safety.

Electric blasting methods are in general use with either instantaneous or delay detonators, employing either exploders (blasting machines) or power mains as the source of the electrical impulse.

Exploder firing is relatively simple, but the number of holes per blast is limited by the capacity of the exploder.

Power mains of from 110 to 440 volts pressure are used for major blasting operations; by this method, a much greater number of holes per blast is possible. With AC mains, larger minimum currents are required than for DC circuits.

In all electrical methods, care should be taken to minimize the circuit resistance due to loose and dirty connections, and current leakage due to poor insulation.

Preparation of Electric Primers

Each electric detonator is supplied intact with plastic covered leg wires in standard lengths of 120 to 370 cm and longer. The primer is prepared in the following way:

1. Take a full-sized cartridge of high explosive.

2. With a wooden or nonferrous pricker, make an axial hole in the end of the cartridge.

3. Insert the detonator in this hole until it is completely buried.

4. Secure the detonator to the cartridge by half-hitching the leg wires once or twice around the cartridge (Fig. 16).

5. Keep ends of the leg wires shunted and clear of all possible electric circuits.

Fig. 16: Electric primer (the EB cap is located axially in one end and the leg wires are looped (half-hitched) one (as is shown) or twice around the cartridge to avoid dislodging the cap during the charging procedure

Blasting Circuits

In any electrical blasting circuit [3], there are three basic elements:

(1) The source of electrical energy,

(2) the electric blasting caps, and

(3) the blasting circuit connecting the energy source with the EB caps.

It is customary to consider this blasting circuit in three distinct parts as set out below.

(a) The *leg wires* that are integral with the detonators. The free ends of each pair of EB cap wires are kept shunted (short-circuited) until the circuit is finally ready to be connected, immediately prior to blasting.

(b) The *connecting wires* that are sometimes necessary to extend the circuit between the leg wires and the permanent firing line. These wires are usually of 20 gauge solid soft-drawn copper, or of 18 gauge three-quarter-hard electrical-grade aluminium, either single or duplex, with vinyl insulation, packaged on metal spools. Resistances for both types average 10.3 ohms per 1,000 ft (at 68 °F). These

Table 11: Nominal resistance of No. 8 electric detonators
(in ohms, with 23 AWG copper or iron leg wires)

Length of leg wires (ft)	Instantaneous detonators		Delay detonators	
	copper	iron	copper	iron
4	1.40	2.25	1.65	2.50
6	1.50	2.75	1.75	3.00
8	1.60	3.25	1.85	3.50
10	1.65	3.75	1.90	4.00
12	1.75	4.25	2.00	4.50
14	1.80	4.75	2.05	5.00
16	1.90	5.25	2.15	5.50
20	2.05	6.25	2.30	6.50
24	2.22	7.25	2.50	7.50

Note: The above data are listed by Hercules [4]. Detonators of other manufacturers have different resistance values, depending mainly upon that of the bridge wire and the gauge and type of leg wires. Manufacturers use bridge wires of different resistance; therefore, it is necessary to avoid mixing detonators of different manufacture in the same blasting circuit.

connecting wires are usually damaged or destroyed at each firing, and should be long enough to prevent damage to the permanent firing line (leading wires).

(c) The *firing line.* This is not damaged when blasting from power mains is practised, and therefore a heavy gauge low resistance firing line is installed as a durable installation. Except where long distances are involved, 14 gauge copper (or 12 gauge aluminium) wires are generally used, giving a resistance of about 2.6 ohms per 1,000 ft.

For certain operations, e.g., in smaller quarries, a compromise is sometimes adopted, by using an 18 gauge 2-conductor flexible stranded copper *shotfiring cord* to replace both the connecting wires and firing line mentioned above. In this case, the resistance is about 6.4 ohms per 1,000 ft.

The average resistances of conventional electric detonators used in North America can be inferred from Table 11. But it should be realized that the special electric detonator types mentioned in Chapter 5 have quite different resistances and current requirements. See Chapter 9 for further details.

In routine blasting operations, the capability of the whole circuit is usually well established, and current practices can be successfully maintained. However, for special or trial blasts, initial calculations need to be made in order to determine the electrical resistance of the circuit and the current characteristics of the power line (or the capacity of the exploder), so that sufficient current will flow to ensure a satisfactory blast.

It will therefore be necessary to calculate the total resistance of the circuit, including that of EB caps, connecting wire and the firing line. It will also depend upon the type of circuit adopted – whether straight series, straight parallel, or parallel-series.

For small rounds, straight series or parallel circuits are used. But where a large number of detonators is involved in the one firing, a parallel-series circuit is employed.

The current required to fire an electric detonator depends, within limits, upon the length of time the current is applied. A current of 0.5 amperes would cause ignition of the fusehead within 0.05 seconds; however, a higher current would effect ignition within a shorter period of time.

To fire detonators connected in *series,* a current larger than that necessary to fire a single detonator is essential. If a small current, sufficient to fire one detonator only, were passed through a *series* of several detonators, a relatively long period of time would be necessary before all the fuseheads reached ignition temperature. During this period, one or more detonator fuseheads might be raised to ignition temperature and fire before the others, resulting in a breaking of the circuit with the consequent interruption of current flow. Under such circumstances, a number of detonators in the circuit would fail to fire.

If, however, the current had been sufficiently high, say 1.5 amperes, all the electric detonators would have exploded because the fusing or breaking of the circuit could not have occurred before all the bridge wires had attained a temperature sufficiently high to ignite the fuseheads. For this reason, when electric detonators are connected in *series,* the current must be high enough to ensure that the explosion of one or more does not break the circuit before the remaining detonators have time to function.

Where instantaneous or zero delays of half-second or short delay detonators are included in the circuit, it is particularly important to have sufficient current because the firing of the fusehead of one such detonator ahead of the remainder is almost immediately followed by the firing of the detonator base charge, and this, of course, results in the rupture of the circuit.

If, however, a current lower than recommended were passed through a circuit of delay detonators only, misfires would be less likely to occur than if instantaneous or zero delays were also present. This is because the detonator base charge of the delay detonators does not fire until after the delay element has burned through. This gives a longer time interval for the current to flow. Consequently, there is a higher probability that these delay detonators will function correctly on a low current.

In practice, insufficient current through a circuit may be caused by (a) high resistance of the circuit due to loose or dirty connections; (b) attempting to fire a larger number of detonators than the exploder is rated to fire; (c) pushing the exploder handle down with insufficient force; (d) a faulty exploder; (e) voltage of the power supply falling below the designed level; or (f) current leakages due to poor insulation.

Every care must be taken with electric blasting to ensure that adequate current is supplied to the detonator circuit.

Blasting machines (exploders) provide DC current and are best adapted for series circuits.

Experience has shown that the minimum current in a straight series circuit should be 1.5 amperes DC or 3.0 amperes AC; and for series-in-parallel (parallel-series) the minimum current (DC or AC) should be 2.0 amperes in each series. For straight parallel circuits, the firing current (DC or AC) should be not less than one ampere per detonator, nor more than ten amperes if arcing within the detonator is to be avoided [3].

Circuit Calculations (for conventional detonators)

1. *Series circuit:* The circuit is as shown:

In series firing, the complete circuit can be accurately tested for continuity. The firing current should be at least 1.5 amperes in order to ensure that each detonator functions properly in a DC circuit.

As an example, let us assume that we have 50 electric delay detonators with 8 ft leg wires (assuming each of 1.6 ohms resistance) and that we are using 100 yd of 20 AWG connecting wire and 100 yd of 14 gauge firing line.

To determine the voltage required, we calculate:

Resistance of 50 electric detonators	80.0 ohms
Resistance of connecting wire (2 x 300 x 10.3/1000)	6.2 ohms
Resistance of firing line (2 x 300 x 2.6/1000)	1.5 ohms
Total resistance	87.7 ohms

Voltage necessary: 1.5 x 87.7 = 132 volts approx.

Series circuits are not commonly employed with mains current. They call for a low current at high voltages.

When more than 40 detonators are to be wired into a blasting circuit, it is preferable to use a parallel-series circuit. It is not advisable to fire more than 50 detonators in a straight series circuit.

2. *Parallel circuit:* In this circuit, each detonator provides an alternative path for the current.

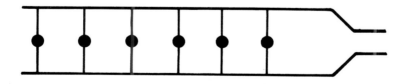

The complete circuit cannot therefore be tested for continuity, but individual detonators can be tested with an approved ohmmeter prior to charging.

For parallel firing, a minimum current of 1.0 ampere (AC or DC) is usually allowed per detonator.

Then:

Resistance of 50 detonators	0.03 ohms
Resistance of connecting wire	6.20 ohms
Resistance of firing line	1.50 ohms
Total resistance	7.73 ohms

Current: $1.0 \times 50 = 50$ amperes

Required voltage: $7.73 \times 50 = 387$ volts.

3. *Parallel-series circuit*: This is arranged as a number of series circuits connected in parallel. Each series circuit will have approximately the same resistance since it should contain the same number of detonators. No more than 40 detonators should be used in each series circuit

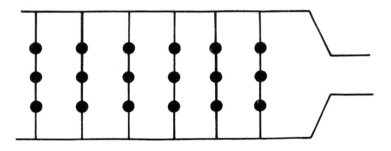

The total resistance of the circuit is given by the resistance of a series divided by the number of series in parallel plus the resistance of cable connections. If the 50 detonators are arranged in 10 rows of 5 detonators, then the current required $= 1.5 \times 10 = 15$ amperes.

Total resistance: $(1.6 \times 5)/10 + 6.2 + 1.5 = 8.5$ ohms

Voltage required: $15 \times 8.5 = 128$ volts.

The number of series that can be used is limited by the current available, and the number of detonators in each series by the voltage.

This type of circuit is applicable to cases where 40 or more EB caps are to be fired, or where the series resistance would be unduly high, as, for example, in long-hole pattern stoping.

Current Leakage

Current leakage may be described as the current that escapes from a circuit to the ground, shortcircuits through the ground and returns to the circuit at a further point. In effect, a parallel circuit is formed.

The extent of current leakage may vary considerably from one locality to another. The nature of the ground, the presence of matter in suspension or in solution in any water present, the number of partially earthed joints, and the general condition of the insulation throughout the circuit are factors that influence the results of the blast.

If a path through the ground offers a lower resistance than the detonator series circuit, an appreciable part of the current will flow through the ground path and by-pass the detonators. The effect of leakage is to produce a current gradient with the detonators in the centre of the circuit receiving less current than those at either end.

In order to minimize current leakage, boreholes should be well blown out before loading to prevent rock particles from abrading the leg wire insulation during charging operations. Bare connections should be well insulated. Avoid kinking the wires. It is sometimes found that twists or kinks occur in leg wires when they are being straightened prior to charging. The passage of the tamping stick past these twists in the borehole may damage the insulation, leading to short circuits, wire breakage, and to current leakage. The twists should be carefully straightened out individually. Tugging of the wires to straighten them may lead to wire breakage. Such breaks are difficult to detect if the insulation remains intact. However, if the wires are pulled, they should be held near, but not at the detonator, to avoid the wires becoming withdrawn from the detonator body.

Current leakage can become a serious problem in high conductive orebodies. In such ground, it may be necessary to reduce the number of detonators in a single series circuit, by connecting two or more series segments in parallel. This has the effect of reducing the total resistance, although the required current level increases. But each series segment should contain approximately the same number of detonators, so as to balance the resistances in each segment. In this way, the available current can be distributed equally throughout the series-in-parallel circuit. A current of 1.5 amperes should be provided for each series segment.

Shotfiring with Exploders

All exploders should be equipped with removable firing keys which are to be kept in the possession of the shotfirer.

For single shots, the leg wires of the detonators are bared and connected to the ends of the shotfiring cable. In retreat, the other ends of the shotfiring cable are connected to the terminals of the exploder which is set up at a safe distance. When all personnel have been cleared from the area, the shotfirer inserts the key and operates the exploder.

The exploder is also used to fire a multiplicity of shots, not exceeding its rated capacity.

Before firing, the electrical circuit can be proved by testing. At first, the permanent firing line is tested, (a) for continuity, and (b) for insulation failure.

When testing for continuity, the two wires at one end should first be twisted together. A blasting galvanometer connected to the wires at the other end will indicate the passage of a current and thus prove continuity; or, if an ohmmeter is used, the continuity can be tested and the circuit resistance determined directly from the ohmmeter reading.

For the insulation test, the ends of the firing line are left unconnected. The ohmmeter connected to the two wires at the other end should show that no current is flowing and that the resistance is infinite.

Next and in turn, the connecting wires and the detonator circuit are connected to the firing line and the complete circuit is tested from the firing position – not at the face. An approved ohmmeter must be used – one that employs a current sufficiently minute that risk of premature detonation during the test is avoided (see later).

For important blasting operations, it is generally considered advisable to test the circuit before every individual blast.

Shotfiring from Power Mains

Electrical energy from power mains is now commonly used for large scale blasts in underground metalliferous mines (for stoping and pillar recovery), in many large quarries and open cut mines, and for tunnelling and civil engineering construction operations.

When power mains are used, a much larger number of shots can be fired, under closely controlled conditions. Most systems utilize special permanently installed blasting circuits, incorporating locked switch boxes, firing boxes, and short-circuiting boxes to give maximum protection against premature firing (see Fig. 17).

A more recent development is the provision of a master installation to serve a number of different unit stope circuits, incorporating built-in switching and circuit-testing arrangements. See Chapter 9.

Special precautions are required to prevent stray currents or accidental premature closing of the blasting switch by unauthorized persons. Switchgear is usually locked in cubicles or cabinets.

Care should be taken to ensure that the blasting switch is closed only for a moment. Prolonged closure may result in a "flashover" or arc from the brass foils of the fusehead to the cap shell, due to an excessive amount of current (exceeding about 10 amperes), thereby causing a pinhole or misfire, and perhaps prematurely igniting rather than detonating the charge.

In order to prevent or minimize this "arcing", some detonator manufacturers provide an inbuilt shield around the bridge wire of the EB cap. Others seek a limit to the blasting current by using an electronic device. Typical of these is the Tunnel Blasting Switch (Atlas) and the CIL Blasting Switch.

In mines, the electric current for firing electric detonators is derived from power mains, and arrangements such as illustrated have been installed to ensure safety in use and freedom from premature blasts. In tunnelling operations also, power main firing is widely used. It is essential, with this method of firing, to incorporate as many safety features as possible to guard against lightning, stray currents, induced currents, and accidental or incorrect operation of firing switches.

FUSE BOX

power mains

metal case
main (double pole) switch

fuses
receptacle for
short cable from firing box

shorting
bar

ground

FIRING BOX

wooden box

pilot lamp
firing switch
(double pole)

plug in
connector
to fuse box

shorting bar

to short
circuiting box

**SHORT
CIRCUITING
BOX**

cable from firing box

wooden box

switch
(double pole)

shorting bar
to short cable
when switch is
in the off position

firing line to face

Fig. 17: Power main firing units

Position of firing lines

The cables for blasting should be used for this purpose only, and should be carried on insulators on the side remote from pipes, other cables, ventilation ducts, and other possible conductors of stray currents.

Firing units

To include as many safety features as possible in power main firing, three units including a fuse box with main switch, a firing box, and a shortcircuiting box should be used, or an arrangement giving equivalent protection against premature firing or faulty operation (see Fig. 17).

1. *Fuse box:* This unit consists of a grounded metal box containing fuses and a main switch, and is also fitted with a suitable receptacle for a plug-in connection between the fuse box and the firing box. The box may also be designed so that it can be closed only after the fuses are removed and the main switch has been placed in the "off" position.

2. *Firing box:* The firing box consists of a pilot light (to indicate the presence of a firing current), a firing switch, and a means for connecting between the fuse and firing box. The firing box which is of wooden construction is made in such a manner that the door can be closed only after the firing handle has been returned to the "off" position with the firing lines shorted.

The connection between the fuse box and firing box is made by means of a length of cable which can be plugged into the fuse box, the other end being permanently connected within the firing box. It is desirable that the fuse box should be situated on one side of the tunnel or drift and the firing box on the other. This arrangement ensures that there is an adequate electrical gap (lightning break) between these two units so that an electric current cannot pass from the fuse box to the firing box unless the connecting cable has been plugged in. A further advantage of the fuse box and firing box being on opposite sides of the tunnel or drift is that the connecting cable acts as an effective bar to traffic until it has been returned to its position within the firing box.

3. *Short-circuiting box:* The short-circuiting box situated between firing box and the face is an important unit which ensures that the blasting lines are disconnected from the cable and effectively shorted. The door of the short-circuiting box should be arranged in such a manner that it can be closed only after the short-circuiting switch has been returned to the "shorted" position. In this position, "stray" currents which might be induced in the blasting cables and which might cause a premature blast are shorted before reaching the detonator circuits.

It is important that the firing box and the short-circuiting box should be effectively insulated from the ground; consequently, ground connections must not be installed.

The firing line from the short-circuiting box is usually extended to about 12 m from the face; from this point the connections to the face network are made with expendable, lighter gauge insulated "connecting wire". As a safeguard against stray currents, it is important that the face ends of the firing line should be twisted together to short them effectively until they are actually connected. The firing line should be insulated from the ground.

Firing procedures

After connecting the blast in parallel, series, or parallel-series circuit, personnel should retire to the firing point, leaving the foreman or shift boss, who has the only key to the firing units, to make the connection to the firing line. On his way back to the firing box, he should unlock the short-circuiting box, test the circuit through to the face, and finally close the switch. He should then retreat to the firing box, unlock it, and take out the connecting cable. After the fuse box nearby is unlocked, this cable should be plugged into the fuse box and the main switch of the fuse box switched on. This supplies current to the pilot lamp in the firing box, thus indicating that the current is available for firing.

To fire the blast, the warning siren should first be sounded; the switch in the firing box should be closed for a moment, then **immediately** withdrawn and returned to the shorted position. The switch in the fuse box is then placed in the "off" position and the short circuiting cable returned to the firing box and both boxes locked. When returning to the face, the shift boss places the switch in the short-circuiting box in the shorted position, and the box is again locked. The end of the firing line nearer the face should then be shorted by twisting the ends together and keeping it insulated from the ground. Before the next blast, the firing line should be tested to ensure that it has not suffered damage during the blast.

As the tunnel advances, the short-circuiting box, firing box, and fuse box are moved forward at intervals. In general, the short-circuiting box should be located some 60 m back from the face, while the blasting box and fuse box should be at such a distance from the face that no danger exists from rocks projected back along the tunnel, or from air blast.

Wiring up the blast

In tunnelling, and especially where electric storms are prevalent, special care needs to be taken to avoid premature blasts due to lightning strikes, induced currents and static electricity. It should be emphasized however, that no protection is effective against a close lightning strike, and consequently, charging operations should be suspended on the approach of an electrical storm.

Detonators are normally supplied with the free ends of the leg wires shunted; this protection should be left in place until just prior to connecting them in the circuit.

Naturally, the ends of all wires to be connected should be thoroughly scraped and bared, with enamel insulation removed; so that they can be electrically connected with an effective twist splice.

Frequently, the parallel method of firing is employed, and under such conditions it is strongly recommended that leg wires of the same colour be connected to a common "bus-wire" at the face. This bus-wire is later connected to the regular connecting wire of the circuit. The advantage of bus-wires is that the face circuit can readily be checked by the shift boss; otherwise, it is possible for both wires of an individual detonator to be connected to the same connecting wire; in this event, a misfire will certainly result.

In recent years, more sophisticated units have no doubt been developed for firing from power mains. Yet the above discussion demonstrates the chief principles involved.

Power mains firing is not permitted in Germany.

Electric Shotfiring Accessories

1. **Exploders**: These are also referred to as Blasting Machines. There are two main types:

(a) The *Generator-type*, operated by a rackbar or a twist spindle, to rotate the armature of a small DC generator (see Figs. 18 and 19). As the generator develops full speed, a firing switch is automatically closed, thereby applying the generator current to the firing circuit to ignite the detonators; and

(b) the *Condenser discharge (CD) type,* used mainly for larger blasts. In principle, a charging button is pressed to build up a high voltage charge on a bank of condensers from a dry cell battery (Fig. 20). When fully charged, the firing button is depressed to discharge the condensers, thereby energizing the firing circuit. With some models the condensers are automatically charged. Others serve as sequential timing devices.

Both types of blasting machine are designed to produce a high voltage low DC current. Those currently available are shown in Table 12. The ratings shown refer to machines "as new" or in good condition, and within a specific circuit resistance.

Table 12: Blasting machines (exploders)

Manufacturer (for code see Chapter 1)	Model	Remarks
Generator Type:		
DuPont/CIL	No. 10	Twist type
	No. 10*	Twist type
	No. 50	Rackbar type
WASAG	ZEB/A	
	ZEB/FA	
Condenser Discharge Type:		
Atlas	800c TBS-5	Tunnel Blasting Switch
Davey Bickford	Alpha D42	Hand held. 175 ohms
	Dragon D48	Max. resistance, 50 ohms
	Jupiter D29-50N	
	Vulcain D29-50P	For highly sensitive dets
DuPont	CD-600	
	CD 48/32/12	Selfcharging types
	Mk 6*	Hand held. Series firing
	Mk 5	
	SS-2000	2000 dets, series in parallel
	SS-1000	
DYNO	Dynocon series	All types of dets
	CI 50VA	
	CI 160VA }	For VA dets only
	CID 300 VA	

Manufacturer (for code see Chapter 1)	Model	Remarks
EIT	HB series	
	HB 20P*	
	HB HCCR*	
	HBR series	
	Tandem 370/640	Delays 0-999 in 1 msec
	Tandem 370S/64S	Ten delays 0-9 (0-525 msec)
ERT	S-200*	Max series res, 200 ohms
	S-500	Max series res, 450 ohms
EXEX	Blast Programmer	Up to 1000 dets
ICI Group	Femco 20-shot*	
	CI-50	
	CIL 10 shot	
	CIL 500 shot	
	CIL 1000 shot	
	Beethoven Mk 2a	Max res of 800 ohms
	ME 6*	Up to 5 dets in series
	ME 12 Mk 2*	Up to 12 dets in series
	Magnadet 153	For Magnadets and Magna primers, 1-500 shots
	153B	For battery power
	6	Lightweight, 1-120 shots
	Magnadet TX4a*	High frequency type, for underground coal mines
NEF	Explotron C-12	
	Explotron H-12*	
NKC	T series	For firing 50/100/200/300/500 No. 6 Japanese standard dets
REO#	CD 225-2J	35 dets
	CD 350-4J	60 dets
	CD 450-7J	85 dets
	CD 450-22J	85 dets
	CD 450-50J	420 dets
	CD 450A-50J	500 dets
	CD 600-100J	1000 dets
	CD 700-60J	750 dets
	BM 175-10ST	Selectable timing
	BM 175-10PT	Programmable timing
	BM 225-10-BOC	10 circuit BOCAR system
Schaffler	Series 800: 804*, 806S*, 808T*, 812, 815, 818, 840, 844T*, 845*	For standard A dets and U-type dets (FIDUZ)
	860N	For HU type dets (POLEX)
	Series 900: 944/3	Has two independent circuits each 150 POLEX shots
	922, 932/3000	For 90/160 POLEX shots
	Series 888:	Outputs up to 2000 Ws
	S888	For shaft sinking
	888/2500/2	Up to 560 POLEX dets in 7 parallel series of 80; or 400 standard A dets = 16000
	888/2500/5	For 800 POLEX shots
VME Nitro-Consult	VME 225B	
	VME 450B	
WASAG	ZEB CU 10, 20, 50	{(K series*)
	80, 150	{S600-1500 v
	CU 200/HU 20	1800 v
	CU 400/HU 80	1500-3000 v, 45-180J
	CU 400/HU 160	1500-3000 v, 80-360J
	HU 1000	3000 v
	Seq Blg Machine	

* Permitted types # REO also produces a range of equipment designed for use with Magnadet detonators

Fig. 18: Generator-type blasting machines

Fig. 19: Method of operating a No. 10 twist-type blasting machine

Fig. 20: A condenser discharge type exploder

Fig. 21:   Rheostat for testing blasting machines

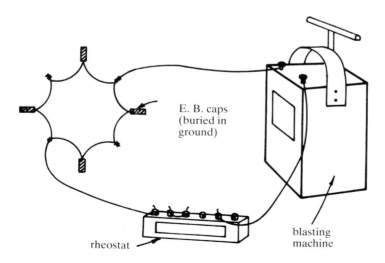

Fig. 22:   Circuit for testing a 50-shot blasting machine with rheostat

2. **Blasting machine testers**: It is important that exploders should be properly maintained and regularly tested as to their firing capacity. Even if well-maintained, they may develop faults in time that reduce their capacity. Blasting machines should be kept, right side up, in a cool dry place. Temperatures over 38 °C (100 °F) will damage the armatures of generator-type exploders.

The effectiveness of generator-type exploders (which are usually rated by the number of EB caps they are capable of firing in series, when in good condition) is commonly tested with a specially designed **Rheostat,** in conjunction with up to four caps (or preferably, electric squibs for greater convenience). The rheostat is provided with numbered binding posts corresponding to related inbuilt resistances and labelled with the number of standard caps that the exploder under test has the rated capacity to fire (Fig. 21).

A useful test circuit is shown in Fig. 22 in which four caps in a parallel-series connection are wired in series with the exploder under test, and connected with the appropriate binding post on the rheostat corresponding to the rated capacity of the exploder. If all four caps explode when the exploder is operated, then the machine can be regarded as in good working order. Otherwise, it needs repair, following which it should again be tested. In the interests of safety, it is good practice to scrap blasting machines that do not develop their fully rated capacities after careful repair procedures.

The full power of a Condenser Discharge (CD) blasting machine can be tested in the laboratory with an oscilloscope, or in the field with a voltmeter or Blaster's Multimeter [3], provided the condensers are in a satisfactory condition. The CIL Performance Tester is also designed to test the condition of condensers in CD blasting machines by checking the "full power" reading of the unit under test [6]. If full power is not achieved, then the condensers are not accumulating or holding their fully rated charge; and therefore the machine must be repaired before further (checking and) use.

The electrical efficiency of both generator-type and condenser-discharge type blasting machines can also be tested in a more sophisticated manner by a range of SOLUS Exploder Testers by Schaffler, or by a REO BT300-10 (or ET 175-10) Blasting Machine Tester.

3. **Circuit testers**: Electric blasting procedures can be successfully executed only if proper care is exercised in planning, loading and connecting the circuit. In important blasts, where the cost of much preliminary work and explosive materials is at stake, circuits should be tested prior to every firing.

A list of possible circuit weaknesses is given below, together with a description of the instruments used to locate or test for corresponding faults [5].

(1) *Discontinuities* or shorts in (a) the cap circuits, and in (b) the total (or any part of the) blasting circuit. A *blasting galvanometer* is used (see below).

(2) *Current leakage* can occur when damage to leg wire or connecting wire insulation allows the bare wire to make contact with the rock (ground), especially under damp conditions. This condition can be checked with a *blasting multimeter.*

(3) *Stray electricity* (current leakage from extraneous sources). Before loading the holes, the shotfirer can test for stray electricity with the probe wires of a *blasting multimeter,* see below.

A **Blasting Galvanometer** (see Fig. 23) is an Ohmmeter furnished with a silver chloride or other special cell in series with high resistance coils, designed to reduce the current to such a low value that an EB cap will not fire while testing for the conductivity of a cap circuit in series (or in any series of a parallel-series circuit).

In testing such a circuit, if the needle swings appreciably beyond the calculated resistance value (in ohms), the possibility of a short circuit is indicated; if the swing is too low, there may be a poor or loose connection); if the swing is zero, there is an open circuit, or missed connection; if very slight, the very high resistance may indicate leakage to ground (possibly by a bare wire from broken insulation). Any of these indications demonstrates a fault that should be located and corrected before firing the blast.

Fig. 23: Blasting galvanometer

Fig. 24: Circuit tester

Open circuits or loose connections can be found in a series circuit by attaching one of the wires to the galvanometer and a probe wire to the other. By progressively probing through the circuit, the weak point can be localized and the fault corrected.

After testing each series cap circuit, the connecting wire circuit is then tested and then the previously tested firing line can be connected in retreat from the face; finally the complete circuit is tested before firing.

The **Blaster's Multimeter** is also furnished with a dry cell, with appropriate resistances and circuitry to limit the test current.

This instrument can be used with a pair of insulated probe wires to check for the presence of stray AC or DC electricity leaking to ground from extraneous sources. These stray currents can be of sufficient magnitude to cause the premature firing of a cap circuit. They are therefore extremely dangerous. Once located, they should be checked for magnitude. If this indicates a serious hazard, special precautions should be taken to isolate and insulate all parts of the circuit from other obvious conductors, such as rails, pipes and ducts. If a stray current is located in the firing line, it should not be connected to the cap circuit, and blasting operations should not be allowed to proceed until the stray current has been effectively eliminated.

The Blaster's Multimeter is a versatile precision meter designed to measure volts, ohms and milliamperes (i.e., all the electrical factors in a blasting circuit) in one instrument, by selecting the appropriate measuring circuit and scale. It can therefore be used as a superior type of blasting galvanometer (for circuit testing and resistance measuring); as a blasting voltmeter (for voltage and for stray current readings); for blasting machine and power line output voltage readings; and for testing other instruments. With CD type machines, it can be used to give a reading of output voltage which is effective provided the condensers are in good condition.

The Austin **Ground Current Continuous Monitor** (Model GM 1000) is designed to monitor continuously the ground current near the face. A built-in alarm system is activated when the input current exceeds a certain level.

A convenient method of indicating continuity in a small wiring circuit is provided by the CIL **Circuit Tester** [6]. This is a pocket instrument designed for circuit resistances up to 75 ohms. It consists of a battery and glow lamp in a small cylindrical housing with metal ends. The lamp glows when the two ends of the unit contact the two wires of a blasting circuit, one at each end (see Fig. 24).

One of the most useful handy instruments yet devised for testing blasting circuits is Schaffler's 'Digohm' **Automatic Digital Circuit Testing Ohmmeter**. By connecting the ends of any circuit to the terminals, the instrument directly displays the resistance value digitally [1].

Allegany Technology are currently producing two models of their **Igniter Circuit Tester**.

In the interests of safety, all testing instruments should be checked periodically (and calibrated, where necessary) by a competent authority. This procedure is too important to be allowed to provide an opportunity for the misplaced enthusiasm of an amateur.

Before use in underground coal mines, the approval of the MSHA or other national authority should be obtained for any particular make of instrument.

References

[1] "Electric Shotfiring Practice", Rev. ed. Schaffler & Co., Vienna, 1988

[2] "Blasting Wire Handbook", Seminole Products Inc. Glendora, NJ

[3] *Handbook of Electric Blasting,* Rev. ed., Atlas Powder Company, 1985

[4] Explosives Technical Data Sheet 224 F, Hercules Incorporated

[5] "Products for Controlled Blasting," Nitro Nobel, Gyttorp, Sweden, 1974

[6] *Blaster's Handbook, 6th ed.* (Montreal, Canadian Industries Ltd., 1968)

CHAPTER 8

Shotfiring with Detonating Cord

General

Detonating Cord (known variously by such trade names as Primacord, Primex, and Cordeau Détonant) is a cord consisting of a core of initiating explosive (usually PETN) contained within a plastic sheath and wrapped in various combinations of textile, wire and plastic coverings [1].

It is used for the simultaneous firing of widely distributed charges and for the mass initiation of very large charges, as in quarrying and chamber blasting.

It is safe to handle, extremely water-resistant, and has a high velocity of detonation (7,000 m per second).

One of the chief advantages of detonating cord (DC) is that, when initiated, it is capable of transmitting the energy of a detonator to all points along its length.

It is reputed to be capable of increasing the efficiency of a blast as it explodes with extreme violence the high explosives (other than blasting agents) lying alongside it in the borehole. It detonates all connecting charges simultaneously from one point of initiation.

Its chief disadvantages are that (a) it exhibits considerable noise, and (b) it tends to compress and reduce the sensitivity of blasting agents in the hole. When AN/FO charges are employed, the use of low energy detonating cord (LEDC), or of DC less than 5.3 g/m core load, is indicated.

In quarry blasting, it is usual to lay out a trunkline of detonating cord extending along each line of holes, connecting to branch or "downlines" into each hole.

With detonating cord, detonators are not required in the holes. Where (as with blasting agents) the charge requires a greater initiating effect than is available from detonating cord, one or more high explosive booster units are attached to the downline (see below).

The whole circuit and series of charges (instantaneous or delay) can be initiated by the use of one No. 6 detonator (plain or electric). The detonator is lashed alongside the trunkline with tape, with its base pointing in the direction of travel of the desired detonation wave.

Alternatively, the trunkline can be initiated

(a) by a SAF-T-DET Detonating Cord Initiator, a non-explosive electrical device specially designed for the purpose, and marketed by Explosive Energy Corporation of Dallas, TX, or

(b) by an Exploding Bridge Wire (EBW) detonator RP-80, supplied by Reynolds Industries, Inc. An EBW detonator contains an insensitive explosive charge such as PETN and RDX, fired by a gold bridge wire. Apart from its use as an initiator of DC circuits, it has unique safety features that indicate its preferred use in a number of applications in general blasting operations. Specific firing sets are available for particular applications.

Detonating cord is much safer to handle than a detonator, even though both contain PETN. (It is not the PETN base charge but the priming charge of a cap that renders it so sensitive to heat, impact and friction.) PETN is relatively insensitive [2]. Detonating cord is also safer to use than electric circuits because the whole series of charges can be placed several hours before firing without risk from any hazard, except perhaps lightning or a brush fire. In other words, the whole charge is foolproof until the initiating detonator is taped to the trunkline immediately before firing [1].

Detonating cord is particularly useful for underwater blasting applications. However, the free ends should be sealed or adequately waterproofed, since PETN will slowly absorb water and become insensitive to initiation. Where the ends have become damp, they should be cut off; or otherwise the detonator should be taped to a dry section [1, 2].

Detonating cord trunklines may be extended or spliced by regular square knots (Fig. 25). Downlines should be connected to trunklines by strapping (taping), by clove hitch, or by a plastic connector. As the detonating wave is uni-directional, it is important that downlines, when connected by strapping, should have the free end facing the direction from which the impulse is advancing. This precaution is unnecessary when the clove hitch or connector is used.

Plastic connectors are simpler to use, and save much time in connecting down to trunklines, especially where the detonating cord has a stiff outer covering (see Fig. 26).

Detonating cord is available in a number of different loading weights and covering specifications for particular applications (see Table 13). Regular types have a core load ranging from 0.4 to 12.8 g/m of PETN, with overall diameters of 3 to 14 mm, depending mainly upon the nature of the encasement. Tensile strengths range from 50 to 170 kg.

Special types of detonating cord are also manufactured for particular purposes, such as:

Detacord (3.8 g/m) and B-line (4.9 g/m) for secondary blasting;

Plastic Reinforced Primacord (11.5 g/m) and Hexacord PT (15 g/m) for underwater blasting;

PETN 60 Plastic (12 g/m) for oil well servicing;

Fig. 25: Square (or reef) knot

Fig. 26: Plastic connector used to connect DC downline to trunkline

Seismic Cord (21 g/m), and Seismocord 20/40/100 for seismic applications;
Wetter-dynacord 4 (4 g/m) for coal mining;
RDX 70 Primacord (14 g/m) for oil well perforating;
Powerflex 5 (5g/m) a multi-purpose detonating cord; and
Octocord PT (15 g/m) for high temperature conditions.

References

[1] R. A. Dick, "Explosives and Borehole Loading", in SME Mining Engineering Handbook (New York, AIME, 1973)

[2] "Primacord Detonating Cord Handbook", Ensign Bickford Company, Simsbury, CT, 1987

Table 13: Types of detonating cord available

Trade name	PETN Core load (g/m)	External diameter (mm)	Tensile strength (kg)
AECI			
Cordtex 4	4	3.7	60
Cordtex 7	7	4.5	50
Cordtex 10	10	5.0	85
Premium Cordtex 10	10	5.5	150
Cordtex 22		6.0	50
Cordtex 40		9.0	100
ATLAS			
No. 18	3.8	4.2	90
No. 30	6.4	4.5	90
No. 40	8.5	4.8	90
No. 50	10.6	7.1	90
AUSTIN/KIMIT			
A cord	5.3	4.3	104
Scotch cord	3.8	4.1	104
40 Reinforced	8.5	4.6	113
50 Reinforced	10.6	4.8	113
Tuff-Kote	10.6	4.6	113
Liteline	3.2	3.6	104
BIQ			
Britacord	5	3.6 ± 0.3	80
	10	4.8 ± 0.3	80
	20	6.5 ± 0.3	110
	40	8.5 ± 0.3	110
CIL			
CORDTEX 50	10.2	5.1	110
CORDTEX 40	7.5	4.7	100
CORDTEX 25	5.3	4.2	100
CORDTEX 18	4.9	4.2	100
CORDTEX 15	3.2	3.7	75
CORDTEX 7.5	2.0	3.2	90
B-Line	4.9	3.1	45
COAST FUSE			
Primex Minicord	3.8	3.8	
SM cord	3.8	3.2	
Economy cord	5.3	4.2	
T-line cord	5.3	3.5	
Rfd 40 cord	8.5	5.1	
Rfd 50 cord	10.6	5.5	
Tuf-Glo cord	12.8	5.7	
FIRE-X Economy	5.3		
FIRE-X MINI-CORD	3.8		
DNAG			
Dynacord	12.5	5.2	
Supercord 20	20	6.3	
Supercord 40	40	9	
Supercord 100	100	14	
DuPont			
Special 18	3.8	4.1	90
Special 25	5.3	4.2	90
Lo-Flash 35	7.4	5.1	90
Special 40	8.5	4.8	90
Special 50	10.6	5.3	90
Detaline	0.5		

Table 13 (continued): Types of detonating cord available

Trade name	PETN Core load (g/m)	External diameter (mm)	Tensile strength (kg)
DYNO			
Dynocord	10	4.9	80
	12	5.0	80
	16	5.8	80
	40	8.2	100
EBCO			
Strip mine special	8.5	4.8	90
HD Primaline	1.5	3.2	68
RX Primaline	3.2	3.7	114
Rfd Primacord	10.6	4.7	90
E cord	5.3	4.0	68
Detacord	3.6	3.6	68
PD cord	5.3	3.6	50
ECP			
Gammacord	3.5	3.7–4.0	70
Hericord	6.5	3.7–4.3	70
Pentaflex 6	6.0	4.2	50
Pentaflex 12	12.0	5.0	75
Pentaflex 40	40.0	8.2	150
Superflex	42.4		
ERT			
Cord det	3	3.5	100
	6	4	100
	12	4.5	100
	20	6	100
	40	7.3	100
ETCAN			
ETI Line 20	4.5	3.0	79
50	10.2	4.4	100
ETI Spl 20	4.9	4.2	100
25	5.3	4.4	100
40	7.5	4.7	109
50	10.2	5.1	129
FAMESA			
Pentacord3P	3		75
3PE	3		100
5P	5		75
5PE	5		100
8P	8		75
8PE	8		100
10P	10		75
10PE	10		100
ICIA			
Blue Cordtex	7.5	3.94	63
Premium Cordtex	10.6	4.8	126–140
Std Cordtex	10.6	4.95	–
Shearcord	70		120
Redcord	10		95
Flexicord	10		140
Tuffcord	10		
Trunkcord	5		95

Table 13 (continued): Types of detonating cord available

Trade name		PETN Core load (g/m)	External diameter (mm)	Tensile strength (kg)
ICIA (continued)				
Powercord		5		140
RX Primaline		3.2		115
Sliderline		2.5		55
IDL				
D-CORD	I	6	3.9	
	II	10	4.65	
	III	20	6.0	
	IV	40	–	
IEL				
Cordtex			5.0	
IIE				
Primaflex		10		
Superflex		40		
Special Cord		100		
IRECO				
IRECORD	50	10.6	4.8	103
	40	8.5	4.6	103
	25	5.3	4.3	103
ITPL				
Extra		12		50
Reinforced		15		60
NEF				
Eclair Plastex	12		5	80
	12		5.4	100
	20		5.8	80
	24		2 x 5.0	150
	40		8.3	50
	70		10.7	40
NKC				
Detonating Fuse	10.6		5.2	
SSE				
Detonex	5			
	12			
	24			
	40			
	80			
	150			
TEL				
TEL Cord II	10			70
TEL Cord III	20			80
Titanite				
Titacord	12	12	5.4	50
	15	15	5.5	50
	24	24	7.0	65
	40	40	9.1	70
	50	50	10.0	90
WAHNL				
Wabocord				

CHAPTER 9

Sequential Firing

General

In many applications of the use of explosives, particularly in mines and quarries, provision must be made for certain of the charges to explode in sequence rather than simultaneously. This is accomplished in the following ways:

With Conventional Safety Fuse Firing

(a) By blasting one or two holes at a time and returning at a safe interval after each blast to light the next hole.
(b) By cutting fuses differentially as to length and/or by lighting them in the desired order.
(c) By connecting standard length fuses with IC in the desired order.
(d) By connecting fuses cut (or docked) differentially as to length with IC in the desired order.

With Conventional Electric Detonators

(a) By using long delay detonators.
(b) By using short/millisecond delay detonators [1].
(c) By using a sequentially controlled timing device with delay detonators [2].

There are several types of electric delay detonators, viz.:

Electric detonators (long delay): These have a longer shell than the instantaneous electric detonators in order to accommodate a delay element interposed between the fusehead and the priming charge.

Fig. 27: Electric delay detonator

There are generally sixteen or more possible delays, 0 to 15, with a nominal half-second time interval between each sequence number. They are identified by a delay number clearly tagged to the leg wires. The number of the delay is a function of the length of the delay element. Long delay detonators are used mainly in certain classes of mine development work, and in tunnelling operations, to provide a predetermined sequence of shots and to allow sufficient time for the rock to move from a restricted area. They are generally available in No. 6 and No. 8 strengths, in aluminium tubes.

Electric detonators (short delay) [1]: These have developed from the long half-second delay detonator; they represent an important advance in blasting efficiency. The main difference is that the delay interval is much shorter. The delay element contains specially blended powders interposed between the fusehead bridge wire and the priming charge.

Electric delay detonators are packed in cardboard boxes and tagged with the delay period number and the length of leg wires, the ends of which are protected by a shunt (Fig. 27).

These are now supplied by manufacturers in a wide range of delay intervals in two classifications, as either No. 6 or No. 8 strength caps.

(a) **Normal type** [1] available in a range of 18 to 38 delays, each interval varying from 8 to 100 or more milliseconds (see Table 14). In order to avoid overlap, the interval is increased in the later delays. They are in general use in practically all rock-breaking applications, in copper, gilding metal, bronze, or aluminium shells/tubes. Leg wires range from 1.3 to 20 m and more in length.

(b) **Non-incendive type**, for use in coal mines, available in a range of up to twelve delays, with intervals varying from 25 to 100 milliseconds (see Table 15). These are available in copper shells with copper or iron leg wires from 1.3 to 5 m long.

Both types can be used in wet conditions and will withstand water pressures of at least 4.2 kg/cm^2 – equivalent to a head of about 45 m of water.

The fusehead resistance is substantially the same in both types. Although the fuseheads of all detonators in any particular circuit ignite as soon as the current is applied, the detonations do not take place until the respective delay elements have burnt through. Hence, the breaking of the circuit by the first detonation does not affect the firing of the later charges. However, because of the wide variation of delay intervals in the above types of delay detonators, they should not be mixed in any one blasting circuit; nor should detonators from different manufacturers. Trade names of electric delay detonators are shown in Table 16.

Sequentially controlled timing devices: One of the main problems in delay firing of large connected segments in the one firing by power mains is the need to balance the resistances in each segment effectively; and to control air blast and ground vibration, as well as to improve fragmentation [2].

A series of automatic solid-state sequential blasting machines has been developed by Research Energy of Ohio (REO). In their BM 175-10 PT Blasting Machine, a total of ten individual blasting circuits (for different benches or for different stopes) can be actuated by a single switch. Each circuit can be programmed from 5 to 999 msec delay in one millisecond steps. Similar additional circuits can be added as slave units (in multiples) [3].

With Special Electric Detonators and Delay Systems [4, 5]

In order to provide a greater margin of safety against accidental current sources, such as from power lines, radio transmitters, lightning discharges, galvanic action, static charges and stray currents generally, as well as to increase blasting efficiency and to provide more flexibility in the design of blasting programmes, a number of special

Table 14: Typical delay intervals with short period delay detonators

Delay No.	Atlas (Rockmaster)		CIL (Short Period Caps No. 8)		DuPont (MS Delay)		IRECO/Hercules (Millidet No. 8)	
	Interval (msec)	Elapsed time (msec)	Interval (msec)	Elapsed time (msec)	Interval (msec)	Elapsed time (msec)	Interval (msec)	Elapsed time (msec)
0	–	0	–	0	–	0	–	0
1	8	8	8	8	25	25	12	12
2	17	25	22	30	25	50	13	25
3	25	50	20	50	25	75	25	50
4	25	75	25	75	25	100	25	75
5	25	100	25	100	25	125	25	100
6	25	125	30	130	25	150	35	135
7	25	150	30	160	25	175	35	170
8	25	175	30	190	25	200	35	205
9	25	200	40	230	50	250	35	240
10	50	250	50	280	50	300	40	280
11	50	300	60	340	50	350	40	320
12	50	350	70	410	50	400	40	360
13	50	400	80	490	50	450	40	400
14	50	450	80	570	50	500	50	450
15	50	500	80	650	100	600	50	500
16	50	550	75	725	100	700	50	550
17	100	650	75	800	100	800	50	600
18	100	750	75	875	100	900	100	700
19	125	875	75	950	100	1000	200	900
20	125	1000	75	1025	–	–	300	1200
21	125	1125	100	1125	–	–	300	1500
22	125	1250	100	1225	–	–	–	–
23	125	1375	125	1350	–	–	–	–
24	125	1500	150	1500	–	–	–	–
25	125	1625	175	1675	–	–	–	–
26	125	1750	200	1875	–	–	–	–
27	125	1875	200	2075	–	–	–	–
28	125	2000	225	2300	–	–	–	–
29	125	2125	250	2550	–	–	–	–
30	125	2250	330	2880	–	–	–	–
–	–	–	230	3050	–	–	–	–

electric detonator types, and a series of electric (and non-electric) initiation systems have recently been developed.

Each of these special electric detonators calls for specific methods of use, application and operation, and are not generally compatible with, nor should they be mixed with, conventional electric detonators in a particular charge. This is because the range of resistances and required current characteristics vary as between each type and are also different from those of conventional detonators.

It has been determined that the more insensitive the detonator, the greater the firing impulse required to ignite it per ohm of circuit resistance. The useful measure of this firing energy is the joule (watt-seconds); and the threshold firing impulse to cause ignition is measured in milliwatt-seconds per ohm (mWs/ohm).

Table 15: Typical delay intervals with short delay non-incendive coal mine detonators

Delay No.	Atlas (Kolmaster II)		DuPont (Coal Mine)		IRECO/Hercules (Coaldet)	
	Interval (msec)	Elapsed time (msec)	Interval (msec)	Elapsed time (msec)	Interval (msec)	Elapsed time (msec)
0	–	0	–	0	–	0
1	25	25	25	25	25	25
2	75	100	75	100	75	100
3	75	175	75	175	70	170
4	75	250	75	250	70	240
5	50	300	50	300	80	320
6	50	350	50	350	80	400
7	50	400	50	400	50	450
8	50	450	50	450	50	500
9	50	500	50	500	–	–

Some of these special detonators are:

(1) *Exploding Bridge Wire (EBW) Detonators*: They are much less sensitive than conventional detonators because they contain no priming charge, but an insensitive base charge only. For this reason, they must be fired by a specific high-voltage, high-current energy pulse. See also Chapter 8. They are supplied by Reynolds Industries Inc.

(2) *Magnadet Electric Detonator System*: These have recently been developed in the U.K. by Nobel's Explosives Co. Ltd. and are marketed by the ICI Explosives Group generally.

In operation, the primary firing current from the exploder is passed by the connecting wire through a ferrite ring (toroid), which is attached to the ends of the detonator leg wires, acting as the secondary of a transformer.

Whatever the nature and characteristics of the detonator itself, it can be ignited only by a primary AC source of 12–15 kHz, and therefore the risk of accidental premature firing by stray currents is virtually non-existent. But a special exploder must obviously be used.

The Magnadet System has an additional advantage in that it does not involve the joining of connecting wires. The connecting wire is merely threaded through the toroidal rings of all the delay detonators in the blast in any order. They are available from ICI Group members as half-second delays (1–12) and short delays (1–30).

The development of Magnadet detonators has led to the introduction of Magna primers: a plastic unit incorporating a cast pentolite charge containing two in-built Magnadets. These units can be slid down the blast hole around a stranded electric primary cable which necessarily passes through the toroids of the emplaced Magnadets. They have all the advantages of a non-electric circuit.

A new sequential blasting machine, called the Magnatimer, designed for reliable in-itiation of Magnadet electric detonators, had been developed by REO.

Table 16:   Trade names of conventional electric delay detonators supplied by various manufacturers (showing cap number and range of delay periods)

Manufacturer (for code see Ch. 1)	Long Delay (0.5 to 10.8 sec interval)	Short Delay (25 to 330 msec interval)	Coal Mine Delay (25 to 100 msec interval)
Atlas	Timemaster No. 8 0–15	Rockmaster No. 8 0–30 Masterdet No. 8* 0–20	Kolmaster II No. 8 0–9
Austin	Timemaster No. 8 0–15 Time Stars# 0–16	Rockstar No. 8* 0–30	Coalstar 0–9
AECI	LPD detonators No. 8 0–13	SPD Dets No. 8 0–20	
DNAG	A type 0–24	A type 0–18 U type 0–18	
DYNO		Group 1 millisecond 0–18	
ERT	Long Period 0–12	For 30 msec, 0–18 For 20 msec, 0–15	
ETI	Acudet Mk V 0 – 7	MS delay 0–19 Posidet* 0–20	Coal Mine Delay 0–9
FAMESA	Long period (Fulmelec) 0–12	Short Period, 0–20 Normal Period, 0–10	
ICI Group	Half Second Delay No. 8 star 0–10	L series No. 8 0–18/24	Carrick No. 6 0–10
IDL	Long delay No. 6 0–10	Short delay No. 6 0–10	Coal delay No. 6 0–6
IEL	Long delay Nos. 6/8 0–10	Short delay Nos. 6/8 0–10	Carrick Nos. 6/8 0–6
IRECO	Superdet No. 8 0–15 Iredet Super LP	Millidet No. 8 0–20 Iredet Super SP No. 8* 0–25	Coaldet No. 8 0–9 Iredet Super Coal
Kemira	Std Halfsecond 0–12	Std Millisecond 0–18	
NK	DSD Electric Dets No. 6, 0–19	MSD Dets No. 6 0–19	Permissible MSD Dets No. 6
Schaffler	Half sec Dets TZMSA 0–13	MIZA 20/MIZA 40 0–19	
Thermex		Davydet* 0–20	

* Precision detonator system, all at 25 msec, # 0.5 sec

(3) *Swedish VA Detonators*: These have an in-built margin of safety because of their higher resistance, about 3.6 ohms, irrespective of the length of the leg wires. This detonator is safe for currents up to 1.3 amps, compared with 0.3 amps for conventional units.

Also, the current impulse required to initiate a VA detonator is about 30 times greater (80–140 mWs/ohm) than for conventional detonators. They are available from Nitro-Nobel in a wide range of delays and leg wire lengths.

(4) *Schaffler (Austrian) FIDUZ Detonators*: These need a minimum firing impulse five times greater, and a POLEX detonator, 1000 times greater, than conventional electric detonators (20 and 3300 mWs/ohm to fire as against 3–4).

Available as instantaneous, half-second and short delay. See Chapter 5.

(5) *Dynamit Nobel AG Detonators*: This firm produces the German anti-static U type detonator which requires an impulse of 18 mWs/ohm to fire; and also the highly insensitive HU type (3300 mWs/ohm). Available as instantaneous, half-second and short delays.

(6) *Frantir HI 67 High Intensity Detonators*: These are of French manufacture, and need 1000 mWs/ohm to fire with a condensor exploder. Available in half-second and short delays.

(7) The Spanish "Union Explosivos Rio Tinto SA" (*ERT*) company manufactures detonators in three levels of safety, viz.

Detonadores sensibles (sensitive S type)

Detonadores insensibles (insensitive I type) and

Detonadores de alta insensibilidad (very insensitive AI type).

The necesssary firing impulse for each is 0.8 to 3, 8 to 16, and 1100 to 2500 mWs/ohm respectively. Minimum firing currents are 1.2, 2.5 and 25 amperes respectively. Each type is available as instantaneous, half-second delay (0–12), and short delay (0–18 in the 30 msec range, and 0–15 in the 20 msec range).

In addition, there are special detonators for coal mines (as S, I and AI types), in the instantaneous, half-second and 30 msec short delay ranges.

ERT also makes seismic electric detonators (S and I types) and submarine detonators to withstand high water pressures.

(8) *FAMESA* also manufactures electric detonators at three levels of safety and in three classes of delays (short period at 30 msec intervals 0–20, normal period at 50 msec intervals 0–10 and long period at 400 msec intervals 0–12). These are the normal current (AN) type, the intermediate insensitive (ASA) type and the high current high insensitivity type (AAA).

The firing impulse required is listed as 1.5, 11 and 1800 mWs/ohm respectively; and the minimum firing current for 5 detonators in series is 0.75, 1.75 and 25 amperes respectively.

(9) For greater protection against accidental initiation by stray currents or atmospheric electricity, *African Explosives and Chemicals Ltd.* produce three types of detonator

(types 1, 2, 3) in addition to their standard Type 0 detonators. The firing impulse required for these are 50–70, 300–500 and 1200–2000 respectively, as against 3–5 mWs/ohm for Type 0.

Minimum firing currents when using D.C. series currents are 6.6, 14 and 25 respectively, as against 2.3 amps for Type 0. Short period detonators (SPDs) are supplied in 0–20 delays and Long period (LPDs) in 0–13 delays, both with No. 8 strength detonators.

Instantaneous detonators (IEDs) are available in No. 6 and No. 8 star strength. Seismic detonators are produced to withstand a water depth of 200 metres.

(10) Kemira Oy supply the Vihtavuori UR-type detonator for greater safety against static electricity, lightning and stray currents than their standard detonator provides. These are available as instantaneous millisecond delay (0–18) types. The firing impulse is listed as 8 to 16 mWs/ohm and the firing current as 0.45 to 1.5 amperes.

With the aim of providing detonators of even higher precision, several manufacturers are reported to be developing electronic detonators [6].

Tri Electronics AB of Gothenburg has developed a new system (TS 100) of initiating electric detonators, based on advanced electronics, and designed to fire 100 VA detonators in series.

In another effort to promote greater accuracy, to avoid overlap and to improve efficiency in the blasting of rock, several manufacturers have developed what they call high precision pyrotechnic millisecond delay detonators, mostly firing at closely re-designed 25 msec intervals of 20 periods [6]. Typical of these are the Atlas 'Masterdet', Austin 'Rockstar', Ensign 'SA Delay', ETI 'Posidet', IRECO 'Iredet' and Thermex 'Davydet'. See Table 17.

With Detonating Cord or other Non-Electric Delay Systems

(a) By using non-electric millisecond (M/S) delay connectors in the trunklines.

(b) By using an all-electric trunkline circuit with delay detonators taped to DC downlines; or

(c) By using special cast boosters with selective delay inserts.

(d) By using an integral non-electric delay system.

(1) **Non-electric MS delay connectors**: These are provided in copper tubes about 8 cm long with an explosive charge in each end, separated by a central spacer element that incorporates the delay mechanism. Detonating cord tail pieces are factory-crimped to both ends to connect with square knots to the gap cut in the trunkline (Fig. 28). As supplied by Austin, there are MS-9, MS-17 and MS-25 millisecond delays available, with provision for MS-35 and MS-45 for special purposes. Each delay period is identified by colour.

DuPont provide a different style of plastic MS **Surface Delays** equipped with EZ latches at both ends to accommodate Detaline trunkline connections. One of these can become an instantaneous starter. In this way a safe foolproof non-electric method of delaying a trunkline can be conveniently provided. Delays of 9, 17, 30, 42, 60 and 100 msec are available, each in a different identifying colour.

As with Austin Delay Connectors, an almost infinite array of delayed firing patterns can be provided by combining connectors of different periods.

Ensign-Bickford supply **Primadet MS Connectors** which consist of a 460 mm length of NONEL shock tube with identical delay detonators fitted inside connector blocks at each end. These delays are timed for 9, 17, 25, 35 and 65 msec intervals, and are colour coded.

For surface mining, delays can also be effected with a NONEL shock tube type of trunkline (see later), supplied with a Bunch Block containing a Primadet millisecond detonator on one end. These **Noiseless Trunkline Delays** (NTDs) are available from Ensign-Bickford in 5, 9, 17, 25, 42, 100, 150 and 200 msec intervals, in lengths of 1, 4, 6, 10, 13, 16 and 20 metres.

Another style of DC delay connector is the NONEL Primadet MS Connector which can be inserted in a Primacord trunkline to introduce delay firing. This unit consists of a 45 cm length of NONEL shock tube with identical delay caps within plastic connector blocks at each end of the tube. Delays are available in 9, 17, 25, 35 and 65 milliseconds.

The Atlas **Blastmaster Trunkline and Delay** (T&Ds) are designed for general use in bench blasting applications with non-electric in-hole detonators or DC downlines. These trunkline units are supplied in particular lengths up to 20 metres with time delays of 0, 5, 9, 17, 25, 35, 42, 65, 100 and 200 msec.

A duplicated 'Redundant (RTD)' system has also been developed to reduce the incidence of misfires, both by Atlas and Ensign-Bickford.

Another type of **MS connector** for DC trunklines is produced by FAMESA. It consists of a plastic moulding containing an aluminium capsule of delay type detonating explosive of No. 6 strength. At both ends the DC can be connected in the form of a U-loop. Delay intervals available are 5, 9, 17, 25, 35, 50, 75, and 100 msec.

Fig. 28: Non-electric MS delay connector (Austin)

Detonating Relay Connectors (DRCs) are devised by the ICI Explosives Group to provide a means of blasting with millisecond delay intervals of 10, 17, 25, 35 and 45 msec when used with Cordtex trunkline. The DRC is inserted into a gap cut in a trunkline. The ends of the trunkline are crimped into the open ends of the relay unit.

IDL supplies **DC Relays** with delay intervals of 17, 25, 50 and 100 msec.

NONEL **SRC Connectors** are two-way relay connectors consisting of a length of NONEL tubing with a DRC delay detonator (set within a special plastic moulding) crimped on both ends. Normal firing times are 2, 4, 5, 6, 7 and 9 msec for 4, 8, 10, 12, 14 and 18 metre lengths of tubing. The unit is laid out in the trunkline between two adjacent blast holes, leading to two DC downlines.

(2) **Electric trunklines with DC downlines**: This procedure is seldom used these days. It is expensive and hazardous because of its ready reaction to lightning and radio-frequency currents.

(3) **Cast boosters with delay inserts**: Austin produces a non-electric **ADP Primer** as a standard unit in two sizes capable of being armed with one of a selection of 16 special ADP delay units, ranging from 25 to 350 msec. Each delay unit consists of a delay detonator equipped with a pigtail. The detonator is loaded into the delay channel of the booster, the pigtail is snapped into a retainer slot and continues upwards into a downline channel. The whole primer can be threaded on a single "40 Reinforced" DC downline and lowered to its position at the bottom of the hole; or several primers can be so dropped on a single downline for deck-loading, in 10 cm diameter holes or larger, loaded with a non-capsensitive charge. When the downline fires, it activates the adjacent loaded pigtail and initiates the delay detonator and then the booster charge [4]. These are now known as **Slider Boosters**, especially useful for delayed deck charges.

The ICIA Sliderdeck System allows a special ANZOMEX primer with integral delay detonators to be slid down a DC downline into the required position in the borehole. This system has three components, viz.,

An ANZOMEX slider primer Mk III

A Slider Primer Mk III delay detonator

An LEDC downline (2.5 to 3.5 g/m).

DuPont have a Detaslide special slider primer (HDP of six sizes) specially designed for sliding charges in deck blasting. These boosters can be armed with specially designed in-hole MS delay detonators of 19 delay periods. Otherwise, in-hole MS non-electric delay detonators can be tied at required intervals to Detaline cord along with Detaprime boosters.

The FAMESA Fame Master is a non-electric slider system incorporating a time delay 'Insert Master' which can slide down a FAMESA 3 g/m downline. It is a 450 g booster which can be timed from 0–1000 msec in 20 steps.

Atlas have developed a similar cast booster which can be armed with a selection from 14 special delay inserts, with timings ranging from 25 to 500 msec [7]. This booster (the green Deckmaster) is for deck-loaded holes on a single DC downline of 3.8, 5.3 or 6.4

g/m. The unit has a plastic body filled with pentolite and provided with a passage for the downline and special channels for location of the delay inserts, which incorporate a high strength aluminium shell delay detonator on one end and a sensor on the other. In operation, the sensor picks up the detonation wave from the downline and ignites the delay detonator of the insert.

The Magna primer consists of a cast pentolite charge in a plastic housing containing two in-built Magnadet detonators [4]. A central vertical hole allows a stranded electric cable to pass through the primer, and therefore through the two toroids of the Magnadets. For deck-loading, or top- and bottom-loading, the Magna primers can be dropped down the primary stranded cable to their desired positions, as the hole is loaded. The use of Magna primers gives safe electrical precision blasting, free from the usual electrical hazards, without any of the problems of detonating cord, and not affected by water.

(4) **Integral non-electric delay systems**: These involve a method of introducing sequential firing mechanisms into non-electric circuits, while retaining the advantages of precise short delay blasting available in electric circuits. In this way, the relatively unsafe features of electric blasting in surface operations (due to lightning, radio-frequency energy, and static electricity) can be avoided. These systems are particularly applicable to bench holes charged with insensitive material such as blasting agents. Several such systems have recently been developed by different manufacturers, as detailed below.

Primadet Delay System: Primadet Delays were originally developed by Ensign-Bickford to provide a practical non-electric detonation system that would yield precise timing characteristics equivalent to those of electric delay systems, free from static and stray current hazard [8]. The delay caps of this system were incorporated in primers within the borehole charge. They were available in both short delay and regular half-second delay series.

The Primadet Delay System consisted of three major elements:

(1) A special No. 6 blasting cap, incorporating its own in-built delay element as an integral feature, inserted into a cartridge or cast booster of adequate strength and sensitivity;

(2) a miniature 0.85 g/m PETN detonating cord called *Primaline*, one end of which was factory-crimped into the delay cap, as a 'downline';

(3) a plastic "J-connector" for readily attaching the free end of the Primaline to the trunkline.

It was usual to initiate the Primaline downline (which takes the place of leg wires or safety fuse in other detonating systems) by a trunkline of PD cord or Reinforced Primacord. It was and still is important to avoid using the Primaline as a downline for sensitive explosive charges such as NG-based types, since it might initiate such a charge, perhaps imperfectly, and cause it to detonate instantaneously rather than in delayed order. Primadet delays can therefore be used effectively only in charges of low initiation sensitivity such as blasting agents.

The **Anodet Delay Blasting** System [9] is produced by CIL. It is particularly designed for underground blastholes, 2.6 to 6 cm in diameter, pneumatically loaded with AN/FO.

The Anodet system consists of a special high strength detonator, factory-crimped to a length of Anoline, which is connected to the DC trunkline by a J-connector. Where necessary, an A-3 or Anodet Booster can be used [10]. To locate the primer centrally in the blasthole, a *Plastic Cap Holder* is available. Anodet delays are available in short or long periods: Anodet Short Delays are supplied in a range of 30 delays with intervals from 25 to 250 milliseconds; Anodet Long Delays range from 350 to 1700 milliseconds over 15 delay periods. The Anoline downlines are supplied in 3, 4 or 5 metre lengths.

The **NONEL System**: This Swedish invention by Nitro Nobel AB is a non-electric system that does not involve the use of detonating cord [11]. Four components are included in a complete unit, supplied in a standard pack. These are:

(a) a NONEL shock tube;

(b) a conventional (plain) detonator with a delay element;

(c) a connecting block, provided with a minidetonator;

(d) a starting gun and NONEL trunkline.

The NONEL shock tube, of appropriate length, is connected at one end to the delay detonator. The other end is connected to the yellow *connecting block* that houses the *minidetonator* (or transmitter cap). The transparent plastic NONEL tube is 3 mm in external diameter with a 1.5 mm bore. The inside wall of the tube is coated with a low concentration of explosive powder that possesses the ability to conduct a shock wave at constant velocity. The shock wave is supplied by the minidetonator in the connecting block. It travels through the tube and emerges in the detonator as an intensive tongue of flame. The complete circuit is initiated by a special starting gun that energizes a NONEL trunkline which in turn initiates each connecting block connected to it.

The **NONEL Primadet System**: This system represents the best features of the original Ensign-Bickford Primadet Delay System and the Swedish NONEL System. It is now known as the NONEL Primadet System and is manufactured and marketed by Ensign-Bickford under licence [12, 13].

For surface applications, the **LLHD NONEL Primadet** unit is supplied integrally with 20, 30, 40, 50, 60, 80, 100 or 120 ft of NONEL shock tube, as a downline; with a Primadet delay detonator which can be inserted into a cast booster, dynamite cartridge or soft booster. See Table 17.

Similarly, for the **MS NONEL Primadet** unit. This series can also use Noiseless Trunkline Delays (NTDs) with a common in-hole delay, as in bunch block blasting.

The **Short Lead (SL) NONEL Primadet** unit consists of a 30 inch length of NONEL shock tube with a non-electric Primadet, inserted into a booster. To the top loop of the unit, a length of HD or RX Primaline is fixed, and fired as usual from the trunkline.

The **Long Period (LP)** is designed for underground applications. It provides $1/2$, $1^1/2$ and $2^1/2$ second delay periods of 0.1, 0.3 and 0.5 seconds respectively. A Primaline Primadet is used, with or without a booster. In this case, the detonator is factory crimped onto 0.85 g/m Primaline, which is half-hitched in turn to a Primacord trunkline.

A similar NONEL Primadet system developed in Canada by the CIL is the **NONEL CXA Detonator** series. Firing times range from 0 to 8050 msec in 36 periods. There is also a long period range from 0 to 18 (for tunnelling).

Table 17: NONEL Primadet delay intervals

Delay Period	LLHD, MS and SL series For surface mining (msec)	LP series For underground mining (sec)
0	–	–
1/2	–	0.1
1	25	0.2
1 1/2	–	0.3
2	50	0.4
2 1/2	–	0.5
3	75	0.6
4	100	1.0
5	125	1.4
6	150	1.8
7	175	2.4
8	200	3.0
9	250	3.8
10	300	4.6
11	350	5.5
12	400	6.4
13	450	7.4
14	500	8.5
15	600	9.6

A further development is the **Low Velocity Signal Transmission (LVST) Line Primadet** non-electric Delay Detonator Trunkline Delay. These are used mainly in construction blasting. Each unit consists of a 16 or 24 ft length of NONEL shock tube, with an instantaneous Primadet in-hole detonator on one end. The precise delay timing is incorporated in the LVST trunkline itself, which fires at a very accurate slow speed. The timing sequence is adjustable by varying the initiation point on the trunkline.

For trench blasting, the **EZ Det series** has been developed. It consists of four components, factory assembled:

(1) a NONEL shock tube, 16 or 24 ft long;

(2) a 200 msec non-electric in-hole detonator, fixed to one end, to be used with a booster;

(3) a 25 msec detonator, set in a plastic connector, on the other end, to connect with the next adjoining hole; and

(4) a delay tag.

Either an electric detonator or a NONEL Primadet Noiseless Lead-in-Line can be used to initiate the whole sequence of holes.

Otherwise, a special type of mechanical initiator is available in three models (Scorpion HR-8, HR-3 and HR-22) from the EIT corporation. Designed for initiating non-electric shock tube systems, or for Noiseless Lead-in-lines. For underground (permissible) blasting, the Scorpion HB-20P and HCCR models are recommended.

Also, an 'Arc Star' **Shock Tube Initiator** is available from Austin, with remote control from a distance ranging from 250 to 5000 feet.

Otherwise, an electronic instrument (the **Surefire Starter**) is marketed by Explosive Developments Ltd of Leeds, U.K.

DuPont and ETCAN have recently introduced their 2.4 gr/ft noiseless **Detaline** detonating cord (either as trunkline or downline), with MS Delay Connectors, and with a series of non-electric detonators having 10 delay periods.

The Detaline system operates in duplicate. An instantaneous starter (electric or non-electric) initiates the Detaline trunkline. The surface connectors have EZ latches for hooking up duplicate downlines to trunkline or between trunkline segments. The in-hole detonators can be connected to Detaline downline by passing the cord through the detonator ring closure and then inserting it into a soft cartridge, or even in a HDP booster.

Atlas have devised the **Blastmaster Non-Electric Initiating System**. This comprises non-electric detonator assemblies (MS and LP), and trunkline and delay signal tubing (T&D). The Blastmaster T&Ds and RTD are millisecond delay reactive tubing downlines in lengths of 4 to 16 metres with a delay range of 0 to 200 msec. For integral downlines incorporating NONEL Multidet MS detonators, another plastic tube containing reactive materials can be provided. The delay periods range from 0 to 20 with firing times of 25 to 500 msec. Tube lengths range from 4 to 35 metres. Alternatively, NONEL Multidet LP detonators can be used with the same range of delays but with longer lengths (30 m) of heavy duty tubing.

Similarly, Blastmaster LP delay detonator assemblies are available with 0 to 18 periods from 0.1 to 7.2 seconds, and with tube lengths from 4 to 6 metres for underground blasting. (Following the recent absorption of Atlas by the ICI Group, it is believed that the shock tube used in this system will be of the EXEL type, see below).

Another style of non-electric initiation shock tube system has been developed by the ICI Explosives Group. This is known as the **EXEL System**. Complete assemblies are available, with a non-electric cap, the signal tube, and colour-coded J hooks.

Associated with the EXEL Shock Tube System, CIL provides three non-electric delay detonator assemblies for specific applications.

1. EXEL Handidet, for surface applications (trenching, quarrying, surface coal mines and construction work).

2. EXEL Constadet, for short delay applications (quarrying, construction work, open pit and underground mining), embracing 40 delays ranging from 0 to 1000 msec.

3. EXEL LP, for underground shaft sinking and development work, embracing 19 delays over 9000 msec.

FAMESA has developed the **FANEL Integrated Non-Electric (anti-static) System**. It consists of three main components:

(a) the FANEL downline (0.04 g/m);

(b) the integral non-electric delay detonator (in both short period, 0–1000 msec in 20 steps, and long period, 0–5000 msec in 15 steps); and

(c) single or multiple connectors for hooking up to a 5 g/m trunkline.

Britanite (BIQ) supplies the **Brinel Non-Electric Shock Tube System**, consisting of lead-in-line, trunkline (in three delays), downline with high precision detonators (15 delays, mostly at 25 msec intervals) and coupling connectors.

The **Hercudet Blasting Cap System** also eliminates all the hazards associated with the use of electric detonators [14]. Unlike DC initiation, it is also virtually noiseless. It consists of three major elements.

(1) A special aluminium shell Hercudet detonator, incorporating a delay element, and furnished in the factory with two plastic tubes, rather than with two leg wires (see Fig. 29).

(2) Hercudet connectors for connecting lengths of tubing between adjacent holes in the circuit. A range of seven types is available.

(3) Hercudet Blasting Machine (with Gas Supply Unit and Tester).

After the detonators (in their primers) have been placed and the charging of the holes completed, the tubing downlines are connected in the circuit to the trunkline (with connectors), and to the blasting machine (see Fig. 30).

To this stage, the circuit tubing has contained nitrogen. The circuit may now be purged with air and tested. To fire the round, the valves on the gas supply unit are opened to charge the blasting machine with the firing mixture of fuel and oxidizer, the "arm" button is pressed for a short time, and then the "fire" button. This initiates the gas mixture in the ignition chamber of the blasting machine, resulting in a detonation that proceeds around the tube circuit at about 2,600 m per second, and initiates all the detonators.

Fig. 29: Hercudet detonator, as compared with conventional EB delay cap

However, an additional delay time (which can be readily calculated) needs to be added in most surface operations for the additional time the gas mixture takes to pass through the associated length of hook-up tubing, at the 2,600 m/sec detonation rate.

For surface blasting, short delay Hercudets can be supplied with 10 cm leads, to be readily connected to duplex trunklines (as downlines), cut to any desired length, for connections in turn to the main single tube downline.

For non-gassy underground applications, Hercudets are available with tubing lengths of 5 and 7 m, in both short and long period delays. These standard lengths can be cut and connected to any shorter length desired.

Hercudet detonators are available with the following firing times:

Delay period	Short delay (msec)	Long delay (sec)
$1/10$	–	0.05
$1/4$	–	0.25
$1/2$	–	0.50
$3/4$	–	0.73
1	50	1.35
2	100	2.05
3	150	2.75
4	200	3.45
5	250	4.50
6	300	5.50
7	350	6.60
8	400	7.60

Fig. 30: Schematic representation of the Hercudet system circuit

9	450	8.60
10	500	9.60
11	550	10.60
12	610	11.60
13	670	12.80
14	730	14.20
15	790	15.80

Advantages of Short Delay Blasting

The advantages of short delay over instantaneous or half-second delay blasting are:

1. Reduction of ground vibration.
2. Reduction in air blast.
3. Reduction in overbreak.
4. Improved fragmentation.
5. Better control of flyrock.

This method derives its advantages from the fact that, in the shorter time-interval involved, while the rock mass is still under the influence of the shock wave from the preceding detonation, the next (and, in turn, each succeeding) detonation occurs [15].

Thus the superimposing of each new detonation wave on an already strained rock mass more readily overcomes its cohesive strength, in accordance with what is known as the Principle of Mutual Assistance. This results in the advantages listed above, for the same weight of charge, or alternatively, the need for a smaller charge.

One of the most important advantages noted with short delay blasting is the marked reduction in vibration as compared with that obtained when an equal weight of explosive is detonated instantaneously. Vibrograph recordings indicate that the effective vibration bears a close relation to the weight of explosive detonated on any short delay period, rather than the total used in a blast; and in practice it would seem that if blasting can be conducted with instantaneous initiation on a given site without causing severe vibration when using, for example, 50 kg of explosives, the use of 10 delay periods of the order of 25 milliseconds will permit a single blast of a total weight of 500 kg. Experience has shown that on the majority of sites **two-thirds** of the instantaneous charge limit can be fired on each of the short delay periods without giving any increase in ground vibration. Considering the above example it should be safe, under normal conditions, to fire as many 35 kg delay charges as there are short delay intervals available. It is always advisable when vibration is critical to check the site by means of vibrograph recordings from typical blasts. Where problems are much less acute, but where the operator feels that it is in his best interest to reduce the ground vibration from his blasts, short delay blasting methods can be introduced with the certain knowledge that they will assist to this end [16].

The usefulness of short delay sequential blasting has been considerably enhanced in recent years by the development by Research Energy of Ohio of their multi-channel sequential timing devices [3] (see above). In this connection, DuPont [6] has developed four basic timing guidelines for sequential blasting in surface mining.

1. The minimum delay time T between holes in a row (or between corresponding deck charges in adjacent holes) should be greater than beween one and five msec/ft of burden distance B.

2. In order to provide good fragmentation and control of flyrock, and adequate relief for each hole, the minimum delay time between rows should be 2 or 3 times greater than the average delay time T between holes in a row.

3. In order to minimize the effects of air blast, the average rate of blast progression along the free face should be less than 400 ft/sec (S/T < 400, where S is the spacing distance, and T is about 3 msec/ft of burden distance B, and S is approximately equal to B).

4. The minimum time interval between charges should be at least 8 msec to control ground vibration.

Structural Damage Criteria

This question refers to damage that may be caused to structures such as residences, public and commercial buildings, churches, bridges, towers and monuments situated near a blast site, chiefly due to the effects of ground vibration and air blast.

(1) Ground Vibration

The increasing number of damage suits filed against quarry and construction companies in recent years demonstrates the need for improved ground vibration technology.

As stated by *Miller* [17]:

"Blasting vibration and air blast are two conditions that can cause people living in the area of a blast site to register complaints – not only to the operator doing the blasting but also to governmental agencies who may exercise some control over the operator's activities. Severe vibration and air blast can cause structural damage to nearby buildings; these are the conditions that need to be controlled. On the other hand, less severe vibration and air blast that are incapable of causing structural damage can still be felt or heard by people. The reaction to these low levels of vibration and noise will depend on the subjective response of the particular individuals. It could range from no reaction, to annoyance or even to claims of damage to their homes.

It is necessary to control vibration and air blast both to prevent damage to nearby structures and to minimize complaints."

It is convenient to analyze a ground vibration, as it affects a particular structure, in three orthogonal components of motion: horizontal longitudinal, horizontal transverse, and vertical. In any given case, the component that exhibits the maximum effect is the important one. In most cases, it is the longitudinal horizontal component, in the direction of the blast site.

Early work in this field was conducted by the U.S. Bureau of Mines between 1935 and 1942, leading to the issue of Bulletin 442 in 1942 [18]. More recent work, as outlined in Bulletin 656, issued in 1971, points to the following conclusions [19].

1. Particle velocity is the best criterion for predicting the probability of vibration damage to structures.

2. Particle velocities less than 2 in/sec show little probability of causing structural damage while particle velocities greater than 2 in/sec are more likely to cause structural damage.

3. If there are at least eight milliseconds (0.008 sec) between detonations, the vibration effects of individual explosions are not cumulative.

These conclusions led to a simple equation for predicting a safe distance for a given weight of explosives to avoid structural damage. The following relationship was set up.

$$v = H\,(\,d/\sqrt{E}\,)^{-\beta}$$

where v is the particle velocity, inches per sec

d is the distance from the shot point to the structure, ft

E is the maximum weight of charge per delay interval, lb

H is a constant for the particular ground conditions

β is an exponent determined from test results.

However, to use this equation intelligently, it is necessary to have values for H and β.

These can be determined experimentally by using a seismograph at the site; but otherwise they can be avoided by using the Scaled Distance Formula, as set out below.

The expression $d/\sqrt{E}$ is referred to as a "scaled distance" in ft per square root of charge weight in lb. From plots of site experimental data, a scaled distance can be selected for which a corresponding safe vibration level can be assured. Once a safe minimum scaled distance has been so determined (usually in excess of 50 ft per square root of charge weight, lb), the safe charge weight per delay, E_S, for any blast can be determined by:

$$E_S = (d/D_S)^2$$

where d is the distance between the blast site and the structure, ft; and

D_S is the minimum safe scaled distance allowable.

Where a value of D_S of 50 or more is used, then the maximum charge weight E_S per delay can be determined safely without the need of instrumental trials. However, if larger charge weights are required, then instrumental measurement should be undertaken to check whether or not a safe level of vibrations is likely to be exceeded [19, 20].

Sophisticated instruments for measuring components of particle velocity in ground vibrations are now available [21].

Individual state authorities have adopted varying regulatory methods and values for enforcing safe vibration limits in built-up areas.

(2) **Air Blast**

When an explosive charge is detonated below ground surface causing significant ground vibration, it also creates an air blast compression wave in the atmosphere. This air blast is not likely to create any more significant structural damage than jet aircraft passing through the sound barrier, or the noise at a fireworks display. The main effects are probably the rattling of windows accompanied by the noise of the blast. This can lead to complaints from nearby residents who register annoyance and also fear that structural damage has occurred. Such phenomena can be minimized by suitable air blast control.

During the last few years, there has been a growing clamour for greater controls over vibrations and air blasts from surface mining by nearby residents. As a consequence, a considerable program of research has been developing in a field where some parameters (soil conditions) are difficult to quantify, atmospheric conditions can give highly variable observations, and, of course, evidence of structural damage and human discomfort can be very subjective.

In a recent Bureau of Mines study [22], it was concluded, *inter alia*, that

1. Particle velocity is still the best ground motion descriptor.
2. Where the operator wants to be relieved of the responsibility of instrumenting all shots, he could design for a conservative square root scale distance of $(70 \text{ ft/lb})^{1/2}$ The typical vibration levels at this scaled distance would be 0.08 to 0.15 in/sec.
3. Practical safe criteria for blasts that generate low frequency ground vibrations are 0.75 in/sec for modern gypsum-board houses and 0.50 in/sec for plaster or lath interiors. For frequencies above 40 Hz (as for close-in construction and excavation blasts), a safe particle velocity maximum of 2.0 in/sec is recommended for all houses.
4. All homes eventually crack because of a variety of environmental stresses.
5. Human reactions to blasting can be the limiting factor [23]. Vibration levels can be felt that are considerably lower than those required to produce damage.

In another study [24], it was shown that acceptable maximum air blast levels ranged from 129 to 134 decibels on a peak hour basis.

It seems that there are many problems associated with surface blasting procedures that are as yet insufficiently documented for the development and adoption of practical ground vibration and air blast safety standards [25, 26].

The U.S. Bureau of Mines has recently advised that "in general, the geologic structure is primarily responsible for the blast vibration frequency and [has] an indirect influence on peak vibration amplitudes..." [27].

A variety of sophisticated instruments for observing and recording ground vibrations due to blasting are available from the following firms (and others).

Philip T. Berger & Associates, Inc.

Blastronics Pty. Ltd.

Dallas Instruments, Inc.

Digital Vibration, Inc.

GeoSonics Inc.

Gisco

Instantel Inc.

Slope Indicator Co.

Thomas Instruments, Inc.

Vibra-tech Engineers, Inc.

Restrictive conditions are being imposed for the control of blasting vibrations from mining activities by Mineral Planning Authorities in Great Britain [27], and many other municipalities around the world.

The basic formula for determining peak particle velocity [18, 19] has been translated into SI units by *Jon Jones* [28]. Guidelines for the prediction of ground vibration and air blast effects are offered in Australian Standard publications [29].

A new approach is currently under way to assess and reduce the structural damage caused by ground vibrations due to blasting. It has been shown that the measure of peak particle velocity may not be the definitive answer. The ICI Group Technical Centre is researching the part that can be played by Frequency Amplitude Modelling to reduce by destructive interference the amplitude of any particular blast-induced frequency. The computer code developed is termed 'VIBREX' [30].

References

[1] *Handbook of Electric Blasting,* Atlas Powder Company, Rev. Edn., 1985

[2] N. P. Chironis, "New Blasting Machine Permits Custom-programmed Blast Patterns", *Coal Age*, March 1974

[3] Research Energy of Ohio Inc., "Internationally Accepted Standard and Sequential Blasting Control Systems and Accessories", Cat No. MA-0388

[4] "Initiation of Explosives – Some Recent Innovations", *Mining Magazine*, May 1981

[5] J. R. Burger, "Non-electric Blast Initiation", *Eng & Mining Jnl.*, April 1982

[6] C. J. Konya, "A New Era in Blast Design and Vibration Control", *Journ. of Explosives Engineering*, 1987

[7] Atlas Data Sheet 701, Nov. 1983

[8] "Primadet Delays", Technical Bulletin EB5, Ensign Bickford Company, 1969

[9] "Anodet Delays", Information Report No. 115A, Canadian Industries Ltd.

[10] "A-3 Primers", Information Report No. 154, Canadian Industries Ltd., 1974

[11] "Nitro Nobel Introduces the NONEL Detonator", Nitro Nobel AB

[12] Ensign-Bickford, Technical Bulletin No. 113B, Jan. 1989

[13] R. A. Dick, "New Non-electric Explosive Initiation Systems", *Pit and Quarry*, March 1976

[14] "Hercudet Non-electric Delay Blasting System", Hercules Incorporated, 1981

[15] M. A. Cook, *The Science of High Explosives*, (New York, Reinhold, 1958)

[16] P. N. Worsey, "Understanding Vibrations from Multihole Blasts using Short Delay Periods", *Journ. of Explosives Engineering*, 1986

[17] P. H. Miller, "Blasting Vibration and Air Blast", Atlas Powder Company

[18] J. R. Thoenen and S. L. Windes, "Seismic Effects of Quarry Blasting", *U.S.B.M.*, Bull. 442, 1942

[19] H. R. Nicholls, C. F. Johnson and W. I. Duvall, "Blasting Vibrations and their Effects on Structures", *U.S.B.M.*, Bull. 656, 1971

[20] J. F. Devine, R. H. Beck, A. V. C. Meyer and W. I. Duvall, "Effect of Charge Weight on Vibration Levels from Quarry Blasting", *U.S.B.M., RI 6774*, 1966

[21] G. A. Bollinger, *Blast Vibration Analysis* (Carbondale, IL, Southern Illinois University Press, 1971)

[22] D. E. Siskind *et al.*, "Structure Response and Damage Produced by Ground Vibration from Surface Mine Blasting", *U.S.B.M., RI 8507*, 1980

[23] D. E. Siskind and M. S. Stagg, "Blast Vibration Measurements near and on Structural Foundations", *U.S.B.M., RI 8969*

[24] D. E. Siskind *et al.*, "Structure Response and Damage Produced by Airblast from Surface Mining", *U.S.B.M., RI 8485*, 1980

[25] S. Walker *et al.*, "Development of Response Spectra Techniques for Prediction of Structural Damage from Open-pit Blasting Vibrations", *Trans. Instn Min. Metall.* (Sect A), Vol. 91, April 1982

[26] W. J. Birch and R. Chaffer, "Prediction of Ground Vibrations from Blasting on Opencast Sites", *Trans. Instn Min. Metall.* (Sect A), Vol. 92, April 1983

[27] "Mineral Planning Authority Blasting Vibrations Survey", Summary Report. (Cornwall, U.K.: Jay Mineral Services Ltd.) July 1988

[28] J. Jones, "Good Neighbours", *Downline*, May 1985

[29] Australian Standard Publications AS 2187.2 – 1983, and DR 91095

[30] "Blast Vibrations: Frequency Amplitude Modelling", *Downline*, No. 12, February 1990

CHAPTER 10

Special Forms of Explosives

Liquid Oxygen Explosive (LOX)

A liquid-oxygen explosive [1] is a detonable mixture employing liquid oxygen as the oxidant of a combustible absorbent material... The detonation is the result of the rapid reaction of the combustible with the oxygen, which can occur over a wide range of oxygen concentration. A large variety of ingredients has been used in liquid-oxygen explosives.

Liquid-oxygen explosives are unique in that the oxidising component of the explosives system is not permanently held, as in the case of fired explosives.

... upon exposure to surroundings at ordinary temperatures, evaporation... of the liquid (oxygen) proceeds at a rate determined by the rate of heat transfer to the liquid.

If evaporation of the liquid oxygen is permitted to continue the cartridge loses its excess oxygen; and eventually the oxygen content falls below the amount required for good explosive performance, ultimately becoming non-explosive.

Combustible materials used include lampblack, carbon black, or char. Cartridges of this material, dipped in a vacuum-walled container of liquid oxygen, are charged into a blast hole and fired with a detonator. The explosive effect is produced by the rapid reaction between the oxygen and the combustible, after detonation; this forms a large volume of CO_2 gas at high temperature and pressure.

The charge should be fired as soon as possible, as the potential energy of the explosion falls off with time as the evaporation of the liquid oxygen proceeds.

This type of explosive presents unique safety features. Apart from the risk of accidental fire, the explosive is basically safe after the liquid oxygen evaporates.

The economic use of LOX depends largely on the availability of a cheap source of oxygen. Since the recent rapid development of blasting agents, it seems unlikely that LOX will ever become a widely used explosive. About 1000 tons were used annually for stripping overburden in the United States.

Shaped Charges [2, 3, 4, 5, 6]

The application of shaped explosive charges to mining operations has extremely interesting possibilities in the field of cost reduction in the drilling of shot-holes.

The principle, known as the "*Munroe* effect", involves the concentration of the force of the explosion in the form of a jet. The principle was used during World War II for demolition purposes, for certain grenades, and for the "bazooka" which employed a warhead containing a shaped charge lined with a metal cone.

Some non-military applications include the "explosive rivet" (used in aircraft construction), the "jet perforator" (for perforating oil-well casing), and the "jet tapper" (for tapping blast funaces).

Possible mining applications include the drilling of blastholes or the blasting of an entire cut in a development face.

A charge described by *Austin* [4] consists of four components: a detonator, $3 \cdot 3$ lb of high explosive, a 4 inch diameter cylindro-conical body, and a metal or ceramic liner of 55° included angle. The charge is placed with the conical liner about 7 inches from the rock face. On detonation, the liner collapses and is expelled as a jet with a forward velocity of up to 30,000 ft/sec. The impact of the jet disintegrates the rock target, forming a hole up to 3 inches in diameter and up to 5 feet deep. As at present developed, great care is required in its use. Apart from a considerable air-blast effect, there is a danger from projection of rock fragments, especially with imperfectly directed shots.

In other fields, the development of shaped charges has been markedly more successful [5], particularly where conventional explosives are difficult to use as, for example, in underwater applications. One of the pioneer operators in this field is Jet Research Center, Inc., of Arlington, TX, USA (see Chapter 17).

FAMESA has developed a shaped charge for deep hole seismic exploration. It has the advantage of providing a concentrated explosion in a small area as a seismic booster (Carga Hueca). It contains about 300 g of high explosive, detonating at 6,500 m/sec.

A 16 kg shaped charge called PERFOLIT is supplied by DYNO for underwater blasting of rock without the need for drilling of holes. The unit is initiated with a seismic detonator in a 400 g primer attached to detonator cord. It is normally produced for water depths down to 70 m but can also be made for greater depths.

A range of six types of shaped charges is available from DNW for particular applications.

GOEX has developed a shaped charge for breaking boulders (see Chapter 14). GOEX also provides a linear shaped charge for cutting work in oil well technology. It is available in core loads of 125, 250, 425 and 680 g/m.

Owen Oil Tools Inc. supplies a full range of cutting and perforating tools and supplies for the oil well industry. Many of these involve the use of small shaped charge assemblies.

Substitutes for Explosives [6, 7]

The main field of use for commercial explosives is in breaking hard rock in order to minimize the arduous nature of the work, and to increase the productivity of such operations (see Chapter 1).

The universal employment of explosives for such purposes has, for a century or more, established the place of explosives as an important tool of engineering endeavour.

However, since the development of hard metals (tungsten carbide) in World War II, and of other techniques, excavation of the less tenacious rocks is being increasingly accomplished by non-explosive methods. Some of these are set out below.

1. **Capsuled compressed gas cartridges** [6–10]: Two general types of non-explosive compressed gas systems have been developed primarily for "soft ground" applications.

These are used in underground coal mining (see Chapter 20), for loosening compacted bulk materials in storage, and for dislodging accretions from hot furnaces. In all of these applications, safety is enhanced. They depend for their action upon the build-up of gas pressure in a cylinder, which, following a trigger action, is suddenly expanded into the material to be broken or loosened. With coal mining, the cylinders are located in regular boreholes. For loosening bulk materials, or breaking up furnace accretions, the cylinder is inserted into similar holes; or (for Airdox), located permanently in a recess in the wall of a storage bin.

For coal mining, a mobile machine is available to drill holes and place cartridges of **Airdox**; or a specially designed self-propelled "shooting car" is used for multiple sequence shooting.

Airdox cylinders are inserted in drill holes in the face and charged to 70 to 85 MPa by a nearby high pressure six-stage compressor through a feeder hose. Cylinders (which are re-usable) are fired remotely through shooting hoses. This equipment is available from the manufacturers on lease arrangements.

For loosening bulk materials, **Cardox** cylinders are also available; but especially for intermittent *ad hoc* duty at infrequent intervals. This unit consists of an alloy steel cartridge filled with liquid carbon dioxide and a chemical igniting agent. When required, the reaction is initiated by an electric current controlled from a safe distance. The expanding action of the CO_2 gas breaks a soft steel disc at the discharge port, and the escaping expanding gas "pressurizes" and heaves the enclosing material. Cardox cylinders may be re-charged at the factory. Standard discharge pressures range from 70 to 135 MPa, depending upon the application.

Where there is a continuing routine need for loosening stored bulk materials, the Airdox system is recommended.

Both systems are available from the Long-Airdox Company, Oak Hill, West Virginia, USA.

The Cardox system, as developed and serviced by Pikrose and Company Ltd. of Delta Road, Audenshaw, Manchester, U.K., is especially applicable for underground coal mining in gassy seams. The steel alloy tubes are available in four diameters and lengths;

and factory-charged with liquid carbon dioxide. After firing, the tubes can be returned to the factory for re-charging

2. **Mechanical methods**: Tungsten carbide tipped steel (rotating and traversing) abrading elements are now used to excavate rock of soft to medium hardness [11].

Specialized "continuous miners", tunnelling moles, roadheaders, and large diameter shaft/raise borers have been developed recently to employ these principles in soft to medium rock without the use of explosives. However, for hard rock, where the compressive strength generally exceeds about 250–300 MPa, Tunnel Boring Machines (TBMs) cannot be used economically. For roadheaders, the practical limit is about 130–145 MPa. Beyond these levels, explosives must still be used in the conventional drill/blast/muck cycle of operation [11, 12, 13].

Secondary breaking of large hard rock boulders by thermo-mechanical methods has recently been under investigation [14]. The rock is first heated and then fragmented by mechanical impact.

Automotive Industrial and Mining Supplies Ltd. of 145 Boulder Road, Kalgoorlie, Western Australia supply a Foseco Technik SPLITTER as a fast acting non-explosive rock breaking agent.

3. **Electrical methods**: Various methods of breaking rock by electrical energy have been investigated, including heating by induction, high frequency, microwave, electron beam, plasma jet, arc, and condensor discharge techniques [15].

The "Electrofrac" method uses electrode contact and resistance heating to stress the rock and to create fractures for subsequent separation by mechanical handling. Field trials on electrical fragmentation for secondary breaking of magnetic iron ore have been demonstrated. It is claimed that it is feasible to use this method for primary breaking of iron ore [16].

An Electrothermal Loosening (ETL) technique is being tested in the Soviet Union, aimed at saving explosives and providing greater fragmentation of iron ore. The technique involves the normal drilling of blast holes, then passing a pair of electrodes (using AC at normal frequency) in adjacent holes; then a breakdown voltage (0.4 to 10 kV) is applied as a succession of vigorous electrothermal jolts, at the pre-blasting stage [17].

The Tetra Corporation of 4905 Hawkins Street, NE, Albuquerque, NM 87109, USA report that boulders can be fragmented with an electrohydraulic effect (EHE) when used with their machine. High energy pressure pulses are generated by a high voltage spark discharge in a liquid medium. The direct impact of these high pressure pulses fracture the rock.

4. **Liquid jet systems**: Pulsed water jets at pressures of 700 MPa can fracture rock and concrete. By incorporating a battery of high pressure water jets on a tunnelling machine, it is believed that conventional tunnelling practices will be revolutionized [18, 19, 20, 21].

A new way to break rocks by water pressure is by using the ROCK SPLITTER, available from Fowlerex Pty Ltd., 401 Pacific Highway, Artarmon, NSW, Australia. A hollow spear inserted in a borehole is locked into position, thereby expanding a rubber seal. The hole is then filled with water through the spear and pressure is applied through a gas-charged accumulator, pessurizing the water to 34,000 kPa. This generates a bursting force of 3,400 kg for every 25 mm hole length in a 40 mm diameter hole.

5.   **Binary explosives**: Three new forms of binary explosives have been introduced:

(1) **Astro-Pak** is being produced by EXCOA of Issaquah, WA, and is represented as a high-performance 2-component liquid explosive that is safe when unmixed, but can develop a very high explosive power when mixed and placed [18].

(2) There is also a range of binary explosives consisting of an inert solid and an inert liquid, each of which can be shipped and stored as a non-explosive. When the two components are mixed and charged, they form an extremely high strength cap-sensitive explosive.

Typical of these is the KINEPAK range.

(a) KINEPAK, where the two components are mixed and armed with a standard electric detonator or DC, develops a VOD up to 6,500 m/sec.

(b) KINESTIK (available in 0.15 to 0.45 kg sticks) is designed for blasting pole holes and for ditch construction and stump removal.

(c) KINEPOUCH (in 0.22 to 1.82 kg pouches) is packaged in a pliable plastic pouch, to which the liquid component can be added, and the detonator placed. This pliable pouch can easily be made to conform to the surface of boulders ands small rocky outcrops. Primarily for secondary blasting.

These three types are supplied by ICI Explosives Group Inc.

(3) Slurry Explosive Corporation (SLEX) produces its T-100 2-component Yellow Sticks, $1^3/8$ x 8 in; and Green Sticks, 2 x 12 in, both developing a VOD of 6,500 m/sec, with a density of 1.22. A seismic stick is also available.

The US Bureau of Alcohol, Tobacco and Firearms has recently published guidelines for the authorized use of binary explosives in the USA.

6.   **Other non-explosive systems**: The SLB Concrete Breaker is marketed by Nippon Kayaku Co, Ltd (NKC) of Japan. It consists mainly of a gas-generating powder enclosed in a plastic cartridge and fired with an electric igniting cap in one end. When ignited, it burns at 40 – 60 m/sec, generating high temperature gas, providing a sort of soft fragmentation for cracking rock and concrete. SLB is supplied in four types.

The S-MITE safe non-explosive agent is represented as having an expansive force of 3,000 t/m², with no noise vibration, dust or flyrock. It is supplied by H. Bleakley Pty. Ltd. of 23 Muriel Avenue, Rydalmere, NSW 2116, Australia.

7.   **Liquid explosives**: GOEX markets a liquid explosive (GOI-4) for fracturing oil and gas well formations. The liquid is pumped into the formation and detonated. A No. 8 detonator is used.

8.   **Shockwave refraction tape (SRT)**: Patented by Dr. *S. C. Alford*, this tape contains two essential components, (a) the explosive, and (b) a shockwave shaping element. The explosive element calls for a density of 1.5 g/cm³ with a VOD of 7,000 m/sec. The SRT is basically designed as a superior cutting charge for steel members [22].

9. **Medical applications**: An unreferenced news report states that two Japanese researchers at the Kyoto University of Medicine have developed a new method of removing large kidney stones in the bladder by using micro-explosives charges. The method would eliminate the need for surgery to remove large stones (mineral deposits) from the kidney and bladder. A new device with an explosive chamber attached to the end of a catheter tube is inserted through the urethal canal. Then lead azide is detonated next to the stone so that the bladder wall is protected from shock waves and flyrock. Then the fractured stone is discharged as sand-like small stones (depending, of course, on the degree of fragmentation achieved).

A research paper on this "micro-explosion of biliary calculi" is now available from the Society of Explosive Engineers, 29100 Aurora Road, Cleveland OH, 44139, USA.

References

[1]   "Safety and Performance Characteristics of Liquid-Oxygen Explosives", *U.S. Bureau of Mines Bulletin*, No. 472 (1941), pp. 1-2

[2]   John B. Huttl, "The Shaped Charge for Cheaper Mine Blasting", *Engineering & Mining Journal*, May 1946, pp. 58-63

[3]   W. P. Walters, "Applications of the Shaped Charge Concept", *Journ. of Explosives Engineering*, Vol. 8, No. 5, Jan/Feb 1991

[4]   C. F. Austin, *Min. Cong. Jnl.,* Vol. 50, No. 7

[5]   P. De Frank and C. H. Brown, "Underwater Explosives Technology", *Marine Technology Society,* 6th Annual Reprints, Vol. 1, June 1970

[6]   Melvin A. Cook, *The Science of High Explosives* (New York, Reinhold, 1958)

[7]   R. S. Lewis and G. B. Clark, *Elements of Mining*, 3rd ed. (New York, Wiley, 1964)

[8]   G. W. Davis, "Pneumatic System Dislodges Bulk Material Safely and Effectively", *Coal Age,* October 1970

[9]   G. W. Davis, "Safely Dislodging Material Stoppages", *Compressed Air Magazine,* March 1971

[10] Airdox Shooting, Bulletin 63-1-5000, Long-Airdox Co.

[11] I. R. Muirhead and L. G. Glossop, "Hard Rock Tunnelling Machines", *Trans. Instn Min. Metall. (Sect. A: Min. Industry)*, 77, 1968

[12] P. J. G. du Toit and L. P. Colvin, "Underground Mining Advances with New Breaking and Handling Systems", *World Mining,* Catalog Survey Directory, June 25, 1971, p. 81

[13] "Tunnelling by Machine", *Mining Magazine,* June 1982

[14] K. Thirumalai, S. G. Demou and R. L. Fischer, "Thermomechanical Method for Secondary Breakage of Hard Rocks", *U.S.B.M., R.I.* 8057, 1975

[15] E. Sarapuu, "Electro-Energetic Rock Breaking Systems", *Mining Congr. J.,* June 1973

[16] E. Sarapuu, "Electrical Fragmentation of Magnetic Iron Ores", Paper presented at AIME Annual Meeting, Washington, DC, February 1969

[17] "Electrothermal Loosening of Iron Ore", *Mining Magazine,* Nov. 1981

[18] Water Jet Technology, Rockville, MD; Exotech Inc., Hydromechanics Division

[19] J. N. Frank and J. W. Chester, "Fragmentation of Concrete with Hydraulic Jets", *U.S.B.M., R.I.* 1572, 1971

[20] M. M. Singh and P. J. Huck, "Rock Breakage by High Velocity Water Jets", Paper presented to SME Meeting, St. Louis, Oct. 1970

[21] B. Mohanty and P. McFarlane, "Water-jet Drilling and its Applications in Mining and Blasting", *Trans. Instn Min. Metall.* (Sect A), Vol. 95, April 1986

[22] S. C. Alford, "Shock-wave Refraction Tape", *Explosives Engineer*, Vol. 2, No. 1, Spring 1986

CHAPTER 11

Practical Usage of Explosives

Placement of Charges

The bulk of the explosives marketed around the world is used for "breaking ground" in mines, collieries, quarries, and rock excavations. In order to obtain the most effective use of explosives, they are confined in boreholes drilled in strategic positions in the rock (as discussed in Part II of this textbook).

The effect of the detonation is to weaken the cohesive strength of elastic rocks by *brisance*, reinforced by the high gas pressure created in the charge hole. This detonation sets up in the rock a compressive strain pulse which travels in all directions from the charge hole and attenuates to zero, unless and until it reaches a free face (see Chapter 12), in which case it is reflected as a tensile strain pulse. The rock is therefore broken in tension, aided and displaced by the high gas pressure (bubble energy).

The operations involved in charging a normal short hole with conventional cartridged explosives are described as follows:

1. The hole is first cleaned out with compressed air by means of a blowpipe.
2. The cartridges of explosive are inserted into the borehole one by one and firmly squeezed into position (so as to occupy the full cross-section of the hole) by means of a wooden tamping pole.
3. The primer cartridge (if of conventional safety fuse/plain detonator type) is placed last.
4. The hole is sealed by stemming with a cartridge of sandy clay material squeezed against the primer.
5. Care is taken to see that no damage is caused to the safety fuse, the free end of which is now protruding from the mouth of the hole.
6. If the charge is to be fired electrically, then the electric primer is the first cartridge to be inserted (inversely) in the hole. The leg wires are then held taut to one side of the hole while the ordinary cartridges are tamped into position.

7. With either type of primer the live end of the detonator should face the bulk of the charge, i.e., with the ordinary primer – inwards; with the electric primer – outwards.

8. On no account must a metal tamping rod (e. g., drill steel) be used.

9. The primer cartridge itself should not be tamped or squeezed with the tamping pole.

When charging soft plastic cartridges of slurries, adjusted techniques need to be adopted. Pneumatically operated cartridge chargers are manufactured by Nitro Nobel AB and supplied by VME-Nitro Consult Inc. They are available in a range of sizes and designs for charging boreholes up to 100 mm in diameter for either rigid dynamite or soft plastic cartridges. DuPont recommends this device for charging small diameter cartridged slurries such as Tovex. One type can be used in conjunction with a Robot Tamping Machine.

Where the rock formation is of such a nature that it tends to break back and "cut off" part of a neighbouring hole that is timed to explode later, the holes should be "bottom-primed", i.e., the primer cartridge should be loaded first, in the bottom of the hole. This can be done safely and effectively *only with an electric primer* (or detonating cord, for deep holes).

There are several reasons why a plain (safety fuse/cap) primer should be used only for top (collar) priming, i.e., placed last in the hole, immediately before the stemming.

(1) If placed at the bottom of the hole, a sharp reverse 180° bend needs to be made in the fuse (see Fig. 31). This stresses the textile wrappings, thereby permitting water to enter, or the flame to spit outwards, with the possibility of setting fire to the main charge. Admittedly, some manufacturers supply a special fuse with extruded plastic jacket to obviate this problem; but a miner trained to use indirect (reverse-end, bottom) fuse priming will always thereafter tend to do so with whatever fuse is available at the site.

(2) Where a bottom-primed hole is well-stemmed (and this is a very necessary requirement for effective blasting), the burning speed of the fuse, under the resulting conditions of superior confinement, can increase by over 60 per cent, in some cases burning almost instantaneously [1, 2]. In such a case, a premature explosion may result, yielding a fatal accident due to a "fast fuse".

(3) In other circumstances, the fuse, lying parallel to the main charge, may "side-spit" and ignite the charge before the main flame reaches the detonator, thereby causing a premature explosion (or at least, an unsatisfactory blast).

(4) Again, the heat generated by the burning of the powder train may be transferred laterally to the main charge, raising its temperature to considerably more than 65 °C, with risk of a premature explosion. This can occur even without the side-spitting action mentioned under (3) above.

Charging of small diameter underground blastholes with AN/FO (in any direction) is usually done pneumatically. There are two basic types of pneumatic loading machines:

1. **Pressure type**, in which 250–280 kPa compressed air is applied above the AN/FO contained in a pressure vessel, causing it to flow from the bottom of the vessel into the placement hose. It is not suitable for charging long "up" holes (unless provided with

Fig. 31: Incorrect method of bottom-priming (with safety fuse/plain detonator type primer)

suitable accessories) because the particle velocity is usually insufficient to cause the material to stick in the hole. This type of charger is represented by ANOL Loader (VME-Nitro Consult); CIL Intermediate Loader 60R.

These units are generally used for large faces. They have high loading rates, and load prilled AN/FO to a density of about 0.9 to 1.0 g/cm^3.

2. **Ejector type**, in which the AN/FO is drawn from the bottom of an open-topped container and ejected into the air stream in the placement hose which conveys it into the borehole under a pressure of 450–700 kPa. Typical loaders of this type are:

CIL Blasthole Charger

CIL Satellite Loader

Penberthy Anoloder (CIL)

PORTANOL (VME-Nitro Consult).

The ejector type generally loads to a higher density. It is therefore more suitable for charging long "up" holes, but it operates at a much slower rate. Both types are made in various sizes and capacities.

Combination methods are also used to develop the advantages of both systems. In such an arrangement, the pressure unit and the ejector operate in series (see Fig. 32).

Typical of the combination (pressure-ejector) models are the CIL Blasthole Charger, the CIL Model 1210R Blasthole Charger, and the JET-ANOL Loader (VME-Nitro Consult).

CIL have developed the Scopemobile Emulsion System, with an inbuilt pump to supply 10 to 70 kg of cold pumpable emulsion per minute through a hose of 25 mm internal diameter. In this way, emulsions can be pumped into small underground holes, similar to the blowing of AN/FO.

Fig. 32: Combination pressure-ejector type pneumatic blasthole charger

It is reported that Nitro Nobel has developed a hole charging robot (type E6-33) for the complete mechanized charging of AN/FO in long underground holes.

For loading of AN/FO into up holes of any diameter, CIL has developed the Cascade System, in which the AN/FO is allowed to fall to a plug placed near the collar. The AN/FO column then builds up to fill the hole.

For loading into 'up' holes (ranging from 50 to 115 mm in diameter), some operators use Plastic Clip Retainers, as supplied by KIMIT AB.

When AN/FO is charged pneumatically, **static electricity** may be generated as the mixture is being blown into the borehole; this can be especially hazardous when holes are bottom-primed with electric detonators in rock of low conductivity under conditions of low relative humidity [3]. In such circumstances, it is safer to "collar-prime" (see Glossary). Otherwise, and particularly for bottom priming, a set of safe requirements has been drawn up by Litchfield, Hay & Monroe, as follows [4].

(1) A semi-conductive charging hose should be used.

(2) The resistivity of the AN/FO should be controlled, either by dampening the AN/FO charge itself, or the walls of the hole.

(3) The borehole should be discharged prior to hook-up of the detonator leg wires.

(4) The operator should discharge himself prior to handling the detonator leg wires.

(5) Tests should be made with a suitable galvanometer to assure the continuity of the detonator wire circuit prior to inserting the EB cap in the hole.

(6) The leg wires should be kept shunted, but not otherwise connected to ground during loading.

(7) The leg wires should never be allowed to contact the loading machine.

The Nitro Nobel Mec Loading Hose is a special anti-statically treated semi-conductive charging hose for AN/FO.

Use of AN/FO Underground

AN/FO can be used successfully underground except under wet conditions. For this reason, it is not generally used for shaft sinking, winzing or in other wet blastholes.

Properly mixed and primed charges have good fume characteristics and do not cause headaches when handling.

When charging by pneumatic methods, hole space is more effectively filled and the charging operation is faster than with cartridged explosives. Fragmentation is generally improved, probably because of the better coupling and greater gas volume. AN/FO has been successfully used for small diameter holes for both short and long (ring-drilled) holes.

For primary breaking of ore in stopes, bagged AN/FO is taken by supply cars to feed pressure-type pneumatic loaders located on main levels (in the case of sub-level open stopes), on sub-levels (in the case of sub-level caving), or actually in the stopes (for shrinkage or cut-and-fill stoping).

For secondary breaking, bagged AN/FO is supplied to scram drifts or grizzly levels. It is then transferred in small polyethylene bags for plastering, "browfiring", or chute blasting.

When blasting in development headings, bagged AN/FO is taken to the face in the normal explosives carrying bags. It is pneumatically loaded into blastholes through 15 and 20 mm diameter semi-conductive hoses by ejector-type loaders. Holes are bottom-primed electrically under conditions, calculated to avoid static currents (see above). If collar-primed (by safety fuse/caps), igniter cord is used; this may be ignited from a re-mote place by electric igniters.

Mixing of Blasting Agents

Following some years of experimentation, AN/FO is now usually mixed on the job site in the following ways. For small-scale operations, the correct amount of fuel oil is introduced into a bag of AN prills, the contents of which are later fed to the charging machine (or poured into a quarry hole).

For medium-scale operations, mechanical mixing in a concrete mixer lined with fibre-glass, in small batches, can be quite effective. However, this procedure is not acceptable in Canada: a ribbon-type mixer or other specially-designed unit is required. Each type of equipment must be approved before use.

However, since AN/FO is now so freely available in pre-mixed form as a bagged product (see Fig. 33), at a marginally higher price, the practice of on-site do-it-yourself mixing of prills and oil is now considered disadvantageous.

For large scale work, bulk storage plants are usually established nearby, from which pre-mixed quantities of AN/FO may be bagged and despatched underground as required. For surface blasts, specialized bulk loading trucks draw from these storage plants and deliver to the blast site, either in pre-mixed form, or as separate ingredients (prills and oil) to be mixed and charged at the blast site. The latter of these bulk delivery vehicles are usually termed *mix trucks*. The mixture is charged into the blastholes either by an auger delivery system (see Fig. 1), or by a pneumatic unit. Where holes are moderately wet, the AN/FO may be loaded into a lay-flat polythene hole liner, or a special mobile de-watering system may be employed to pump water and sludge from the holes before charging.

For convenience, an Explosives Loading Table is included as Appendix G, giving the weight of explosives (of density ranging from 0.7 to 1.4) for blast holes from 32 to 432 mm in diameter.

Charging of Bulk Slurries and Emulsions

Mixing of AN slurries is a rather more exacting exercise; it is therefore usually handled by the suppliers. Their chief application is for surface blasts in wet holes or for breaking hard tenacious rocks (haematite or taconite).

Where slurries or emulsions are used in small diameter short holes as for underground development headings and some stopes, soft plastic film cartridges are used.

But for long stope holes 125 mm in diameter and for large diameter holes in open cuts and quarries, bulk materials are usually charged.

For small quarry operations, or in locations where bulk-mix-load services are not available, a series of **pourable slurries** is supplied in polyethylene packs that can be slit at the collar of the borehole and the contents shucked and poured down the hole

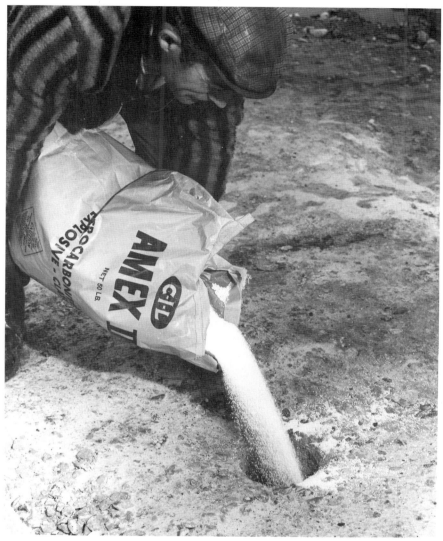

Fig. 33: Loading ready-mixed AN/FO into hole by a simple pouring procedure

(Fig. 34). Typical of these products are: DuPont "Pourvex Extra" and "Tovex Extra A", and CIL "Hydroflo".

For large scale operations, slurries and emulsions are more advantageously placed by highly sophisticated *pump trucks,* usually operated by explosive manufacturers as a service to their customers. Many of these pump truck contractors provide for "programmed blasting", a system in which a loading formula can be preplanned for each hole or group of holes (with more than one mixture, if desired, for any particular

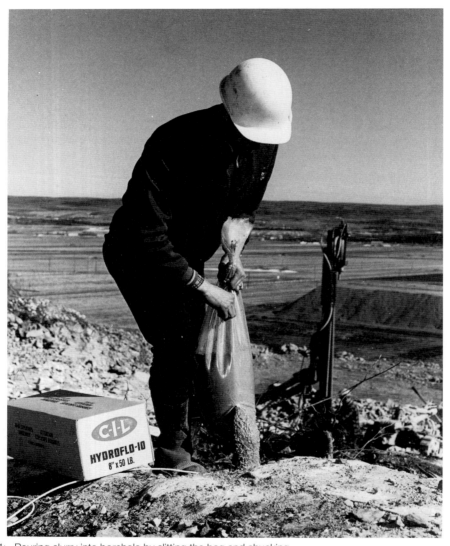

Fig. 34:   Pouring slurry into borehole by slitting the bag and shucking

hole), followed by fast economical accurate loading procedures. In this way, a single pump truck can load a number of mixtures into a hole at the one stop or visitation. Changes in the mixture formula can be effected by the operator, by using simple controls, during the pumping operation. By these means, quantities and formulations can be tailored to fit the requirements of the hole pattern and the desired characteristics of the broken rock. Blasting performance is thereby optimized.

Some contractors also place the primers and fire the whole charge; thereby undertaking the whole of the blasting operation following the drilling of the holes.

Some types of mix pump trucks presently in service include:

AN/FO bulk truck type SDA (Nitro Nobel)

AN/FO mix truck type 803H (Nitro Nobel)

Bulk mix truck (Baughman Mfg Co)

Bulk truck for Nobel 100 (DNAG)

Emulsion blend truck (Amerind MacKissic)

Gelmaster (CIL)

Handi-bulk (ICIA)

ICI Bulkmaster (ICIA)

SuperAN, for Heavy AN/FO blends

and others by Austin, JKS Boyles, CBS Explosives, DuPont, and Warren Manufacturing, Inc.

Some pump trucks load with plant-mixed slurries and emulsions at the bulk plant depot; others have the capability of loading at the depot and mixing and loading at the site (see Fig. 35).

A recent development, based upon their consistency at normal temperatures, has demonstrated that bulk "pumpable" emulsion products can be pumped into suitable vessels and stored for relatively long periods (up to three months). When required for use, these bulk emulsions can be re-pumped from storage into mobile delivery trucks, and finally into blastholes, after blending if desired.

Fig. 35: Pump truck for charging slurry holes as a programmed blasting service

When mixed with 5 to 30% AN/FO, the blended product is termed "Heavy AN/FO. A broad energy range is thereby developed to suit on-site requirements.

Slurry and emulsion blasting agents are denser than water; but it should not be assumed that pouring or gravity-loading into "down" holes will always effectively displace standing water and thereby provide a continuous column. To achieve this necessary objective, the holes should first be unwatered by pumping, and the mix should then be pumped into the holes under pressure through a hose, even for vertical "down" holes of large diameter. The charging hose should first be lowered to the bottom of the hole and slowly withdrawn as the slurry progressively fills the hole.

Special unwatering pumps are now available (in three sizes from Bill Lane, Inc., Westport, WA 98585, USA), from EXPLO Tool Manufacturing Ltd., Mavilette, Nova Scotia; from Dry-Rite (distributed by Precision Blasting Services), and from the LEGRA unit of Blasting Accessories & Supply Inc., Farmington, NM, USA, and from BDS Inc., Montana, USA.

Priming of Blasting Agents

The notoriously low initiation sensitivity of blasting agents predicates the need for great care in the priming of such charges.

For normal underground holes up to 6.3 cm diameter, a full cartridge of high velocity ammonia gelatine 60%, with a No. 6 detonator, is a sufficient primer in a well-mixed, well-placed, and well-stemmed charge of AN/FO.

For larger holes, as in quarries, priming needs extra care, especially if the hole is wet, or if deck charges are used. A small quantity of high-strength booster is preferable to a larger amount of lower strength. The VOD of the booster must be greater than the inherent VOD of the charge for efficient detonation.

The best position for the primer is normally at either end of the charge, i.e., with collar- or bottom-priming. Unless deckloaded, the practice of stringing additional boosters along detonating cord throughout the charge column is disadvantageous. It is important however to ensure good contact (without air space) between the primer and the charge. Nevertheless, the number and position of primers in a bench hole provide a continuing topic of research, experiment and debate.

Even with bottom-priming, the core loading of detonating cord should not exceed 5.3 g/m, in order to avoid premature low-order detonation of the charge laterally/radially.

With large diameter holes (say greater than 100 mm) the *shape* of boosters as well as the strength is important (Fig. 6). The diameter of such boosters should approach that of the borehole in order to provide that the major portion of the available energy is released axially (to propagate a strong detonation wave along the column) rather than radially. The use of Primacord as the sole detonant, even if it runs throughout the column, is not recommended, since it may cause deflagration rather than detonation of the charge [5].

Table 18: Components of a charge* (in other than coal mines)

Main Charge	Placement	Primer Details	Circuit Details	Method of Initiation	Method of Firing	Method of Sequential Firing of Several Charges
Low explosive – Black powder in bulk	In borehole or cavity	–	–	Safety fuse	Light fuse with fuse lighter etc.	–
High explosive – NG-based (in cartridge form)	In boreholes or coyote chambers,	Plain detonator incorporated in a cartridge (or a special booster)	–	Detonator crimped to safety fuse	Light fuse with fuse lighter etc.	Fuses docked to various lengths and ignited in order
Blasting agents (in bulk, prepacked cartridges, cans, or bags)			Igniter cord (IC)	Detonator crimped to safety fuse	Light IC with fuse lighter etc.	Fuses undocked but connected to IC in order
	or	Electric detonators incorporated in a cartridge (or a special booster)	Series, parallel, parallel-series	Electric detonator connected to blasting circuit		Electric delay detonators
	as		Electric trunkline circuit	Electric detonator taped to DC downlines	Throw blasting switch on power lines, or operate exploder	
	blister	Detonating cord laced through a HE cartridge (or a special booster)	Detonating cord trunklines with connectors to DC "downlines"	Electric detonators taped to DC trunk-line		
	or demolition charges			Plain detonator (taped to DC) and safety fuse	Light fuse with fuse lighter etc.	M/S delay connectors

* The use of non-electric Anodet, Detaline, EXEL, NONEL and other delay systems are not covered because they are generally self-contained systems. They are used only for initiating charges of blasting agents.

Components of a Charge

Methods of formulating (and firing) a complete charge (for other than coal mines) are shown in Table 18.

Treatment of Misfires

A charge that has not exploded or has only partially exploded is classified as a "misfire" and is treated with the utmost caution.

The first precaution is to allow a safe interval of time (in some cases specified statutorily) between the report of a misfire and an approach to the face.

Before commencing and while removing the broken rock from the face, extreme care should be taken to identify unexploded cartridges or detonators, and to remove them to a safe place.

The face should be carefully examined for remaining "butts" of holes which may contain remnants of a charge. All such explosive remnants should be carefully removed before drilling commences. Holes should never be drilled into old butts.

In some countries, a misfired hole can be rectified by drilling a hole near to but not closer than a specified distance from the misfire. The firing of this hole will either explode the misfired hole by sympathetic detonation or at least break it open and free the explosive.

Local regulations differ in all countries, but they usually specify the procedure that should be carefully followed in each case.

Misfires can be caused by defective explosives (due mainly to deterioration in storage), damage to components while charging, water entering the detonator, discontinuity of the electrical circuit, insufficient current in the circuit, and by "cut-offs" (i.e., the explosion of a previous hole breaking out the collar of a hole and dislodging the primer).

AN/FO misfires are much less dangerous to resolve because AN is soluble and may be sluiced out of a butt with the water hose. However, if an NG primer is present, the misfired hole should be regarded as of the same degree of hazard as a conventional NG-based charge.

Tamping

The placing of cartridges of explosives in a small diameter hole, as in underground metal mining, is usually accomplished with a tamping stick (or rod). These are best made of wood, of about 22 mm in diameter. Metal or metal-tipped tamping rods are dangerous. Drill steel must *never* be used. Rigid plastic tamping rods may also be hazardous because of the possibility of building up large charges of static electricity. Plastic materials used for tamping rods should therefore have suitable dielectric properties.

The operation of tamping a cartridged charge into a hole involves a certain amount of danger due to a premature explosion. Therefore great care should be exercised. Necessary precautions are as follows:

1. Holes should be thoroughly cleaned out before charging, to remove grit, sludge, duff, and obstructions that may cause undue impact pressure to be applied to get the cartridge into place.

2. Cartridge diameters should be less than the minimum diameter of the hole.

3. Cartridges should be firmly pressed into place and then enlarged by squeezing with the tamping rod to fill the borehole diameter. They should not be thumped or pounded.

4. Care should be taken not to dislodge the detonator, or damage the fuse or the leg wires.

5. Special care should be taken with the soft plastic film cartridges of slurries and emulsions. For charging holes in coal mines, see Chapter 20.

Stemming of Charge Holes

In order to localize the effects of the gases produced in the explosive reaction, the charge must necessarily be confined. A plaster charge to break large rocks or boulders is "mudcapped". Charges placed in boreholes must be sealed (or "stemmed") to prevent the gases from escaping before they make their contribution to the task of breaking the rock (see Glossary).

The most effective stemming material is sandy clay. It is usually preformed into cartridges and tamped into the hole above the charge.

For large quarry holes, drill cuttings are normally back-filled into the hole above the charge.

In coal mines, it is necessary to use inert incombustible material. Water stemming bags (DuPont) have been used to seal the hole and to quench/cool the flame of the explosion, thereby reducing the risk of a coaldust/gas explosion.

An improved procedure is to use Trabant Gel-stemming ampoules [6]. These consist of a flame-resistant non-abrasive blow-moulded cylindrical sheath, filled and sealed (under factory conditions) with a stable inert gelatinous material containing water and organic substances. The ampoule not only effectively seals the hole, but also absorbs fumes and dust.

Fire-resistant polystyrene Tamping Plugs are also available, from Trojan.

A new style of mechanical stemming device is termed a *blast control plug*. When the charge is fired, the plug becomes wedged in the hole. It is claimed to improve charge confinement and fragmentation, and to reduce the length of stemming required. This device is patented by the University of Missouri.

Packing of Explosives

High explosives are usually bulk-packed in a fibreboard case of 50 lb (25 kg) weight or containing ten bags of 5 lb each. Thus in each bag, the number of wrapped cartridges depends on the diameter, length, and density of the particular explosive.

Cases are marked on each end with the name of the explosive, the diameter of cartridge, date, and batch symbol. Cases are lined with plastic to preserve the contents against deterioration during storage under normal conditions.

Rigid dynamite cartridges, although regularly $1^1/_8$ or $1^1/_4$ x 8 inches long, are also supplied in $^5/_8$, $^7/_8$, $1^1/_2$, 2, $2^1/_2$ and 3 inch diameters in lengths of 8, 12, 16, 20 and 24 inches; and in even larger diameters for large quarry holes (Fig. 36). These explosives are supplied in prewaxed wrappers (to meet Class 1 fume requirements) in the smaller diameters for underground use. For surface conditions, sprayed paper cartridge wrappers are used, since these have better water resistance.

For seismic prospecting with high explosives, where high heads of water are usually encountered, and for other underwater blasts, special packs have been devised. Threaded paper sleeves and rigid plastic shells in various lengths can be coupled

Fig. 36:   Various sizes of rigid cartridged explosives

together to form a rigid column, and thereby provide increased water protection, easier and improved positive charging techniques, and better propagation effects. For quarry blasting, large diameter cartridges are also supplied in a waxless tapered-crimp-ended (23G) heavy-walled spiral-wrapped tube (Fig. 3) that can be shipped bare without the need for a fibreboard case. These provide easier charging conditions and improved column propagation.

Cylindrical metal cans are used for blasting agents in coyote blasting, and for offshore seismic operations.

AN prills and AN/FO mixtures are usually supplied in bulk, or in 50 or 80 lb plastic, or plastic-lined multi-wall paper or polyburlap bags (Fig. 33). For large diameter quarry holes, AN/FO mixtures are also available in large diameter paper drums with a 23G tapered nose and lowering tapes (Fig. 3).

AN slurry and emulsion mixtures are supplied in bulk by pump trucks or in plastic film cartridges of 6 to 18 cm in diameter, which may be slit and loaded direct; or slit, shucked and loaded (where higher loading density and better coupling is desired, Fig. 34).

For regular seismic shots with blasting agents, a continuous rigid column of sealed threaded cans, provided with a nose cone (loading point), is formed and lowered into the hole. Individual cans contain 1 lb of material, packed 50 to the case (Fig. 2). A special primer can screws on to the top of column in the later stages of loading.

Storage of Explosives

Regulations governing the safe handling and storage of explosives are vested in the Chief Inspector of Explosives or equivalent in each country (see Chapter 22).

Conditions governing the handling, storage, and use of explosives in mines, collieries, and quarries are laid down by the Chief Inspector of Mines.

As the regulations in each country are different, they cannot be quoted here because of space restrictions. See also Chapter 22.

In addition to the need to store explosives securely to prevent their falling into the hands of unauthorized persons and to prevent their premature explosion, they should be stored in such a way as to prevent deterioration.

Explosives are perishable goods liable to deterioration after prolonged storage, especially under hot, humid conditions. They are packed and proofed to give maximum protection for long periods.

Fibreboard cases containing explosives are specially designed to give maximum strength (and therefore minimum distortion of cartridges) when stacked according to "This side up" instructions.

AN prills should be stored at a temperature not exceeding 90 °F (32 °C) at all times. Repeated cycling through this temperature will cause the crystal lattice to become disrupted; particles thus become fractured and the desired physical characteristics of the prills are lost.

High explosives must be stored separately from detonators. Magazines must be well ventilated. Only non-ferrous tools should be used. Cases should be opened with wooden or copper wedges and mallets, as steel tools are not permitted.

Unwanted or deteriorated stocks should be disposed of in accordance with careful safe practice (see below).

The location of storage magazines in the United States should conform to the laws and regulations of the local state or municipal authority; and generally should follow the specifications set out in:

(a) Appendix A: Safe Location Specifications for Storage of Explosives (USA); otherwise cited and referred to as "American Table of Distances", or "American Table of Distances for Storage of Explosives" [7, 8, 9].

(b) Appendix B: Safe Location Specifications for Storage of Blasting Agent Materials (USA); otherwise cited as "Table of Recommended Separation Distances of Ammonium Nitrate and Blasting Agents from Explosives or Blasting Agents" [7, 8, 9, 10].

[This table lists recommended separation distances to prevent explosion of stores of ammonium nitrate and AN-based blasting agents (as the receptor) by propagation from nearby stores of high explosives or blasting agents (referred to as the donor)].

In Canada, when explosives are for the user's own operations, magazines for the storage of more than 75 kg of blasting explosives or more than 100 detonators must be licensed by the Explosives Division of the Department of Energy, Mines and Resources.

All magazines, regardless of capacity, containing explosives for sale must be licensed by that Department. Magazine construction must comply with the minimum standards specified by the Department.

Because cap-sensitive slurries are adversely affected by low temperatures, they should be stored at a minimum temperature of 40 °F (4 °C) before loading into boreholes; or at least held in boreholes for a sufficiently long "residence time" before firing, to bring them to this temperature.

Destruction of Blasting Materials

Explosives materials are perishable goods and may deteriorate after long periods of storage, even under approved conditions. Damaged or deteriorated explosives are dangerous and should be handled with extreme caution [7, 11, 12].

When it becomes necessary to destroy blasting materials, the advice of an explosives field representative, inspector of mines, or police officer should first be sought as to the safest method.

General Hints for Shotfirers or "Powder Monkeys"

This is the outstanding occupation that exemplifies the adage "Familiarity breeds contempt". Shotfirers should be well trained, steady, self-disciplined persons, and preferably non-smokers.

In the majority of mining operations, however, miners collect and look after their own stocks of explosives (for the shift in question), charge their holes, and fire their shots.

In other cases, however, it is possible and it is preferable to employ experienced and well-trained persons who specialize in this class of work. This frequently happens in quarrying, tunnelling, shaft sinking, earthmoving, and colliery work.

The following hints apply both to experienced shotfirers and also to regular miners who fire their own shots [13]:

1. Avoid smoking or the use of naked lights.
2. Use care in handling.
3. Keep explosives dry, especially detonators and safety fuse.
4. Use safety fuse of adequate length.
5. Do not force or twist fuse into the detonator composition.
6. See that the fuse is freshly cut and cut squarely across.
7. Never crimp the detonator near the closed end. Use an approved crimper. Never use the teeth.
8. Do not bend, kink, or coil the safety fuse in tight circles.
9. When charging holes do not thump the cartridges with the tamping pole, but squeeze them firmly. Do not squeeze the primer but squeeze the stemming on to it.
10. Never use a metal or a metal-capped tamping pole.
11. When using electric primers, avoid kinking of the leg wires. Carefully free any accidental kinks. Do not damage the insulation.
12. When inserting an electric primer cartridge into the borehole, take care not to tug or jerk the wires; pull the wires *gently* to straighten them without kinking; avoid damage to wires when tamping.
13. When connecting up, bare and scrape the last 5 cm of the ends of the leg wires; keep shunt in position as long as possible.
14. Carefully check all connections before running the connecting leads.
15. Never drag a firing cable along the ground – coil it carefully and carry it, paying it out as you go.
16. Always maintain personal possession of exploder key or key to mains firing boxes. Make sure the latter are locked (with fuses drawn and switch in the safe position) before approaching the face for charging.

17. Never return to a face after a blast unless:

   (1) You have the exploder key in your possession.

   (2) Mains firing box is locked in the safe position.

   (3) Leads are disconnected and short-circuited.

   (4) An adequate time interval has passed (usually 30 min for fuse firing).

18. Make sure all personnel have been withdrawn to a safe place before firing.

19. Be especially careful of misfires.

20. Report any misfires to the oncoming shift.

21. Never leave unused explosives lying about. Return them to the magazine as soon as possible.

22. Never charge a bulled hole until it has cooled down.

23. Never bull a hole next to one already charged with explosive.

24. In general, observe faithfully the local regulations laid down for the safe use of explosives, especially those relating to misfires [13].

Causes of Explosives Accidents

Positive care should always be exercised in the use of explosives, as accidents associated with them are dramatically horrible. The following is a list of common causes of explosives accidents; each cause infers some lack of care or disregard of regulations or established safe practice.

1. Delaying too long in lighting fuse.

2. Drilling into explosives.

3. Premature firing of electric blasts.

4. Returning too soon after blasting.

5. Inadequate guarding.

6. Unsafe practice during transport, handling and storage.

7. Improper handling of misfires (see above).

8. Using fuse too short in length.

9. Improper tamping procedure.

10. Smoking during handling of explosives.

Basic information regarding accidents that might result from electric currents (such as lightning strikes, electric storms, static electricity, radio frequency currents, and other stray currents) is also published [14, 15, 16, 17].

References

[1] E. W. S. Colver, *High Explosives*, 2nd. ed. (London, Technical Press. 1938)

[2] W. O. Snelling and W. C. Cope, "The Rate of Burning of Fuse, as Influenced by Temperature and Pressure", *U.S. Bureau of Mines, T.P.* 6,1912

[3] "Pneumatic Loading of Nitro-carbo-nitrates; Static Electricity, Fumes and Safety Handling", Technical Report (undated), Atlas Chemical Industries Inc.

[4] E. L. Litchfield, M. H. Hay and J. S. Monroe, "Electrification of Ammonium Nitrate in Pneumatic Loading", *U.S. Bureau of Mines, R.I.* 7139, 1968

[5] R. A. Dick, "Puzzled about Primers for Large-diameter ANFO Charges? Here's some Help to End the Mystery", *Coal Age*, August 1976

[6] "CPMS Trabant Gel Stemming", Contractors' Plant and Material Supply Co. Ltd., Llanelli, U.K.

[7] "Safety in the Transportation, Storage, Handling and Use of Explosives", Institute of Makers of Explosives, Pub. No. 17, March 1987

[8] "The American Table of Distances", Institute of Makers of Explosives, Pub. No. 2, June 1991

[9] "Manufacture, Storage, Transportation, and Use of Explosives and Blasting Agents", National Fire Protection Association, Booklet No. 495, 1985

[10] R. W. Van Dolah, "Large-scale Investigations of Sympathetic Detonation", *Ann. N.Y. Acad. Sci.,* Vol. 152, Art. 1, October 1968, pp. 792-801

[11] "Blasting Explosives and Blasting Caps. Storage, Possession, Transportation, Destruction and Sale", Dept. of Energy, Mines and Resources, Explosives Division, Ottawa. 1979

[12] "Destruction of Commercial Explosive Materials", Institute of Makers of Explosives, Safety Library Pub. No. 21, September 1987

[13] "Warnings and Instructions for Consumers in Transporting, Storing, Handling and Using Explosive Materials", Institute of Makers of Explosives, Safety Library Pub. No. 4, June 1989

[14] "Safety Guide for the Prevention of Radio Frequency Hazards in the Use of Commercial Electric Detonators", Institute of Makers of Explosives, Safety Library Pub. No. 20, December 1988

[15] American National Standards Institute, Standard C 95.2, 1966

[16] Australian Standard Publications, AS 2187.1-1984; AS 2187.2-1983; DR 91249-1991

[17] "Electrical Hazards of Electrical Detonators", *Down Line*, No. 12, February 1990

ABBREVIATIONS

AWG	American Wire Gauge
FGAN	Fertilizer grade ammonium nitrate
ft	foot, feet
ft^3	cubic foot (feet)
ft^3/lb	cubic feet per pound
ft/sec	feet per second
ft^3/ton	cubic feet per short ton
g	gram(s)
g/m	grams per metre
g/cm^3	grams per cubic centimetre
gr/ft	grains per foot
in	inch(es)
kg	kilogram(s)
kg/m	kilogram(s) per metre
kg/m^3	kilogram(s) per cubic metre
kg/t	kilogram(s) per tonne
kJ	kilojoules
km	kilometre(s)
kPa	kilopascals
l ton	long ton (2240 lbs)
lb	pound(s)
lb/ft^3	pounds per cubic foot
lb/in^2	pounds per square inch
lb/ton	pounds per ton
m	metre(s)
min	minute(s)
mm	millimetre(s)
mm/sec	millimetres per second
msec	millisecond(s)
MPa	megapascals
mWs/ohm	firing energy (milliwatt-seconds per ohm)
sec/ft	seconds per foot
sec/m	seconds per metre
sh ton	short ton (2000 lbs)
t	tonne (1000 kg)
USSS	United States Standard Sieve

PART II

BREAKING GROUND WITH EXPLOSIVES

CONVERSION TABLE

(To be read in conjunction with the list of Abbreviations on the previous page)

To convert from	to SI units	Multiply by
British Thermal Units (BTU)	kJ	1.055
BTU/lb	kJ/kg	2.326
Degrees Fahrenheit (°F)	°C	°C = (°F − 32)/1.8
Feet (ft)	m	0.3048
ft^2	m^2	0.0929
ft^3	m^3	0.0283
ft^3/lb	m^3/kg	0.0624
ft^3/sh ton	m^3/t	0.0312
ft/sec	m/sec	0.3048
Grains (gr)	g	0.0648
gr/ft	g/m	0.2126
Inches (in)	mm	25.40
in^2	mm^2	645.16
in^3	mm^3	16387.06
in/sec	mm/sec	25.40
Miles	km	1.609
Pounds (lb)	kg	0.4536
lb/ft	kg/m	1.488
lb/ft^3	kg/m^3	16.02
lb/sh ton	kg/t	0.500
lb/in^2	kPa	6.8947
Seconds (sec)	sec	1.000
sec/ft	sec/m	3.281
Tons, short (sh ton) 2000 lb	(tonnes) t	0.907
Tons, long (l ton) 2240 lb	t	1.016
sh ton/yd^3	t/m^3	1.186
Yards (yd)	m	0.9144
yd^2	m^2	0.836
yd^3	m^3	0.7645

CHAPTER 12

Introduction

General

Military explosives are not dealt with in this book.

Explosives are used in the industrial sphere chiefly for fracturing ores and rocks either in the recovery of economic minerals or for the making of excavations within a rock mass. The former includes the winning of road metal and building materials by quarrying, and of ores and minerals by open cut and underground stoping operations, where the rock or ore in place is too hard and tough to loosen by mechanical or current hydraulic methods. The latter refers to the excavation of road cuttings, tunnels, city building excavations and submarine passages in civil engineering practice and of underground development openings (such as shafts, drifts, crosscuts, raises, and winzes) in mines.

Industrial explosives are also used (but to a minor extent) for demolishing foundations and concrete or masonry structures (such as buildings, bridges and chimney stacks), for breaking heavy castings, for seismic exploration work, for oil well perforation and for general agricultural usage (see Chapters 17 and 21).

Industrial explosives are therefore vital to modern civilization and have contributed greatly to our current standard of living.

Their main use is in breaking out selected sections of hard rock and causing the "fragmentation" of such rock in the process. There is as yet no other way of doing this work practically and economically.

In order so to fracture rock (or to "break ground"), the explosive charge must be placed within the rock and at a suitable distance behind the rock face. For this purpose, openings must be made into the rock either by drilling holes (with or without subsequent "bulling" or chambering) or by excavating chambers (as for very large charges in coyote blasting).

The rock mass must also have one (or more) free faces, i.e., it must be exposed or open on one or more planes more or less at right angles to that from which drilling is

Fig. 37: Diagram showing the use of a free face when blasting rock from a quarry bench

done. This provides a rock/air interface termed a "free face". The rock is blasted in the direction of the free face.

This is necessary because (a) broken rock occupies a much greater space than when it is in the solid mass, and it must therefore have room to move or expand (see Fig. 37), and (b) it thus allows the rock to be broken in tension (more effectively) rather than in shear (under "tight" conditions with no free face).

When a free face does not exist (as in the case of tunnel or mine development headings), it must be provided in one of the following ways (Chapter 15):

1. By explosives in cut holes (centre, wedge, or drag cuts).

2. By explosives in cut holes in conjunction with free (uncharged) holes (as in burn cuts).

3. By drilling a large diameter hole or slot (an extension of the burn cut principle) [1].

4. By excavating a large diameter hole with a shaped charge.

5. By the use of high pressure pulsed water jets (still under development);

or

6. By mechanically cutting a kerf (as in a coal face).

In Fig. 37, the distance DC (or FD) is known as the "burden distance" (see Glossary). It represents the line (or path) of least resistance, along which the charge can more easily break the rock; or along which the burden of rock is least. The free face BC is actually a rock/air interface. Some writers regard the face from which the drilling is done as one free face, in which case, two (or more) free faces are required.

References

[1] R. Gustafsson, *Blasting Technique* (DNW, Vienna, 1981), pp. 137–151

CHAPTER 13

Blasting Theory

Factors Involved

Explosives are used for breaking ground only when cheaper effective means are not possible or available.

In breaking ground, the following conditions have an effect on blasting operations:

1. Presence and extent of one or more free faces.
2. Tenacity or cohesive strength of the rock (i.e., its resistance to blasting).
3. Structure of rock (massive, stratified, jointed, or fissured).
4. Type, strength, and nature of the explosives used.
5. Method of initiation.
6. Type of detonation (instantaneous or sequential – long delay or short delay).
7. Whether broken rock falls or is to be lifted.
8. Size, type, and depth of shot-hole or chamber.
9. Depth to which hole is loaded.
10. Proportion of burden distance to length of hole.
11. Loading density and degree of confinement.
12. Subsequent method of removal of spoil.
13. Degree of fragmentation required.
14. Coupling ratio effected.
15. Temperature of explosive charge (if a slurry or an emulsion).
16. Proximity or otherwise to important installations or built-up areas.
17. Amount of air blast or flyrock allowable.

18. Quantity of rock to be broken.

19. Whether the holes are in water.

20. Ultimate shape of excavation.

21. Ultimate use or purpose of excavated material.

22. Climatic conditions.

23. Safety of human life.

24. Statutory regulations.

Atchison [1] epitomizes these rock fragmentation factors rather more succinctly as:

(1) **Explosive parameters**, such as density and detonation velocity (detonation pressure), detonation impedance, gas volume and available energy.

(2) **Charge loading parameters**, including charge diameter and length, stemming, coupling, and type and point of initiation; some of these may directly influence the explosive parameters.

(3) **Rock parameters**, particularly density, propagation velocity, characteristic impedance, energy absorption, strength (compressive and tensile), texture and lack of homogeneity or isotropy.

Blasthole Diameter

The choice of borehole diameter in quarry blasting is critical since it affects the drill equipment specifications, burden distance, spacing distance, explosives distribution, and generally the efficiency and economics of the complete operation [2]. For this reason, the choice of borehole diameter should not be restricted to considerations of minimum drill/blast costs in isolation. Other parameters can be varied once the optimum blasthole diameter and burden distance have been determined.

The most important considerations in determining optimum borehole diameter for a given operation are:

(a) Rock parameters (see above).

(b) Explosive parameters (see above) that are related to charge diameter.

(c) Local restrictions connected with the proximity of built-up areas.

(d) Production factors, related to size of loading, haulage, crushing, screening equipment and scale of production.

It is important to match drill equipment specifications (and therefore blasthole diameter) to the later categories of production equipment, since the cost of purchasing, operating and maintaining the latter may be of paramount importance, depending mainly upon (a) the tenacity and abrasiveness, and (b) the ultimate end use of the material to be broken.

In theory, it should cost more per inch of diameter to drill larger diameter holes, but recent installations have demonstrated that the massive proportions of metal and power in the larger drill rigs achieve penetration rates comparable to those of smaller diameter capacity. There has therefore been a recent pronounced trend towards larger diameter blastholes in order to achieve the economies associated with improved labour productivity, extended blasting patterns (see Glossary), and lower density low-cost blasting agents. However, when toe problems increase and higher costs of secondary blasting and load/haul/crush operations due to poor fragmentation ensue, then the economic limit of large diameter blastholes has certainly been reached or exceeded.

Such limits depend upon (a) the comparative ease with which the particular rock formation will become fragmented, and (b) the economic degree of fragmentation required, consistent with the end use of the material to be broken.

The determination of an optimum blasthole diameter should involve adequate consideration of these factors.

Other Parameters

For practical reasons in surface mining, blasthole diameters (d) vary from about 3 to 15 inches; burden distances (B) from 20 to $40d$ in feet, nominally 30; spacing distances from 1 to $2B$, usually about 1.5; hole depths from 1.5 to $4B$; subdrill distances (below grade level) usually $0.3B$; and collar distances (depth of stemming) about $0.7B$.

The type of explosive used and the method of initiation are other important parameters.

Choice and Quantity of Explosive

This mainly depends on the tenacity and other physical characteristics of the rock being broken. The presence of bedding planes, joint planes, and planes of weakness also influences the choice.

Further, the diameter of the borehole has an important bearing on the question. Large diameter boreholes or small diameter holes that are "chambered" would call for the use of lower strength low-density explosives.

Small diameter boreholes on the other hand, especially in the harder more tenacious formations, call for high density explosives.

The quantity used is a function of the hole diameter, hole depth, burden distance and spacing distance for any particular blast, after the type, strength, and density of explosive has been determined for the particular conditions.

In determining the type, strength, and quantity of explosive to be used for a given purpose, the over-riding considerations are:

1. Applicability to the particular job.
2. Safety of life and property.
3. Efficiency (the usual yardstick is the "powder factor" expressed in lb per ton (or kg/t) of ore or rock broken to the required size. This ratio varies generally from 0.2 to 1 lb per ton, depending principally on the tenacity of the rock).

4. Economy (based upon the total costs of the operation, including drilling, firing, loading, haulage, crushing, screening and product storage).

According to *Dick et al.*, the formula to calculate Powder Factor is given by

$$PF = L\ (0.3405d)\ D^2\ /\ 27BSH$$

where L is length of charge, ft
           d is density of charge, g/cm^3
           D is charge diameter, in
           B is burden distance, ft
           S is spacing distance, ft
           H is bench height, ft.

Fragmentation

Poor fragmentation usually results in high secondary blasting costs and high costs of loading, haulage, primary crushing and general maintenance.

Fragmentation can be improved in several ways:

1. Shallower holes or better distribution of the explosive charge over the length of the hole.
2. Shorter spacing distance between holes.
3. Shorter burden distance.
4. Use of an explosive that gives less brisance and greater gas production.
5. Use of short delay detonation.

Dr. *O. Dojcár* has demonstrated by laboratory investigation that the three most important blast parameters controlling fragmentation are the burden distance, the specific charge and the spacing / burden ratio. Of these, the ratio of spacing to burden (S/B) is of greatest importance. For cylindrical charges, the optimum value of S/B was found to be 2 or greater. (See *Trans. Instn Min. Metall.*, *Sect. A*, Vol. 100).

Analysis of Theories

Early formulae for the calculation of blasting charges were evolved for military blasting operations. In these formulas, the burden distance alone was taken as the variable factor while a correction factor embraced the effects of type of explosive, blasting resistance of the rock, depth and diameter of drill holes, and charging depth. This meant that the correction factor was useful only for a limited range of conditions. The best of these formulas was due to *Belidor* [3]. *Bendel* [4] has published a critical discussion on the efficacy of these blasting formulas.

The first atomic bomb blast provided an impetus to research on blasting problems, giving rise to the development of the Reflection Theory [5] (see Chapter 2).

A review of other treatments of blasting design is included here for the information of students.

1.   O. Andersen [6] shows that the main considerations in breaking ground are (a) the burden distance and (b) the strength, quantity, and distribution of the explosive charge. The first is a function of the square root of the projected area of the blast hole, and is *independent of the nature of the rock*; the second takes care of the physical characteristics of the particular rock. Both are to some extent modified (when more than one hole is fired) by the spacing distance between holes and the degree of fragmentation required.

The following simple empirical formula for a single hole gives the burden distance in terms of the projected area of the hole, viz.:

$$B = c \sqrt{(DL)}$$

where B = burden distance, ft
          D = hole diameter, ft
          L = length of hole, ft
          c = constant determined empirically.

It was also shown that sufficiently accurate values were given for most practical purposes by quoting the hole diameter in inches and by taking $c = 1$.

Thus the formula was applied in practice as

$$B = \sqrt{(dL)}$$

where d = hole diameter, in inches

Over a range of blast holes from 1 inch diameter, 4 ft deep to 9 inches diameter, 100 ft deep, burden distances have been calculated, and are shown in Table 19.

Table 19: Burden distances calculated by the *Andersen* formula

Diameter of Hole (in)	Length of Hole (ft)								
	4	9	16	25	36	49	64	81	100
1	2	3	4	5	6	7	8	9	10
2	3	5	6	7	9	10	12	13	14
3	–	–	7	9	10	12	14	16	17
4	–	–	8	10	12	14	16	18	20
5	–	–	9	11	13	16	18	20	22
6	–	–	–	12	15	17	20	22	25
7	–	–	–	13	16	19	21	24	27
8	–	–	–	14	17	20	22	25	28
9	–	–	–	15	18	21	24	27	30

This formula, unlike the others set out in this chapter, has the particular advantage that the burden distance can be determined from readily available physical dimensions, without the need for the separate trial assessment of other factors.

Burden distances calculated from the above formulas have been shown to agree very closely with those employed in actual practice; and especially for the wide range of commonly occurring rock types ranging between plastic clay shales and mudstones and incompetent overburden on the one hand, and dense tough hard tenacious haematite and taconite on the other. Within the above limits of rock types it is highly recommended for both undergraduate use, and indeed for most practical applications.

But when aluminized or Heavy AN/FO and slurries are used, in well-stemmed holes with adequate primage and excellent coupling, the explosive parameters are considerably enhanced. The increase in density, VOD, and heat of reaction produces a much higher detonation pressure. As a result, an increased value of c will usually be applicable, yielding a greater practicable burden and spacing distance (extended blasthole geometry). But field trials will normally be necessary to determine the extent of the increase possible, consistent with fragmentation requirements.

When more than one hole is fired at a time, these burden distances can influence the amount of spacing adopted between adjacent holes in any row. Modified formulae covering this effect have been adduced by *Andersen.*

2. *G. E. Pearse* [7] offers a burden formula based on the physical characteristics of rock and type of explosive:

$$B = K d \sqrt{(P_s / T)}$$

where B is maximum burden, in inches
$\qquad$ K is constant depending on rock characteristics (0.7 to 1.0)
$\qquad$ d is hole diameter, in inches
$\qquad$ P_s is reaction stability pressure of explosive, lb/in^2
$\qquad$ T is ultimate tensile strength of rock, lb/in^2.

The reaction stability (peak explosion) pressure of particular explosives has been calculated by *Taylor* [8].

3. *R. L. Ash* [9, 10, 11] has propounded a simplified modification of the *Pearse* formula, in which he replaced the factors K and $\sqrt{(P_s / T)}$ by a burden ratio, K_b; from empirical field tests, the factor K_b ranges from a value of 20 to 40, averaging 30.

He bases his observations on the dependence of burden distance on a combination of rock and explosives parameters. The mean value of K_b = 30 corresponds by and large to blasting conditions in which the rock density averages 2.7, and the explosive has a density of 1.3 and an average VOD of 12,000 ft per second. Actually, the K_b values range from about 25 for AN/FO to 35 or more for dense slurries and gelatines, under average rock conditions. Various formulae have been adduced by *Ash* to adjust K_b values for more specific conditions, such as variations in rock types, in density of explosive, and for the degree of fragmentation and rock displacement desired.

It will therefore be seen that the *Ash* formula caters for refinements not available in the

Andersen formula, but it necessarily involves a number of separate determinations to arrive at a suitable K_b value. These may be assessed from convenient tables.

As a recommended practice, the *Andersen* formula can be used as a first step. Where further refinements in blasting design are considered necessary, the next step is to evaluate the parameters, calculate the K_b value, and apply the *Ash* formula.

The maximum burden distance is given by

$$B = K_b \times d/12 \text{ (ft)}$$

where   *d* is hole diameter, in inches.

From this simplified but very useful formula, *Ash* has also derived relationships for assessing the spacing distance (*S*), the length of hole (*H*), the length of subgrade drilling (*J*), and the collar (stemming) distance (*T*), all in terms of the burden distance (*B*). These are set out below.

Spacing distance, $S = K_s B$

Hole length, $H = K_h B$

Subgrade drilling depth, $J = K_j B$

Collar distance, $T = K_t B$

where K_s, K_h, K_j and K_t are the spacing ratio, hole length ratio, subgrade drilling ratio, and collar distance ratio respectively. All distances are expressed in feet, with ranges of $K_s = 1$ to 2; K_h from 1.5 to 4; K_j generally from 0.2 to 0.4; and K_t from 0.7 to 1.

All these factors are useful in calculating a complete blasting design programme.

4.   *Fraenkel* [12] has derived a somewhat similar formula to that of *Andersen* [6] in establishing a rock characteristic which he calls "resistance to blasting".

$$B = \frac{RL^{0.3} \times l^{0.3} \times d^{0.8}}{50}$$

where   *B* is burden distance, in metres
   R is resistance to blasting (an experimental factor varying from one to six for all rock types)
   L is length of hole, in metres
   l is length of charge, in metres
   d is diameter of hole, in mm.

This formula has been derived from the use of Swedish 35 per cent LFB dynamite. In practice, the following approximations are used: *B* is reduced to $0.8 B < 0.67 L$; *l* is taken as $0.75 L$; *S* (the spacing distance) is not greater than $1.5 B$.

5.   *Langefors* has produced a comprehensive series of formulas based largely upon the work of *Fraenkel* [13]. He quotes the maximum theoretical burden distance as

$$B_{max} = (45 \times d) \text{ (metres)}$$

where d is the hole diameter in mm.

Then he proceeds to develop a measure of the "practical burden distance" by modifying B_{max} for variables that might be expected to occur in practice, such as faulty drilling (errors in hole spotting and in hole deviation). Included in the calculations are associated determinations of other factors such as the length of blast hole below grade, the total hole depth, bench height, hole spacing, height and weight of bottom charge, height and weight of column charge, uncharged height, specific charge, specific drilling length, and width of the face.

Gustafsson offers a series of examples and tables listing these various calculations under prescribed rock conditions [14]. However, it is difficult to represent the widely varying rock characteristics in any mathematical model when the rock is not homogeneous. Rock is never really homogeneous.

6. **Crater Theory** *(Peele)* [15]. If a vertical hole is placed normally to a horizontal surface of earth or rock and charged with explosive, it may blow out a conical shaped crater, the sides of which meet the horizontal surface (or free face) at 45°.

In such a case, the line of least resistance is given by L, the depth of the hole. The volume of the crater:

$$V = 0.33 \, L \times \pi \, L^2 = L^3 \text{ (approx)}.$$

In practice, the volume of rock loosened is taken as:

$$V = m \, L^3$$

where $m = 0.4$ for tough, soft rock and 0.9 for hard brittle rock.

Crater theories are generally based on a point source of explosive. This means that although they are useful in laboratory studies, it is not practicable to reproduce the effects so observed under actual field conditions. Nevertheless, the principle is basic. The 90° conical shape was first propounded by *Vauban* in 1704 [16].

7. **The Livingston Crater Theory** [17] has had wide acceptance.

Livingston developed his "strain energy equation" for crater charges as set out below:

$$N = E \, W^{1/3}$$

where N is the critical depth, in ft, of a charge
  W is weight, in lb, that would just cause the rock surface to fail, and
  E is the strain energy factor derived empirically.

He then modified this equation by reducing the charge depth to give good fragmentation by expressing it in the following form:

$$d_o = \Delta E \, W^{1/3} \text{ (ft)}$$

where d_o is the optimum depth (or indicated maximum burden distance)
    Δ is the optimum depth ratio (d_o / N)
    W is the weight of charge, lb.

Useful values of d_o depend upon the value of E which varies for different rock characteristics, as discussed by *Bauer* [18].

Grant has established the Dow Crater Formula by adopting a standardized cylindrical volume (6 inch diameter x 36 inch) of explosive charge, instead of the weight W used by *Livingston* [19].

This simplifies comparative field performance testing of explosives.

8.   **The Thermohydrodynamic Theory** [20, 21]: The mathematical and physicochemical analysis associated with the exposition of this theory is too involved for inclusion in an elementary monograph. It is useful only as a research tool; or to determine the theoretical energy output of particular explosives.

Quarry Blast Design

Because of the complex problems involved, none of the above theories or formulas can be expected to give precise values of burden distance; nor is this essential under practical conditions of blasting. They do, however, provide an opportunity to set up initial blasting patterns; or to check existing practices where these are suspect; or where reduced blasting costs and better blast results are sought. A simplified analysis of the main design features in quarry blasting is given below.

1.   Determination of burden distance

The maximum amount of work in breaking out a rock face has to be done at the bottom of the borehole where the charge must supply sufficient energy to shear the rock at floor level in addition to breaking it along the line of holes and displacing the mass of rock. The **burden distance** is the distance between the bottom of the hole and the free face, and this corresponds with the line of least resistance.

Taking an extreme case, where the burden distance exceeds the depth of the hole, the result of firing a suitable charge at X will be a conical-shaped hole YXZ as in Fig. 38. Where the burden distance equals the depth of the hole, the result may be as shown in Fig. 39. In this case, the break would be along the lines YXZ, if the charge was strong enough; however, in practice, it would tend to blow a crater YXW.

Fig. 40 shows how the rock will break if the burden distance is less than the hole depth, and the hole is column-loaded but does not reach the lower quarry bench level. If the hole is loaded up to point X_n, then the section of rock broken corresponds to the parallelogram $XX_nY_n Z$. However, for practical purposes, it is necessary to preserve the continuance of a horizontal floor or bench level (to accommodate a roadway), and therefore XZ should be horizontal as in Fig. 41.

Now Fig. 42 shows the corresponding stress pattern for a concentrated charge at X.

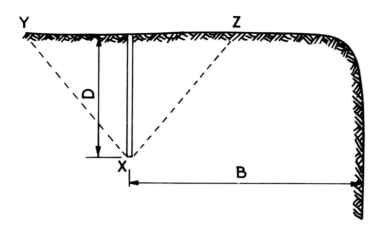

Fig. 38: Probable blasting effect where burden distance exceeds hole depth

Only a small proportion of the stress wave is reflected in tension, and therefore the rock must be broken along XZ mainly in shear (in which property it is about ten times as strong).

Hence, an inordinately larger quantity of explosive is required at X to break effectively along XZ. If it fails to do so, a "toe" will be left, as in Fig. 43. In this event, before further

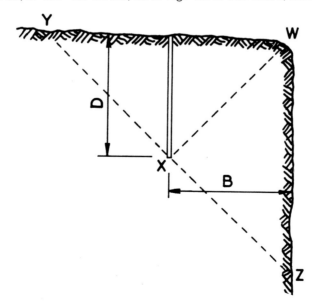

Fig. 39: Two possible effects where burden distance equals hole depth

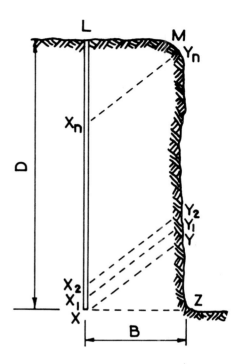

Fig. 40: Blasting effect where hole is column-loaded, and bottom of hole does not reach the lower quarry bench

Fig. 41: Blasting effect where hole is column-loaded, and bottom of hole reaches the lower quarry bench

(economic) blasting operations can proceed, the face and bench must be "squared up". This can only be done by *ad hoc* drilling and blasting, involving a disruption to the operational plan, and a general increase in costs. This sort of problem occurs frequently in many quarries where the rock has a high shear strength.

The persistence (or regular occurrence) of a toe in quarry blasting signifies that the burden distance is too great; or that the bottom charge (the explosive in the bottom of the hole) is not strong enough; or that the hole does not extend far enough below bench level to accommodate a sufficient explosive charge to shear the rock cleanly.

In order to overcome this problem, *Kochanowsky* [22, 23, 24] has shown that, in theory, the holes should be drilled at an angle of 45°, so that the maximum effect of breakage in tension can be derived (see Fig. 44).

Such a practice has many useful advantages; it is now gaining ground (except that, for greater ease of drilling and loading, the inclination of the holes is restricted to 60°– 65° as a compromise).

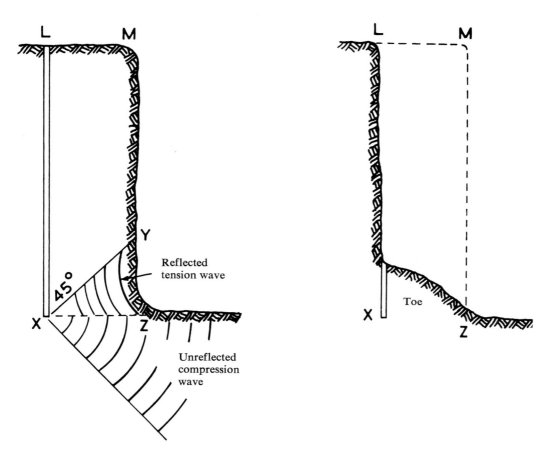

Fig. 42: Stress pattern for a concentrated charge in bottom of hole

Fig. 43: Result of insufficient explosive energy release at bottom of hole

Kochanowsky [24] lists the advantages claimed for angle drilling as follows:

(a) Safer operation for both men and equipment.

(b) Improved fragmentation, and greatly reduced secondary blasting cost.

(c) Negligible toe problem.

(d) Backbreak difficulties practically eliminated.

(e) Progressive reduction in explosive consumption with increased inclination from the vertical.

(f) Lower drilling footage per ton of rock broken.

(g) Less vibration.

(h) Significant reduction in drilling, blasting, loading, and crushing costs.

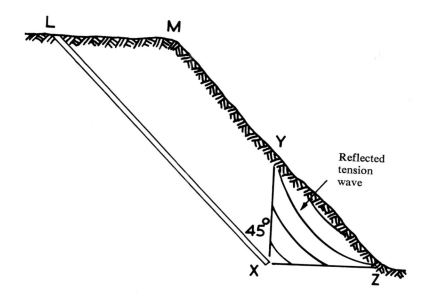

Fig. 44: Stress pattern for a concentrated charge in bottom of 45° angled hole

From Fig. 41 it will be seen that:

(i)   The chances of failure to break the "toe" vary directly with the burden distance.

(ii) No explosive should be placed nearer to the collar of the hole than the distance to the free face XZ; otherwise, in most cases it will be wasted, or it may cause rock to "fly", or cause unnecessary backbreak.

The toe burden that can be broken satisfactorily in a deep hole blast depends, among other things, upon the weight of the charge that can be accommodated in the bottom portion of the hole. Actually, the weight of charge in a borehole is proportional to the square of the diameter.

2.   Determination of spacing distance

Fig. 45 is a plan showing the wedge of rock which should be broken by a charge at F; the volume of rock broken to the free face EG by a vertical hole at F is the square of the burden multiplied by the depth. An increase in the burden of 50 per cent calls for an increase in the charge of 125 per cent, to cater for a similar increase in volume of rock broken.

The jointing of the rock is the most important factor in determining the spacing between holes in a row. If the hole spacing is equal to twice the burden the result should be as in Fig. 46. The triangle of rock which lies between the bursting angles of the two charges at M and N would, in theory, remain unbroken.

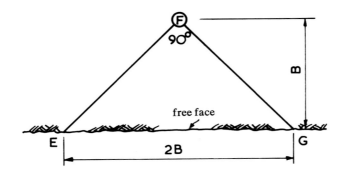

Fig. 45: Plan diagram of volume of rock broken to the free face by a single vertical hole at F

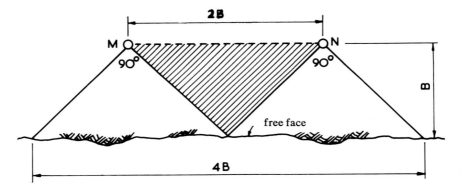

Fig. 46: Plan diagram of breakage pattern for two holes spaced at twice the burden distance

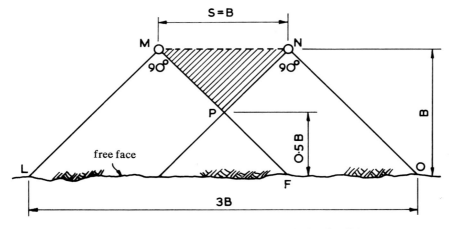

Fig. 47: Plan diagram of breakage pattern for two holes spaced at the burden distance

In practice, however, the rock would be partly dislodged or poorly fragmented. It would, nevertheless, depend on the conditions existing at a particular site.

But if the spacing is equal to the burden, as in Fig. 47, the bursting angles would intersect at P, leaving the rock in the triangle MNP outside the theoretical bursting angles. In practice, however, the area broken will be LMNO. Since explosives exert force in all directions, this triangle should be well fragmented and the face from M to N broken cleanly. Where blastholes are spaced at intervals which are too wide, the face is frequently left in a ragged condition, and, in massive rocks, will often present a "scalloped" appearance. In addition, the rock is "fragmented" to a lesser degree.

Experience tends to show that changes in the burden distance have a much more pronounced effect on the fragmentation, on the tendency to leave an unbroken "toe", and on general quality of breakage than changes in spacing distance. Therefore, if an increase in the tonnage per foot of hole is desired for economic reasons, it is better to extend the spacing between the holes rather than increase the burden.

In all references to the geometry of blasting patterns it is customary to express the burden distance and spacing (in feet) as "B by S" or "B x S", always quoting the burden distance first. Normally, the value of S varies from B to 2 B, averaging 1.5 times B.

3.   Methods of firing

The principle of firing a number of charges simultaneously so that they will mutually assist one another is important in practically all surface blasting operations. But simultaneous firing of charges has placed a restriction on the size of the blast that can be fired in many locations, since the vibration produced often results in complaints and, in some cases, damage to adjacent property and installations.

By using short delay firing methods, the principle of mutual assistance is retained, and without increasing the vibration the size of the blast may be increased significantly.

When firing a row of holes in sequence by short delay means, there is a greater tendency to shear the rock along the line of holes, probably because the line of least resistance NP (in Fig. 47) is diagonal to the previously fired hole, as at M, and not directly forward. Advantage may be taken of this tendency to increase the spacing when firing single rows by short delay methods.

4.   Calculation of the charge

Firstly, for successful blasting the borehole must be drilled to give the correct burden distance. This is most important and should not be a matter of guesswork. Secondly, it is advantageous to use high density explosives in the bottom portion of the hole.

A simple formula for calculating the amount of explosive required for a single hole is $C = B \times S \times D/60$, where C is the charge weight, in lb, B is the burden distance, in ft, S is the spacing distance, in ft, and D is the hole depth, in ft. This formula gives a powder factor of 0.225 lb/ton, for rock of 13.5 ft^3/ton (see Appendix D).

It is generally applicable for high density explosives (dynamites, slurries and emulsions).

With large diameter holes (127–300 mm), where high explosives are used, the charge would usually be deck-loaded, in which case two-thirds of the total charge should be placed in the bottom of the hole. The charge may be distributed or placed to suit local conditions. Deckloading may not necessarily be required when other explosives of a lower loading density (e.g. AN/FO) are employed.

A useful report to assist quarry operators has been prepared by *Pugliese* [11].

A noteworthy approach to the optimization of burden/spacing patterns has been propounded by *Lang* and *Favreau* [25]. They have developed a computer model in which all relevant parameters of rock properties, explosive energy outputs and blast geometry factors are matched in terms of rock movement time and cost elements to yield optimum effects quantified by numerical values, within the natural limitations of rock structural variation in the immediate blast area. *Favreau*'s research has led to the BLASPA programme, the basis of the DuPont Computer Simulated Blasting Programme.

A comprehensive paper outlining the optimum design of blasting rounds has been prepared by *Hagan* and others [26, 27, 28].

Skodack has developed a computerised analysis of rock excavation (CARE) parameters [29]. This covers drilling, charging, loading and operating cost calculations.

A more comprehensive analysis of the problems involved in designing bench blasting programmes is offered by *Dick* [30].

Flyrock

One of the problems of surface blasting is caused by flyrock. It is not only a safety problem. It is also an indication of possible inefficiency of the blast design, because explosive energy is wasted in the form of air blast, flyrock and noise [31, 32]. Flyrock (and backbreak) can be reduced by increasing the stemming distance.

Flyrock problems are usually ascribed to elements of geological structure; but KONYA believes that errors inherent in blasthole loading, pattern drilling, blasthole timing and pattern design can also make a significant contribution.

References

[1]   T. C. Atchison, "Fragmentation Principles", Chapter 7.2 of *Surface Mining*, ed. E. P. Pfleider, Seeley W. Mudd Series (New York, AIME, 1968)

[2]   R. A. Dick and J. J. Olson, "Choosing the Proper Borehole Size for Bench Blasting", *University of Minnesota, 31st Annual Mining Symposium*, 1970

[3]   B. F. Belidor, *Nouveau Cours Mathématique à l'Usage d'Artillerie et du Génie* (Paris: 1725), p. 505

[4]   L. Bendel, *Das Sprengen im Fels* (Lucerne, Haas Verlag, 1942)

[5] K. Hino, "Fragmentation of Rock Through Blasting", *Jour. Ind. Explosives Soc. Japan*, Vol. 17, No. 1 (1956),1–11

[6] O. Andersen, "Blast Hole Burden Design", *Proc. Aus. I. M. M.*, No. 166–7 (1952)

[7] G. E. Pearse, "Rock Blasting", *Mine & Quarry Engineering*, January 1955

[8] J. Taylor, *Detonation in Condensed Explosives* (London: O.U.P., 1952)

[9] R. L. Ash, "The Design of Blasting Rounds", Chapter 7.3 of *Surface Mining*, ed. E. P. Pfleider, Seeley W. Mudd Series (New York, AIME, 1968)

[10] R. L. Ash, "The Mechanics of Rock Breakage", *Pit and Quarry*, Vol. 56, Nos. 2, 3, 4, 5

[11] J. M. Pugliese, "Designing Blast Patterns Using Empirical Formulas", *U. S. Bureau of Mines, I.C. 8550*, 1972

[12] K. H. Fraenkel, "Factors Influencing Blasting Results", *Manual on Rock Blasting* (Stockholm, Aktiebolaget Atlas Diesel, 1952), Vol. 1, Art. 6, No. 2, p. 15

[13] U. Langefors and B. Kihlstrom, *The Modern Technique of Rock Blasting*, 3rd Edition (New York, Wiley, 1978)

[14] R. Gustafsson, *Blasting Technique* (DNW, Vienna, 1951)

[15] R. Peele, *Mining Engineers' Handbook* (3rd ed.), pp. 5–11

[16] S. S. Saluja, "Mechanism of Rock Failure under the Action of Explosives", *Ninth Symposium on Rock Mechanics*, Golden, CO, USA, April 1967

[17] C. W. Livingston, "Fundamental Concepts of Rock Failure", *Colorado School of Mines Quarterly*, Vol. 51, No. 3.

[18] A. Bauer, "Application of the Livingston Theory", *Quarterly of the Colorado School of Mines*, Vol. 56, No. 1 (January 1961)

[19] C. H. Grant, "Simplified Explanation of Crater Method", *Engineering and Mining Journal*, Nov. 1964

[20] M. A. Cook, *The Science of High Explosives* (New York, Reinhold, 1958)

[21] R. Meyer, *Explosives* 3rd. edn. (Weinheim. FRG: VCH Verlagsgesellschaft, 1987)

[22] B. J. Kochanowsky, "Blasting Research Leads to New Theories and Reductions in Blasting Costs", *Mining Engineering*, September 1955

[23] B. J. Kochanowsky, "Inclined Drilling and Blasting", *Mining Congress Journal* November 1961

[24] B. J. Kochanowsky, "New Developments in Drilling and Blasting Techniques" *Engineering and Mining Journal*, Vol. 165, No. 12 (December 1964)

[25] L. C. Lang and R. F. Favreau, "A Modern Approach to Open-Pit Blast Design and Analysis", *C.I.M. Bulletin*, June 1972

[26] T. N. Hagan, "The Design of Blasting Rounds – the Key Parameters", *Journal of Mines, Metals & Fuels*, January 1982

[27] J. K. Mercer and T. N. Hagan, "Progress towards Optimum Blasting – a Key to Increased Productivity and Profitability", *Mining Magazine*, August 1978

[28] G. D. Just, "Incremental Explosive Energy Distribution in Blasting Design", *International Jounal of Mining Engineering*, July 1984

[29] T. Skodack, "Using CARE to Predict Equipment Needs, Costs and Productivity", *Mining Engineering*, November 1982

[30] R. A. Dick et al.; "Explosives and Blasting Manual", *U.S.B.M. I.C. 8925*, 1983

[31] "Blasting Nuisances – Flyrock", *Nobel Notes*, Vol. 29, No. 3

[32] J. Ludwiczak, "Flyrock from Blasting", *Journ. of Explosives Engineering*, 1985, pp. 16–17

CHAPTER 14

Special Techniques

"Bulling" or Chambering of Holes

The bottom of a small diameter borehole (such as diamond drill or wagon drill hole) may be enlarged by lighting and dropping a gelatine dynamite safety fuse primer into the hole. The burden is, of course, too great for this small charge to break the ground. Its effect is to pulverize the rock in the vicinity and to expel it from the mouth of the hole in the form of dust. Meanwhile, the bottom of the hole has been increased in diameter in the form of a bulbous-shaped chamber, which will then accommodate a larger quantity of explosive. Care should be taken to allow the bottom of the hole to cool down before adding further explosives. The operation is variously called "bulling" or "chambering" or "springing". The method has been used chiefly in quarry work on bench holes.

Tunnel or Coyote Blasting

Where very large quantities of rock are to be blasted and there are adequate free faces (as, for example, on the end of a spur ridge, or the side of a hill), large quantities of explosives can be placed to better effect in excavated chambers rather than in boreholes.

In this way, a large blast can be planned; internal access-ways and chambers can be excavated at one or more horizons, explosives packed into the chambers in their original cases, and the connecting passageways backfilled.

Charges are usually fired with detonating cord.

Perhaps the most notable coyote blast in North America [1] was a well-planned underwater firing of a navigation hazard known as the "Ripple Rock" in Seymour Narrows, 110 miles north of Vancouver, BC. On April 5, 1958, 365,000 tons of rock and 320,000 tons of water were displaced with 1378 tons of canned Nitramex 2H blasting agent placed in tunnels and chambers excavated in the submerged rock and fired with primacord. Shafts were sunk in the opposite shores and connected by an underwater drive, from which a rise was developed. From the top of this rise, coyote chambers in the upper part of the submerged rock were then excavated.

Secondary Blasting

Wherever rock is blasted from a face (except possibly in development headings in a mine), some of it may break into pieces too large to be handled satisfactorily through chute openings, into and out of cars, trucks, skips, shovel dippers or grabs, and into crushers.

The equipment in use necessarily limits the size of such pieces. They must be broken to the limiting size, usually by explosives. This procedure is called "secondary blasting" and is achieved either by "blockholing" or "blistering" (see Glossary).

1. **Blockholing**: Short holes 100–150 mm deep are drilled in the boulders. It is not necessary to drill into the centre of a boulder. All that is required is to explode a light charge (about one-quarter of a cartridge, with detonator and fuse) in a shallow hole to crack the boulder. A very large boulder may require several such holes, strategically placed.

However, in built-up areas, it may be *desirable* to drill the hole into the centre of the boulder to minimize the possibility of damage from flyrock.

2. **Blistering (or plastering)**: This method does not involve the use of drilling equipment but of much bigger explosive charges. The charge, suitably primed, is laid on the surface of a boulder and sealed or plastered ("mudcapped") with clay. Ammonia dynamite or packaged AN/FO may be used for this purpose. Much noise and air blast result.

The U.S. Bureau of Mines has developed a device called a 'sheathed charge' for use in secondary blasting without the need for drilling. This sheathed charge consists of a disc-shaped core of explosives within a bed of salt in a package. This salt acts as a flame quencher.

Techniques involving the use of shaped charges have been developed by GOEX for breaking boulders. Sierra produce a boulder breaker package.

For breaking large boulders blocking chutes and orepasses, the 'Minecharge' system is used by Outokumpu Oy in Finland. This is a device that focusses on the blockage and propels a metal slug at about 3000 m/sec to break the boulder and clear the blockage.

Explosives specially designed for secondary blasting are Magnapak (CIL), Knauerit S2 (DNW), Tovex Slakpak (DPW), Tovex Slabs (DANTEX), Tovex Sakpak (ETCAN), Bjønnit (DYNO), Plastergel (ICIA), and Plaster Gelatine (ECP, IIE and NOBEX). Austin produces an approved non-incendive sheathed explosive for unconfined blasting of large boulders in coal mines. This is named 'Rock-Buster'.

For more details on secondary breaking, as distinct from secondary blasting, see Chapter 16.

Petroleum Engineering Applications

Explosives are used in the petroleum industry in two main ways, in geophysical prospecting (seismic blasting), and in the stimulation of oil and gas flow in production wells.

(1) **Seismic Blasting**: Geophysical prospecting has become very important in the search for deep oil structures (and for locating buried metalliferous orebodies). The use of the seismograph is one such important method.

Seismic prospecting depends upon the fact that the earth is elastic. Explosive charges fired in boreholes are reflected and refracted in different ways by abnormalities in the strata, and the time of travel of the various shock waves is determined from signals received by sensitive geophones on reaching the surface.

In order to initiate these shock waves, special purpose explosives have been developed to provide a high degree of reliability, high strength, and excellent water resistance. To aid in charging deep holes, seismic explosives can be provided with cardboard tubes or threaded cans which can be coupled together to form a continuous charge.

Under certain conditions, seismic explosives can also be designed for firing on the surface, as explosive pouches.

Trade names of seismic high explosives, prepared by different manufacturers (for code symbols, see Chapter 1) are given below.

Atlas:	Petrogel
	Seisprime
	Atlaseis
Austin:	Seismograph HV
CIL:	Geomex
DANTEX:	Tovex 660
DNAG:	Seismo-Gelit 2
DNW:	Gelatine Donarit S
DuPont:	Seismogel
	Tovex SSS
DYNO:	Emulite 700
ERT:	Goma
ETCAN:	Dynamite S
	Energel
	Energex
	Seismogel
	Seismopac
ETI:	Energel
	Energex
Hercules:	Vibrogel
ICIA:	Anzite Blue Fastlok

	Powergel Seismic
	Miniseis P
IEL:	Seismic Gelatine
Independent:	Seismigel
IRECO:	Ireseis
	Seispulse
	Surfaseis
ITPL:	Geodin B
	Nitrogel
	Gelpack
Nitro Nobel:	Emulite 700
NKC:	GX-1 dynamite
	KIRI dynamite
NOBEX:	Geophex
	Seismic Gelatine
Thermex:	Thermex
Trojan:	Seismic Gelatin
WAHNL:	Seismic Explosive S-3

Fig. 48: An example of perimeter blasting on a highway project

(2) **Oil Well Stimulation**: In many cases, oil wells need a fracturing of the strata to initiate or increase the flow of oil and gas; or at a later stage, to increase water input in the 'water flooding phase'; or to flush out residual oil in a depleted field. For this purpose, IRECO supplies High Pressure Gelatin 60% and Gas Well Gelatin (with primer).

Liquid propellants have been developed to reduce clean-out time. For this purpose, IRECO has developed the Ire-Flo 402 type.

The perforation of drill pipe to aid stimulation is achieved mainly by assemblies of shaped charges with associated tools and other appurtenances, as supplied by GOEX and OWEN. See also Chapter 17.

Overbreak Control [2–6]

Contracts which call for rock excavation commonly contain a penalty clause for unbroken rock left inside a certain gauge line near the nominal perimeter of the excavation; on the other hand where the excavation is to be concrete lined, the contractor may have to pay for the extra concrete required where overbreak has occurred. Consequently it is usually important that the walls of the excavation be as smooth and as close to the nominal gauge line as possible.

Similarly, there is a growing need in most rock excavation projects to give greater consideration to the effects of blasting upon the stability of the remaining rock mass (which is, in many cases, seriously affected by uncontrolled blasting programs).

Based upon these desirable aims, a new era of precision blasting was developed, initially in Sweden, and then by Canadian Industries Ltd. in 1953 during the construction of a hydro-electric facility in Ontario. The technique has since been applied to excavations for highway and railroad cuts, tunnels, dam spillways, canals, and underground machinery halls.

The formation of a line of shear may be an advantage where blasting vibrations are a problem, in that the shear line will act as a barrier to the vibrations between the blast area and nearby structures. It may be possible, as a consequence, to increase permissible charge weights per delay, thus decreasing the number of blasts necessary.

The chief advantages to be derived from the employment of this technique are set out below.

1. The stability and strength of the remaining rock is relatively unaffected.
2. More regular outlines of the remaining rock are preserved thereby contributing to safety and aesthetic appearance (Fig. 48).
3. In built-up areas, less ground vibration is transmitted to neighbouring structures.
4. Overbreak is gready reduced; this may represent a superior economic advantage, by reducing the volume of concrete required as in concrete-lined tunnels.
5. In some tunnelling operations, the need for costly concrete lining procedures may be dispensed with altogether.
6. In underground lode mining, the stability of weak stope walls can be better preserved; and dilution of the ore is minimized.

There are various ways in which blasting may be carried out to achieve these aims, and the bases of these methods are given below. The differences in rock types call for wide variations in methods and drilling/loading parameters used; and fine distinctions between each method at different job locations have developed a confusion in terminology. In any large or medium scale operation extensive trials should be undertaken to develop the most effective method. The method finally selected will depend upon the nature and economics of the particular operation and the rock characteristics at the site.

All methods involve the drilling of a line of holes along or around the perimeter gauge line, in order to provide a line of weakness or fracture plane ("shear curtain") along which the rock will separate when the main round is fired. This aims to provide a smooth finished surface along the perimeter of the excavation. Similarly, all methods provide for a buffer zone between the perimeter holes and the last or nearest row of the main primary round. The width of this zone (known as the "buffer distance") is usually related to the perimeter hole diameter, but is in any case about one-half of the regular burden distance in the main round.

In practice, when the main round is fired, the buffer zone of rock becomes lightly fractured up to but not beyond the perimeter gauge line. It may then be readily removed with a scaling bar. A smooth finished surface along the perimeter of the excavation will thereby be provided, whether it is a highway cut, building excavation, tunnel or underground machine hall outline or stope wall.

Variations in the method to be selected will be based upon:

1. The rock properties (whether relatively homogeneous, laminated, or intermediate in nature).
2. The conditions of existing ground stress.
3. The diameters of the perimeter holes to be drilled.
4. The spacing between adjacent holes along the perimeter.
5. The "buffer distance" between the perimeter holes and the nearest row of the main round.
6. The diameter of the explosives cartridges to be used.
7. The density of the explosive, and the degree of continuity of the charge.
8. The charge weight per unit length.
9. Whether full de-coupling or a secondary loading of stemming material is used to close the air spaces.
10. The collar stemming to be used.
11. The number of holes to be left uncharged, if any.
12. Whether instantaneous or delayed firing is to be used; and the delay period, if used.
13. Whether fired before or after the main round; or not at all.

The *modus operandi* of overbreak control programs has been discussed in detail by many scientists, including *Langefors* [2], *Gustafsson* [3] and *Culver* [4].

1. **Line drilling**: In this method regular rockdrill holes, about 40 mm diameter, are spaced 100 to 150 mm apart along the perimeter and left uncharged. Larger diameter holes could be placed at greater spacing intervals. The buffer zone between the perimeter holes and the last row of main round holes should be about 20 to 30 cm wide (the buffer distance). The drilled unloaded holes along the periphery alone provide a plane of weakness to which the rock will break readily and cleanly when the round is fired.

The main disadvantages of Line drilling as compared to other methods of overbreak control are:

1. A greater amount of drilling is involved.

2. Precise hole alignment is required to establish an effective plane of weakness; and

3. The method is applicable only to massive homogeneous rock.

On the other hand, in massive homogeneous rock, and where smooth outlines are specially important, the higher drilling cost of this method may be readily justified.

2. **Presplitting**: This method consists of creating a plane of shear in solid rock on the desired line of break. It is somewhat similar to other methods of obtaining a smoothly finished excavation, but the chief point of difference is that presplitting is carried out before any production blasting, and even in some cases before production drilling.

These methods may be applied to all excavations, both on the surface and underground, where the walls of the excavation must be located within precise limits. Where smooth walls are required in underground excavations such as tunnels and machine halls, the smooth wall effect may be obtained by the use of Xactex, an explosive packed in 16 mm diameter cardboard tubes which may be conveniently joined together; when these are loaded into 32–38 mm diameter holes, a substantial air-space remains into which the gases may expand to reduce the shattering effect on the rock wall. Normally the perimeter holes loaded with Xactex (or similar explosive) are paced approximately 45 cm apart.

For surface operations, perimeter holes from 50 to 125 mm in diameter at 50 to 100 cm spacing are commonly used.

For pre-split holes under 50 mm diameter, they are spaced 20 to 45 cm apart and charged with explosives at 0.15 to 0.37 kg/m of hole.

One problem which has arisen is that rock may be left at the toe. To overcome this, a heavier charge may be loaded at the bottom of the preplitting holes. In addition, the buffer distance may be reduced. For trial purposes, it is suggested that the buffer distance selected be $1/3$ to $1/2$ the normal burden distance adopted for production blasting.

Presplitting has been carried out in which alternate holes only are loaded, and also in other cases short delay firing has been used. However, experience has shown that a cleaner face is achieved if every hole in the presplit line is loaded and the holes fired simultaneously, about 50 or more millieseconds before the main round is fired [5]. Little or no stemming is used.

Although interest in presplitting is increasing, the number of cases in which details are known is not sufficiently large to give necessary experience from which general charging ratios can be stated. The nature of the rock involved, including hardness, brittleness, and presence or otherwise of cracks, is the most important variable. However, such experience as has been gained to date indicates that a charge ratio of the order of 0.2–0.3 kg/m^2 of area to be presplit might be used in initial trials.

The presplitting technique may be used in all engineering works where smooth faces are required to obtain the advantages of saving in labour and concrete. In addition, the creation of smooth unshattered walls increases the factor of safety since falls of loose rock are much less likely to occur.

3. **Smooth wall blasting**: When the rock is reasonably competent, smooth wall blasting techniques can be used to advantage in underground applications. Horizontal holes are charged with small-diameter low-density decoupled cartridges strung together and by providing good stemming at the collar of the hole. Charges are fired simultaneously after the lifters. If the rock is incompetent, smooth wall blasting may not be satisfactory. Holes 37 to 50 mm in diameter are usually spaced from 60 to 75 mm. Sometimes referred to as 'perimeter blasting'.

4. **Cushion blasting**: This technique is similar to Line drilling, with a single row of perimeter holes, but loaded with light decoupled charges. Successful cushion blasting depends upon stemming of all air spaces in the hole, especially when the rock is not homogeneous.

It is therefore applicable to vertical down holes on the surface. One practice is to load the holes by attaching cartridges at intervals to DC downlines which are then lowered into the holes. The holes are completely backfilled with stemming material. To aid the passage of the stemming material down the hole, the DC line may be gently shaken, or raised and lowered as the material is added. Commonly the holes are 50 to 150 mm in diameter, spaced from one to two metres with a buffer (burden) of one to three metres, and loaded with a charge of 0.15 to 1.5 kg/m of hole. Such charges are fired after the main charge, often in delayed order.

Cushion blasting is regarded as a better method to use than pre-splitting when the rock is unconsolidated.

For all types of overbreak control (contour blasting, or profile blasting), a special range of explosives has been prepared. Most of these cartridges are designed to reduce overbreak by giving a poor degree of *coupling* (see Glossary). They are generally of the order of 15 to 22 mm in diameter.

Trade names of explosives used for controlled blasting in all the above methods are given below, as listed by various manufacturers. For the code, see Chapter 1.

AECI: Smoothex

Atlas: Kleen-Kut
                                                Coalite 8S

Austin: Austinite
                                                Emuline
                                                Red-E-Split

BIQ:	Petecas Britanite
CIL:	Powertrim
	Xactex
DNW:	Gelatine Donarit 2E
DPW:	Tovex Bakpak
DuPont:	Tovex T1
DYNO:	Rorladning
	Larvikit
EBCW:	Obrysit
ECP:	Sigma Trim
ERT:	ISANOL
ETCAN:	Trimrite 1,2
	Tovan Lite
	Dynamite T
ETI:	Trimtex SD
EXSA:	Exsacorte
ICIA:	Xactex
	Powergel
	Trimex
IRECO:	Iresplit D, S
ITPL:	SB2
Kemira:	Silosex
Nitro Nobel:	Gurit
NKC:	SB-IREMITE
SLEX:	Detagel Pre-Split

Controlled Trajectory Blasting (Cast Blasting) [7–13]

Under certain limited conditions overburden may be dislodged and directly moved into position in the spoil pile by the planned use of a large quantity of AN/FO loaded into medium diameter holes. The method is known as "controlled trajectory blasting". Up to 50 per cent of the overburden can be moved in this way, thereby increasing the capacity of the excavating equipment.

As an extension of this technique, Russian explosives engineers have developed the principle of directed rock ejection by methods using conventional explosives. In this way, they have planned and constructed several large canal installations and rockfilled dams. One such dam across the Vakhsh River involved the emplacement of a total weight of 1800 tons of explosives in the banks. From the right bank 1.55 million m^3 of hard limestone rock were torn out and directionally ejected to form a dam 60 metres high across the river. Then, 30,000 m^3 of soft earth were thrown into the stream bed from the opposite bank to provide an impervious core. Such a method greatly simplifies dam construction [8].

The fixed parameters desirable for successful Cast Blasting operations have been intensively studied [14].

Blasting in Plastic Rock Material

By far the largest usage of commercial explosives is for breaking hard brittle elastic rocks. When plastic rock materials, such as stiff clay, mudstone, soft shale, industrial minerals and permafrost are to be blasted, different procedures are called for.

In the former case, the rock immediately surrounding the shot point is pulverized, cracked and weakened by the compressive stress induced by detonation. Following this phase, breakage is readily effected by tensile spalling from the free face, aided by gas pressure (known as "bubble energy").

On the other hand, plastic materials become compacted and strengthened around the shot point when high velocity explosives are used. Tensile spalling is relatively ineffective unless the zone of compaction can first be broken in shear. This would call for greater explosive energy. In such circumstances, it is much better to use explosives of low brisance or de-coupled charges to lessen the initial compacting effect.

With industrial minerals, such as white clays, rock salt, gypsum and the like, the problem is alleviated by first undercutting a kerf with a conventional coal cutter, before firing.

Possible examples include:

(a) The *Kladno* method of reverse sequence blasting in underground railway tunnels in weak slate under the city of Prague, Czechoslovakia [15].

(b) The findings of Academician *Melnikov* [16] who shows that a certain amount of de-coupling gives better overall blasting efficiency in plastic materials.

(c) Experiences related by *Short* in connection with blasting in rock salt [17].

(d) Blasting problems in frozen ground.

References

[1] C. H. Noren, "The Ripple Rock Blast", *University of Missouri School of Mines & Metallurgy,* Fourth Annual Symposium on Mining Research, Bulletin No. 97, November 1958

[2] U. Langefors and B. Kihlstrom, *The Modern Technique of Rock Blasting*, 3rd. Edition (New York, Wiley, 1978)

[3] R. Gustafsson, *Swedish Blasting Technique* (DNW, Vienna, 1981)

[4] R. S. Culver, "Pre-Split Blasting", *The Mines Magazine,* March 1966

[5] S. A. Jenkins Jr, "Pre-splitting Technology for the Mining Industry", *Journ. of Explosives Engineering*, Vol. 6, No. 4, 1988

[6] ICI Australia Operations Pty. Ltd., "Blasting Methods for Wall Control in Surface Excavations", *Nobel Notes*, Vol. 36, No. 3, 1989

[7] A. Pisaneschi and H. S. Frazier, "Moving Overburden with Explosives", *Mining Congress Journal*, July 1963

[8] R. S. Ariel *et al.*, "Explosively Constructed Dam of the Baipazinsk Hydrocomplex on the Vakhsh River", Translation No. 789, Bureau of Reclamation, Denver, CO, Oct. 1968.

[9] J. M. Tracy, "Increased Production through Cast Blasting in Surface Coal Mines", *Journ. of Explosives Engineering*, May 13, 1985

[10] N. P. Chironis, "Angled Drilling Aids Casting", *Coal Age*, Jan 1984

[11] P. D. Dupree, "Applied Drilling and Blasting Techniques for Blast Casting at Trapper Mine", *Mining Engineering*, Jan 1987

[12] A. A. Chernigovskii, *Application of Directional Blasting in Mining and Civil Engineering* (Rotterdam: Balkema, 1986)

[13] C. V. B. Cunningham, "Explosives Today", AECI

[14] "Effective Modelling for Cast Blasting", *Downline*, ICI Explosives International Pte. Ltd., Jan 1989

[15] *Engineering News-Record,* October 1, 1970

[16] N. V. Melnikov, "Influence of Explosive Charge Design on Results of Blasting", *International Symposium on Mining Research, University of Missouri School of Mines & Metallurgy and U. S. Bureau of Mines,* Feb. 1961

[17] N. M. Short, "Fracturing of Rock Salt by a Contained High Explosive", *Colorado School of Mines Quarterly,* Vol. 56, No. 1, 1961

CHAPTER 15

Cut Holes

For economical blasting, as shown in Chapter 12, it is necessary to have a free face to which the rock can be blasted. In some applications of blasting, no such free face exists. In these cases, such as in tunnels, shafts, and other mine development openings, it is necessary to provide a free face artificially [1]. This is normally done, as a preliminary to the main blast, by drilling and firing an opening in the drilling face. This opening is termed a "cut".

In hard rock, a cut must be fired in each and every cycle of advance. The full round is usually drilled in the one operation; and the complete round is similarly charged and fired in the next operation. But of course the cut holes are the first to be fired in the whole sequence.

Type of Cut Used

The cut should normally be as small as the physical characteristics of the rock will safely permit with a minimum footage of drilling and explosives consumption. But to allow for inaccuracies in drilling and the natural vagaries of the rock, it is usual to be liberal when assessing the quantity of the charge.

The type of cut selected depends not only on the physical characteristics of the rock and the presence of joints and planes of weakness, but also on the skill of the operator, the equipment used, the size of heading and on the desired length of round to be "pulled".

There are five main types of cut (with variations of each). They are:

1. **The centre cut**: This is often called a "pyramid" or "diamond" cut (see Fig. 49). Four (or six) holes converge to a point about 6 inches beyond the depth of the rest of the round.

This arrangement allows for a concentration of high strength explosive near the apex of the pyramid. By firing these holes simultaneously, a pyramidal crater opening is obtained which provides free faces into which the other surrounding holes can be fired

SIDE ELEVATION

ELEVATION

(easer holes not shown)

ISOMETRIC VIEW

Fig. 49: Centre cut

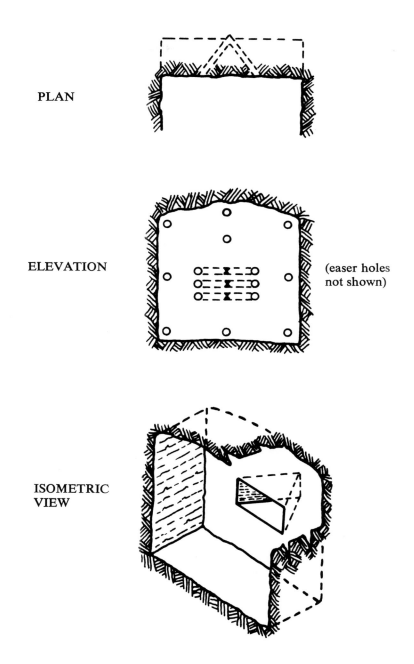

PLAN

ELEVATION   (easer holes
not shown)

ISOMETRIC
VIEW

Fig. 50: Wedge cut

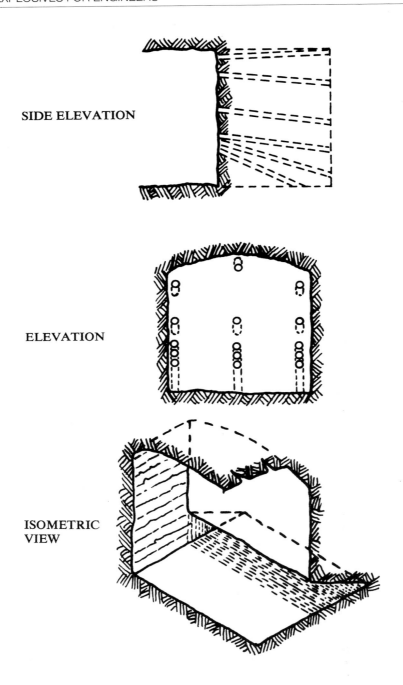

SIDE ELEVATION

ELEVATION

ISOMETRIC
VIEW

Fig. 51: Drag cut

in turn. Centre cuts are very effective in hard tough rock; but explosive consumption is high and much air blast and flydirt result. A high degree of skill is required to place the holes accurately.

2. **The wedge cut**: This is sometimes referred to as the "Vee" cut. In this case, four (or six) holes converge, not to a point as with the centre cut, but to a line forming a wedge-shaped rather than a pyramidal opening when blasted. It is easier to drill than a centre cut but is less effective in dense tough ground. An example of this type of cut is shown in Fig. 50.

For best effects the apex angle of the vee cut should not be less than 60 degrees. This involves a wide spread between the collars of holes. The consequent need to avoid the possibility of fouling the walls with the drilling equipment necessarily limits the depth of round pulled, except for very wide headings such as in tunnels and room-and-pillar faces in hard rock. For this reason, vee cuts are usually restricted to these applications.

3. **The drag cut**: This is like one side of a wedge cut. The holes may be drilled to "drag" from:

(a) The floor, as is usual.

(b) The back (not to be recommended as it causes shattering).

(c) One side or other (in which case it is sometimes termed the "fan" cut).

(d) A convenient slip plane or slide.

This cut is suitable for shale or laminated rock. It calls for less accuracy in drilling but requires more holes. It is much less effective than a centre cut in hard ground. Its main use lies in controlled blasting alongside important installations or against timber.

A typical drag cut (off the floor) is shown in Fig. 51.

4. **The burn cut**: This cut is suitable for hard, brittle homogeneous rock such as sandstone or igneous rock. It is not so effective in broken or shaly ground. However, its effectiveness can be varied to suit the ground by the use of a selection from a multiplicity of patterns.

Because all holes are normal to the face, longer holes can be drilled and longer rounds "pulled" than with the other cuts, which involve angled drilling.

Certain of the holes are left uncharged in order to provide a series of miniature free faces to relieve stress, to reflect the compressive wave in tension, and to provide open space into which shattered rock from the charged holes can break.

Although there are many variables involved, the main essentials for a satisfactory burn cut (or cylinder cut) are:

(a) Holes must be collared accurately to pattern and must not converge or diverge.

(b) Low power explosives should be used to avoid packing or "freezing" of broken rock in the uncharged holes.

(c) Cut holes should not be fired instantaneously but in sequence, with ample delay periods between consecutive shots in order to give rock fragments an opportunity to be expelled from the cut.

As an aid in planning hole spacing to give "clean blasted holes", a diagram relating hole diameter to distance between hole centres has been developed by *Langefors* [2].

Some examples of burn cut patterns are shown in Figs. 52, 53, 54.

5.   **The large-hole cut**: This type of cut has evolved from the success achieved with burn cuts, in which parallel horizontal holes are used to pull longer rounds, and in which one or more holes are left uncharged.

Recent improvements in drill-equipment design have made possible the drilling of larger diameter holes. One or two such holes can be left uncharged to provide a more effective miniature free face than the larger number of smaller uncharged ordinary holes used in burn cut patterns. At the same time the need for drilling precision is not so rigid, although still an important feature of any parallel hole cut.

There are several models of large-hole cuts, as set out below [3].

A **single large-hole cut** is shown in Fig. 55. The large centre hole is probably of the order of 75 to 125 mm in diameter, with the smaller ordinary holes of 32 to 50 mm diameter, detonating in the short delay sequence indicated. Two sets of easer holes are shown, each fired simultaneously in turn at half-second intervals after the cut. In such cases, the burden distance from each cut hole to the wall of the large hole is usually 70 per cent of the large hole diameter. These cuts are suitable for a round depth of about 2.5 m. A similar pattern is known as the Fagersta cut.

A **double large-hole cut** is shown in Fig. 56, along with two sets of easer holes. Cut holes are fired sequentially at 50 msec intervals. In this case, the burden distance from the wall of an individual cut hole to the wall of the nearest large hole is normally 0.7 times $2d$, where d is the diameter of the large holes. Each set of easer holes is fired simultaneously in turn at half-second intervals after the cut. In Fig. 56, where two 76 mm holes are used, the dimensions shown are in inches. S is about 53 cm and B is of the order of 34 cm.

The **Coromant cut** is of special significance. The holes are located to give maximum effect at the time of detonation. Two overlapping large holes are drilled with a special drill guide to form a slot. The charged holes are drilled from a template. Fig. 57 shows the hole layout but does not include the necessary easer holes.

General Notes on Cut Holes

Cut holes are generally drilled 15 cm deeper than the remainder of the round. This ensures that the other holes leave clean "bottoms" in preparation for drilling the next round.

Stab holes or "baby cut holes" are sometimes used to assist the cut. They are short holes meeting at a shallow depth, and arranged to detonate before the main cut holes. In conventional safety fuse firing, there is a danger of their "cutting off" a cut hole. They are applicable mainly to centre cuts.

Easers (also known as relievers) are used to divide or ease the burden between succeeding holes where necessary.

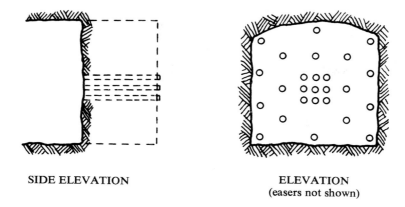

SIDE ELEVATION   ELEVATION
                                  (easers not shown)

Fig. 52: Typical burn cut

a, b, c = Box cuts
  d, e = Line cuts
    f = 3 in dia. uncharged hole
    ● = Charged holes
    ○ = Uncharged holes

Fig. 53: Burn cut patterns

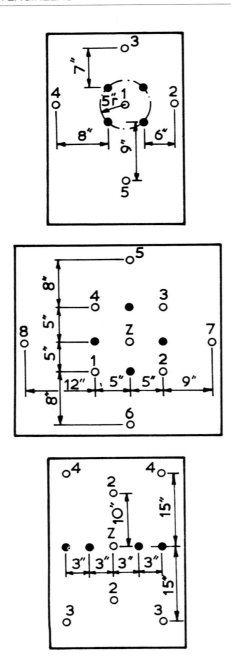

Fig. 54: Suggested layouts for burn cuts (with easers) – uncharged holes are shown in black

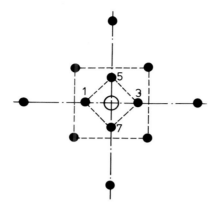

Fig. 55: A single large-hole cut, with two sets of easers

Fig. 56: A double large-hole cut, with two sets of easers

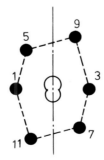

Fig. 57: The Coromant cut

It is important that holes planned to detonate at a certain instant do not "bottom" within, say, 45 cm of holes planned to detonate earlier. Otherwise, sympathetic detonation may spoil the sequential planning of the round with poor results.

Depth of Rounds

Normal rounds in development headings generally "pull" about 1.6–2 m; but burn cut rounds may pull 2.5–3 m.

The economic depth of round pulled depends on the cross-section of the face (or on its smaller dimension) and on the economic depth of shot-hole of a diameter sufficient to accommodate a standard explosive cartridge in the bottom.

It also depends on the length to which all holes can be drilled in the time allowed for drilling, so that the round can be fired at the end of the shift to maintain an effective cycle of operations.

Another limiting factor to the depth of round pulled is the degree of angling required to drill and fire satisfactorily a centre, wedge, or drag cut. This is of no particular significance in the case of burn cuts where no angling is required. Hence the greater depth of round which can be pulled with a burn cut [4, 5, 6].

References

[1] R. A. Dick *et al.*, "Explosives and Blasting a Procedures Manual", *U.S.B.M. I.C. 8925*, 1983

[2] U. Langefors and B. Kihlstrom, *The Modern Technique of Rock Blasting*, 3rd Edition (New York, Wiley, 1978)

[3] R. Gustafsson, *Blasting Technique* (DNW, Vienna, 1981)

[4] R. L. Bullock, "Fundamental Research on Burn Cut Drift Rounds", *University of Missouri School of Mines & Metallurgy, Third Annual Symposium on Mining Research*, No. 95, 1958

[5] R. L. Schmidt, R. L. Morrell, D. H. Irby and R. A. Dick, "Application of Large-hole Burn Cut in Room-and-Pillar Mining", *U.S.B.M. R.I. 7994*,1975

[6] "Optimising Blasthole Layout in Burn Cuts", *Mining Magazine*, July 1981

CHAPTER 16

Quarry and Open Cut Blasting Practice

General

The breakage of stone from suitable surface deposits for its manifold uses in the secondary and tertiary industries is of increasing moment on the national scene. By far the largest tonnage of any category of ore or mineral matter produced by the use of explosives by surface methods is in the area of quarrying. For this purpose, a quarry may be considered as an open cut mining operation in which rock, rather than mineral matter, is produced. The mined rock (or "stone") may be used as a raw material feedstock for chemical plants (such as limestone for cement making, and clay shales for brick production), or simply as "construction stone" for concrete aggregate, highway pavements or railway ballast. For this latter purpose, the rock as mined is crushed and screened to provide several graded products for specific usage requirements. For many of these market outlets the rock must meet standard specifications in relation to physical and other characteristics. On the other hand, special methods are involved in the quarrying of dimension stone (building and monumental stone) to produce blocks of rock free from flaws or planes of weakness.

Explosives are necessary for the breaking of stone, the charges being placed in such positions within the rock that their energy, mainly in the form of high pressure gases, will be utilized to the full. However, it is necessary to have equipment capable of drilling holes in such positions and to such depths as will enable the explosives to be placed in the best positions, for effective results. Explosives and drilling are therefore complementary in the breaking of stone, and in any discussions on quarrying, explosives practices and drilling techniques are of prime importance.

The modern concept of quarrying is that, as far as possible, the rock should be broken to the required size in the primary blast, with a minimal need for secondary breaking of oversize boulders. This calls for good fragmentation.

A high face (see Fig. 58) of rock or ore for quarrying or open cut work is normally divided into several steps or benches for ease and safety of operation [1]. The width of bench should be sufficient to accommodate the spread of rock broken from the face and to provide space to deploy shovels, haulage units, and drilling equipment. The height of an individual bench depends on the depth capacity of the drilling equipment, and also on the degree of fragmentation required for the particular rock. (Some bench heights are necessarily determined by the angle of stratification of the rock and by the presence of clay seams or planes of weakness.) Most large scale operations use a nominal bench height of 13 to 16 m. Higher benches (deeper holes) generally mean coarser fragmentation, reduced accuracy in locating the hole bottom, but fewer drill set-ups. Lower bench heights are more suitable for less sophisticated drilling equipment, but drill set-up time and cost are considerably increased.

Fig. 58 shows one typical arrangement of benches for quarry or open cut work. Blast holes are normally drilled vertically, or at a steep angle, in rows parallel to the face. Alternate rows of holes may or may not be staggered.

In order to avoid the development of a toe, and to achieve good fragmentation, special care is taken to site accurately the collars of vertical blast holes. Also, in order to ensure the required depth of subgrade drilling, the reduced level of each hole collar needs to be observed. These details are of increased importance with angled holes because of the greater difficulty in ensuring that the bottom of the hole, which is the most important part of the hole for effective blasting, is at the planned point within the rock. Factors that are involved are (a) the siting of the collar; (b) the direction or azimuth of the line of the inclined hole; and (c) the extent of possible hole deviation.

For these reasons, some operators find that it pays to make routine surveys and to peg and plan every bench round drilled. This aims to ensure regularity in primary blasting, free from toe, and to achieve a low powder factor, with good fragmentation.

Electrolocation Ltd. of Bristol, U.K., manufacture a new electronic borehole monitoring instrument GPR110, designed to check borehole alignment on quarry benches.

Another method uses a laser survey in conjunction with a computer to prepare accurate profiles of quarry benches. This Quarryman System was developed by ETI.

Tramac Corporation of Randolph NJ, USA, offers two types of its ILMEG electronic angle indicators for accurate blasthole drilling. These are the ANGLE S30 and the MEC-ANGLE drill boom indicator.

Where the rock is of such a variable nature that random toes form unpredictably, cautious operators prefer to drill only one row, or perhaps only two rows, of holes for a single blast round. On the other hand, in rock subject to backbreak, where the bench surface near the new face line is cracked or disturbed, it is difficult to collar holes satisfactorily. For this reason, some operators prefer to drill and fire three or four rows of holes so that a greater proportion of the total number of holes can be collared and loaded in solid ground.

Fig. 59 is a diagram displaying one typical firing order for short delay blasting of a quarry or open cut face, where three rows of holes are employed in staggered formation.

Similar techniques to quarry operations apply also to those of open cut mining of ores and industrial minerals [2]. In both cases, the prior or concurrent removal of the

Fig. 58: Cross-section of quarry (open cut) bench system showing typical drilling pattern geometry for two rows of holes. B = burden distance; S = spacing distance

overlying worthless rock material, the overburden, may call for the use of explosives. The overburden may be a relatively thin cover of weathered earthy material in which case it can be ripped and removed by bulldozers and tractor-drawn scoops. But where it is well consolidated, it will need to be loosened or fragmented by explosives before removal. For deeper deposits of rocky overburden or where large amounts of rock along the hanging wall of deep open cuts are involved, the overburden will need to be quarried in benches, similar to the procedures involved in the mining of ore.

Fig. 59: Typical firing order for a staggered 3-row pattern on a quarry/open cut bench, using short delay detonators

Where near-surface deposits of coal are to be strip-mined, weathered overburden, up to 30 m deep, is first removed by large-scale excavators, in order to expose the coal seam. In many cases, the overburden needs to be blasted or loosened by explosives, to enable the excavator to perform effectively.

The batter angle of a face of rock or ore depends largely upon the class of rock and its geological structure. Some rocks such as basalt or stratified limestone safely stand almost vertically. Other formations need to be battered at a safe slope angle to avoid local landslides, especially if influenced by the action of water following heavy rains. Under these conditions, slope stability can be extremely tenuous. Yet when barren overburden overlying an ore deposit is to be mined, every additional degree of slope angle gained represents considerable savings in quantities mined and therefore in cost.

The technique of explosives usage in quarrying depends to a large extent on the drilling procedures employed, and therefore on the capital and operating scale of the operation, and the drilling equipment already available on the site. Small scale operators with limited capital investment will necessarily be restricted to simple units of equipment. A significant proportion of the construction stone output is contributed by many small producers using equipment of limited capabilities. Some coverage is therefore given here to their field of interest.

The following analysis of explosives usage in quarries is based upon the drilling practice adopted.

Drilling [3 – 6]

Most drills for primary blast holes in surface mining and quarrying are designed for vertical "down" holes, although some now have the capability for angled holes. Manufacturers are presently paying greater attention to devices for lining-up and inclining the holes with greater accuracy. Rigs for surface blasting can drill holes from 50 to 375 mm in diameter and from 10 to 20 metres deep. They use either rotary or percussive tools, with either water or dry (compressed air) flushing systems. They are mostly mobile (self-propelled) and provided with diesel or diesel-electric power units, operating through hydraulic systems. Modern units incorporate fast drilling, quick set-up, and rapid hoisting and lowering speeds, some with automatic drill rod handling.

1. **Rotary drills** are the more versatile. In soft material, drag bits can be used. For medium to hard rocks, tri-cone roller-cutter bits with a variety of tooth facings are used, with compressed-air flushing. Some small truck-mounted rigs use a drag bit, with augers to remove the cuttings.

2. **Percussive drills** break hard rock by high-energy blows delivered by a reciprocating high-speed piston to the drill steel provided with a chisel or button-faced bit. The piston is operated by compressed air under 700 to 1400 kPa pressure. The hollow drill steel is rotated either by a rifle bar mechanism or by an independent rotation device. The hole is flushed by an air stream passing through the hollow drill rods.

There are two main types of percussive drills for surface drilling of blast holes: (a) an above-surface machine which imparts energy to the bit, with the piston blow transmitted through the series of sectionalized drill rods, for drill holes 75 to 150 mm diameter in hard rock, and (b) "down-the-hole" drills, in which the machine follows the bit down the hole, with consequent reduced loss of blow energy because the piston strikes directly on the back of the bit. Down-the-hole drills have their widest application in drilling 100 to 200 mm diameter holes in hard rock.

The smaller variety of surface type percussive drill is mounted on a towed wheeled chassis and termed a "wagon drill", restricted to drill holes from 50 to 75 mm diameter to a depth of ten metres. Track-mounted self-propelled drills were developed from wagon drills, and have been adapted to serve the large range of surface and down-the-hole percussive drilling needs currently used in the surface blasting of hard rock. Some of these units are truck-mounted for rapid site-changing between widely distant sites.

Jackhammers are percussive rockdrills, operated by compressed air, and typical of those used in underground hard rock mines, but adapted for manual (hand-held) operation. In quarries, they are limited to 45 mm diameter holes for a maximum depth of seven metres. Hence they are used only by small operators.

Quarrying Using Small Diameter Holes

In the past, many small scale operators used small diameter holes followed by bulling the hole bottom to accommodate a sufficient explosive charge to break the toe. However, bulling is not now practised to any extent; many now aim to drill holes to a smaller bench height to secure improved fragmentation and greater output. However, this is still not so feasible with jackhammer holes.

1.   Short holes by jackhammer: Short hole drilling with jackhammers has been in use for many years; however, it is probably true to say that drilling and firing of these short holes in groups with definite spacings and burdens is a more recent practice. It used to be common, in small quarries for instance, to use safety fuse for initiation of the primary blast. Modern practice, however, is to drill holes in definite relation one to another and to fire them together electrically or by detonating cord.

Although jackhammer holes may be drilled to greater depth, the usual practice is to limit them to 5–6 m. At these depths, problems connected with the handling of drill steel, removal of drill cuttings, etc. are not too great.

Faces of stone in excess of 6 m, however, may be broken by short holes by employing a combination of vertical, inclined, and horizontal holes.

If the convenient maximum depth of holes by jackhammer is taken as 6 m, faces of stone say 7 m high may be broken, using a combination of vertical and horizontal holes as shown in Fig. 60.

To drill the horizontal toe holes, a pusher air-leg machine may be employed with advantage.

Using an additional line of holes in the face – frequently referred to as half-uppers – permits a face say 9 m high to be broken by such methods (see Fig. 61). Easy breaking ground and closer than usual spacing of holes would enable this height to be exceeded, as would, of course, deeper vertical drilling.

Fig. 60: Typical drilling diagram for 22 ft quarry faces using jackhammer holes

Fig. 61: Typical drilling diagram for 27 ft quarry faces using jackhammer holes

An important objection to methods which employ a combination of such holes is that the quarry floor, including the toe, must be cleaned up before drilling of the bottom holes can commence. In addition, particularly with high faces, there is the hazard that loose rocks may fall on the men drilling below. It is essential, therefore, to clean the face before drilling commences.

2. Short holes by wagon drill: Perhaps the machine more commonly used for drilling in the manner described previously is the wagon drill.

Short hole drilling by wagon drill is usefully employed by the smaller operators who find it difficult to justify large scale equipment. Such wagon drills, equipped with drifter mountings, are capable of drilling 50 to 75 mm diameter holes up to 12 m deep.

Quarrying with Large Diameter Holes [6, 7]

In recent years, improved technology and rising labour costs have predicated larger unit sizes of drilling, blasting, loading, transport, crushing, screening, dust recovery, and storage equipment and facilities.

This trend is clearly marked, especially for the medium and large scale quarry and open cut organizations. Mobile-electric or diesel-electric rotary drills are capable of drilling holes from 150 to 375 mm in diameter for depths up to 30 m, at rates of 150 to 350 m per shift, depending upon the hardness of the rock or ore. These drills incorporate air compressors for flushing the cuttings. Drill masts are capable of inclination up to 30 degrees from the vertical.

Either AN/FO or aluminized or Heavy AN/FO or slurries or emulsions are used as the primary charge, bottom-primed with high velocity boosters.

Bench heights range from 8 to 16 m. Holes are usually drilled below grade for distances variously quoted from 10 per cent of bench height, ten times the hole diameter, or generally up to 3 m. This is done to avoid the formation of a toe. With inclined drilling, this is not necessary; and if jet piercing is used, the bottom of the hole is usually chambered to achieve the same objective. Some large open pits use inclined holes for much of their drilling. This is not applicable to the jet piercing process.

Where a quarry is set up to handle large tonnages per day, loading arrangements on the quarry floor and the size of the primary crusher usually permit the rock to be broken larger in the primary blast than would be desirable in a quarry with small-size equipment.

This would allow holes to be spaced further apart than that indicated by the calculated burden distance. Such a procedure is indicated where shortdelay firing methods are employed. However, where the ore or rock formation is blocky, fragmentation is likely to be poor and this procedure is contra-indicated.

In the best of open cut operations, some secondary breaking is always necessary. Operators generally aim to minimize the need for secondary blasting, however, since its direct and indirect effect on total costs is exceedingly high.

The iron ore mines of Minnesota generally aim to keep the proportion of secondary breakage to within two per cent of their total tonnage; and then to use a drop ball, in various weights up to 7 tons, handled by a mobile crane, in order to avoid the cost of explosives for secondary breaking. Some of these mines break up to a million tons of ore in a single multiple-row primary blast.

Some operators now use an impact breaker machine for secondary breaking of oversize boulders from the pile of broken material at the face. In this way, such problems as flyrock, dust, noise, air blast, and broken working time, are avoided.

In 1981, a record single blast of 7,172,600 t of rock was made at the Sishen open cut iron ore mine in South Africa. About 60 km of detonating cord was used to fire 2,662 blastholes, with an average bench height of 11.9 m.

The type of explosive employed and the arrangement of charges in large diameter holes depends on the type of rock, stratification (if any), depth of holes, etc. The depth of hole is important since this determines whether the charges within the hole should be decked or not. Where deck charges are employed, from half to two-thirds of the calculated charge is placed in the bottom of the hole with the balance in one or more deck charges separated by sand.

For breaking softer formations, especially where there is no serious water problem, the use of a low-density blasting agent such as AN/FO avoids the need to deck-charge.

For wet holes in the harder formations, metallized AN slurries and emulsions are particularly applicable, especially where a pump truck service is available [6, 8].

References

[1] M. E. Lechner, "Contribution to the Optimum Design of Bench Height for Hard Rock Open Pit Mining", *Proc. 11th World Mining Congress*, Belgrade, May 31, 1982

[2] E. P. Pfleider, Ed., *Surface Mining* (New York, AIME, 1968)

[3] S. Tandanand, "Principles of Drilling", in *SME Mining Engineering Handbook* (New York, AIME, 1973) Chap. 11

[4] A. Bauer, "Update on Open Pit Blasting – a Global Review", *Journal of Mines, Metals & Fuels*, January 1982

[5] "Handbook on Surface Drilling and Blasting", Tampella Ltd., Tamrock

[6] "Drilling and Blasting Technology", Australian Mineral Foundation, Inc. May 1977, Chaps. 1-6

[7] R. K. Singhal, H. G. Naidu and S. P. Singh, "Influence of Blasting Techniques on Open Pit Economics", *Mining Engineering*, February, 1989

[8] R. A. Dick *et al.* "Explosives and Blasting Procedures Manual", *U.S.B.M. IC 8925*, 1983

CHAPTER 17

General Industrial Applications

Surface Excavations

Apart from quarries and open cuts, all other surface excavations such as canals, trenches, cuttings, and foundation excavations are included in this category.

Canals are used chiefly for navigation, irrigation and drainage purposes, and generally as aqueducts; trenches are usually prepared as drains and for laying pipelines or cables; cuttings are for road and railway formations; foundation excavations for city buildings, structural and machinery installations; and general excavations are required for clearing sites, for pole holes, and for miscellaneous purposes.

In many of these applications, blasting is advantageous to loosen the rock before its removal by mechanical excavating plant. A wide range of rock types and strengths is encountered in this class of work. Soft overburden is first removed to expose the solid rock.

1.   **Canals and trenches in rock**: It is necessary to use explosives to loosen the rock along the trench profile in advance of mechanical trench excavators or backhoes. Mobile high speed drill rigs are used.

For narrow pipeline and cable trenches up to 60 cm wide, a single row of holes is drilled to grade level. Spacing is determined experimentally in conjunction with the type and grade and quantity of explosive selected. Holes are fired sequentially towards a free face with short delay detonators.

In harder ground or with wider trenches up to 2 m wide, two or more rows of holes are drilled, sometimes in a staggered formation so that limiting side holes are on alternate sides.

Holes are placed vertically as shown in Fig. 62 but may also be slightly inclined [1]. The required amount of side batter to the trench is usually achieved by the incidental amount of side overbreak that results.

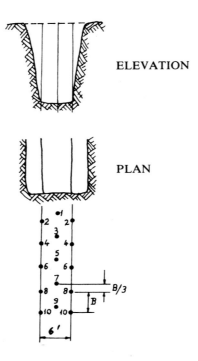

Fig. 62: Diagram for blasting trenches in hard rock, with leading centre hole and two flank holes

The explosive charge should be ample but well distributed up the hole at a low loading density to avoid excessive overbreak. Drill holes need to be closely spaced in these "tight" narrow faces. Holes should be well stemmed. Fig. 62 shows a typical hole layout in a staggered pattern.

Where important installations must be protected, more holes are used, each charged more lightly, and barricades and blasting mats are used.

2.   **Drainage ditches in swamp lands**: For draining swamps, it is often impossible to use either hand or mechanical methods.

The method of ditch blasting with explosives, however, is easy to apply, rapid in results, and, furthermore, requires no elaborate equipment. Channels ranging in width from one to many metres across may be successfully blasted in this manner. The depth of the drain may also be controlled to some extent by the amount of charge used and the depth to which the charge is placed.

Ditch blasting in its simplest form is illustrated by the single line of charges placed along the centre line of the proposed ditch or channel. The charges are placed in holes in the mud or silt at regular intervals; the top of the charge is placed 20–30 cm below ground level. The amount of charge or number of cartridges in each hole will depend on the characteristics of the ground and the width and depth of ditch required. This is largely a matter for experiment under the particular conditions at the site.

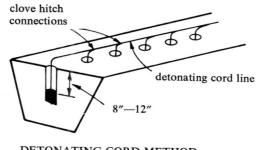

clove hitch
connections

detonating cord line

8"—12"

DETONATING CORD METHOD

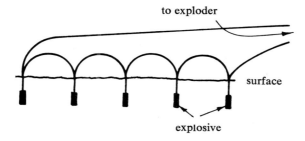

to exploder

surface

explosive

ELECTRICAL METHOD

Fig. 63: Single line ditching

As a guide, however, a ditch approximately 1.3 m across the top and 1 m deep can be blasted in silt by charges of one cartridge of ammonia gelatine 60% placed at intervals of 60 cm – the charges being fired electrically or by detonating cord. Charges of $1^1/2$ cartridges placed as a column in similar type soil will form a ditch approximately 2 m wide and 1.3 m deep (see Fig. 63).

For wider ditches the number of cartridges per hole should be increased, still, however, keeping the top of the top cartridge 8–12 inches below the surface level. The depth of the ditch will also be increased in proportion.

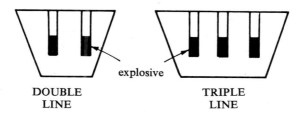

explosive

**DOUBLE
LINE**

**TRIPLE
LINE**

Fig. 64: Double and triple line ditching

When ditches are required to be wider than can conveniently be blasted with a single line of charges (or where a wide shallow channel is required), multiple rows of holes, staggered in relation to one another, are employed. Generally, however, the number of rows so employed does not exceed three (see Fig. 64).

A cross-row method, in which rows of holes are placed at right angles to the main line of charges at intervals along the centre line of channel, is also a widely used method, particularly where wide ditches are required.

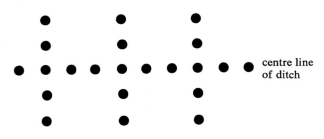

centre line
of ditch

cross-row arrangement

If it is possible to obtain the desired effects with the single line of charges, this should be used, as the method is simpler to operate and is less costly in materials.

In ditching with explosives, detonating cord or the electrical method of initiation is employed. However, since the capacity of the generator type exploder would limit each firing to a short length of ditch, a condenser-discharge type of exploder should be used.

Detonating cord firing also enables long lengths of ditch to be fired at the one time. The DC lines with primer cartridges attached may be prepared on solid ground near the site and placed in position when ready. This is the method of initiation normally recommended for ditching with explosives. For further details on ditch blasting, see Chapter 21.

The Trenchrite System has been developed by DuPont, using cartridged water gels (slurries) and Trenchdet delay electric detonators with regular precise firing intervals of 25 msec.

Atlas produces a cap-sensitive 'Powerditch' explosive in three grades. IRECO supply 'Ditching Dynamite' and 'Iremite TX'.

3. **Road and railway cuttings in rock**: After removing soft overburden, it is necessary to establish a free face across the width of the cutting. Where a natural free face is not available, it may be established by means of a box cut.

The diameter of cartridge (where dynamite is to be used), burden distance, and hole spacing depend upon the diameter of hole drilled, which in turn depends upon the equipment available.

It is usual to drill holes to about 60 cm below grade level and to use electric short delay blasting or DC and MS delay connectors arranged so that each row of holes is fired in sequence.

Under average rock conditions, explosive consumption works out at a minimum of 0.3 kg/m^3 of rock in place.

4.   **General excavations**: Based on the general principles expounded above, a specific blasting pattern can be evolved for any type of excavation.

Much depends on the condition and requirements associated with each particular application.

Submarine (Underwater) Blasting

Applications of submarine blasting for civil purposes include the following:

1.   Blasting trenches across rivers to carry pipelines and cables.
2.   Demolition of wrecks.
3.   Cutting of piles.
4.   Blasting channels through reefs, bars, and sandbanks.
5.   Harbour development and improvement.
6.   Blasting sheet piling and coffer dams.

Special provisions relating to submarine blasting include the following:

1.   The effect of shockwaves transmitted through the water to nearby installations.
2.   The effect of hydrostatic pressure.
3.   Special waterproofing requirements and the need for high resistance to water of the explosive components.
4.   The difficulty of effective placement.
5.   Because of water pressure, burden distances must be reduced.
6.   Holes should be drilled well below grade.
7.   In order to avoid silting up, charges should be fired as far as possible in one operation.
8.   Full advantage of an ebbing tide should be taken to scour out the broken material.
9.   Use either Blasting Gelatine or other high strength gelatine with aluminium-tube electric detonators or with DC.

Where a small quantity of submerged rock is to be removed under water, it is sometimes economical to employ a diver to drill holes with a jackhammer and to charge and connect the holes for subsequent firing from the surface. With larger jobs such as deepening or construction of a harbour, special drilling equipment mounted on a drill barge designed for the purpose is generally necessary.

The drill barge is equipped with spuds that can be lowered to the seabed. The spuds, which usually consist of heavy timber, reinforced with steel plate, may be raised or lowered with steam- or compressed-air-driven hoists by means of steel-wire ropes through top and bottom sheaves. Before dropping the spuds, the barge is manoeuvred and se-cured in the desired drilling position by anchors or spring lines. The barge is then raised a few inches on the spuds to ensure a stable and level drilling platform.

The drilling equipment usually consists of one or more drilling masts mounted on one side of the barge. These are generally arranged on rail tracks for ease in manipulation when "spotting" drill holes. The masts are usually high enough to accommodate the longest length of drill steel required for the deepest hole without stopping to make ex-tensions or adjustments.

The masts also support the sand pipe which is raised or lowered on guides by a hoist and cable. The sand pipe, which is "belled" at the top, is slightly larger in diameter than the gauge of bit used; it is usually of sufficient length to reach from surface to bedrock. For shallow water where wave and tidal conditions are moderate, the sand pipe can be in one piece; but when employed in deeper water in more difficult conditions, a tele-scopic type is used. Where drills are used under water, the sand pipe used is shorter but should extend from the bedrock through the soft unconsolidated material on the seafloor.

The purpose of the sand pipe is to prevent loose material from falling into the drill hole, to guide the drill steel, and also to convey the drill cuttings away from the hole. In some cases the sand pipe is slotted near the bottom to discharge the heavier cuttings.

Holes drilled for underwater blasting vary from 60–150 mm diameter, using jackham-mers and down-the-hole drills.

The drilling pattern must be so designed that there is no risk of unbroken rock being left above the grade level, otherwise further work becomes difficult and costly. Each drill hole charge will create a cone-shaped crater; therefore the holes must be spaced and drilled to such a depth below grade that the craters will overlap. The spacing is usually of the order of 2–3 m, depending on hole diameter, type and thickness of rock to be re-moved, and depth of water. Holes are usually drilled below grade to a distance corre-sponding to the spacing distance.

Where a vibration problem exists, small diameter holes and smaller charges should be used.

The quantity of explosives required will vary according to the depth of water and tenaci-ty of the rock. Usually 0.3–3 kg are required per cubic metre of rock. As a guide, 3 kg/m^3 should be suitable for reasonably hard rock under 10–13 m of water. Preliminary examination and survey by diver and sounding is usually required before determining drilling patterns, charge quantities, and methods.

In work involving extensive underwater blasting, special explosives should be used be-cause with increasing depth of water the sensitivity and VOD of the explosive decreas-es. This effect is probably due to the minute air bubbles within the cartridges being squeezed out, thus increasing the density. To counter this effect, special explosives for-mulated to give a high VOD and greater sensitivity are recommended. No special prim-ing is necessary, except that a No. 8 aluminium electric detonator is required.

Explosives recommended for underwater blasting include the high velocity gelatines.

Seismic cartridges are supplied in tubes which may be screwed together by means of an outer coupler to form a rigid column of explosive of any practical length. This is convenient for charging readily through a sand pipe or charging tube.

Where the sand pipe reaches to the surface, the charge of explosive may be charged through the pipe and pushed to the bottom of the hole by means of a long tamping stick.

A conventional brass loading tube may also be employed. This should fit inside the sand pipe and penetrate 60 cm or so within the drill hole. The explosive is then pushed to the bottom of the drill hole.

Explosives may also be loaded into metal shells such as stove pipe and the unit of the required length lowered into the drill hole.

A small float which will readily pass through the sand pipe is often attached to the detonator leg wires or the DC so that when the sand pipe or charging tube is withdrawn the ends float to the surface. Connections for firing a blast may be made by using a small boat. For firing electrically, it is important to tape all joints carefully.

When firing small charges, the drill barge need not be moved from the drilling position. However, for multiple holes with larger charges, it should be moved to a safe position.

Vibration and air blast from underwater blasting may be a cause of concern when blasting near harbour installations. If delay firing is indicated, DC lines should be connected to the charges with delay detonators at the surface. It is possible, however, that the underwater charges, being placed at close spacing may become subject to sympathetic detonation, in which case some or all of the charges will explode together. Because of the close spacing of holes in underwater blasting, cut-off holes could result from sequential firing unless rock and other conditions happen to be favourable.

Pipeline and cable trenches through rock and reefs can be effectively and expeditiously executed without the need for the drilling of holes.

Wooden piles may also be cut at river or seabed level by means of a charge of strong gelatine strung in the form of a girdle in a plastic tube, or alternatively, taped to rope, wire, or detonating cord.

In many cases, a diver is employed to place charges in position in close contact with the pile, especially where heavy marine growth makes this otherwise difficult (and may, incidentally, indicate the need for increasing the charge).

Where a diver is not available, an elastic material may be used to form a girdle around the pile just below the water level; the girdle may then be located by sliding it down the pile to the seabed, using two light wooden poles on opposite sides of the pile.

As a guide, a pile of 45 cm diameter would require a charge of about 1.5 kg of high velocity gelatine dynamite.

More recent advances in underwater blasting techniques have been developed with the use of shaped charges (see Chapter 10).

Shaped charges (Fig. 65) are merely placed on the top of the seabed, along the projected trench lines and hooked up to the firing point with detonating cord.

Fig. 65: Shaped charge for underwater ditch blasting

This technique has been developed by the Ocean Applications Group of Jet Research Center, Inc. of Arlington, TX, USA. In the same way they have developed cutting harnesses in which small shaped charges are assembled as circular girdles to cut piles made variously from steel tube (hollow or concrete-filled), reinforced concrete, or timber. These girdles are particularly useful for removal of hazards to shipping, such as the demolition of wrecked off-shore drilling rigs (see Fig. 66).

In the field of oil well technology, where high water pressures are prevalent, the Jet Research Center also specializes in the production and application of a wide range of harnesses and assemblies for cutting drill pipe, tubing and casing, and for perforation to increase oil flow. These assemblies are based on the use of specially designed shaped charges.

FAMESA supply a shaped charge 'Carga Huesca', housed within a seismic booster, to provide a concentrated charge of 300 g in a small area, as a powerful seismic charge.

ICIA have developed an 'Anzomex Well Head Recovery Charge', incorporating shaped charges for cutting oil well pipe and recovering the well head. Also an 'Anzomex Shaped Charge' for breaking large boulders.

For cutting cables and steel rods, ETI supply a 'Detacabe' unit in two versions, of 35 and 50 grams. Shaped charges are also produced by DYNO. Their 'Perfolit' unit is fired by Group 2 VAOD detonators.

Fig. 66: Outside circular girdles for cutting piles (shaped charge principle)

GOEX and OWEN supply a wide range of cutting tools and oil well perforating assemblies, most of which are based upon shaped charge technology.

Demolition Work [1, 2, 3]

Explosives may be used to demolish a wide variety of materials (including stone, brick, concrete, steel, and timber) in the following applications:

1. Breaking up structures fabricated from steel plate and girders; breaking heavy castings such as flywheels, engine beds, and the like; breaking up iron acid pots and retorts by concussion charges.
2. Demolition of factory chimney stacks.
3. Demolition of masonry and concrete walls.
4. Removing old concrete foundations or adjusting existing foundations to accommodate new machinery.

Generally, each demolition job is an individual problem, requiring special treatment; consequently, this class of work should be placed in the hands of experienced contractors. Because of the complexities of and risks involved in each individual task, amateurs and enthusiastic revolutionaries are likely to become doomed in time to a process of self-elimination. Therefore, in their own interests, no further notes on the methods to be used are offered here.

Apart from the use of regular explosives for demolition work, some special 'demolition agents' have been developed.

Among these are:

1. An expansive cement-type non-explosive demolition agent (S-mite) developed by Sumitomo Cement Co., Ltd. of Japan.
2. KAYASOFT, an explosive to prevent flyrock and to reduce vibration in urban areas. It is a "soft" explosive with a VOD of about 2000 m/sec with good water resistance.
3. SLB Concrete Breaker, for breaking concrete boulders and foundations. It is a powder explosive consisting of heat-generating agents. When ignited under confined conditions, it burns with a velocity of 40–60 m/sec, generating high temperature gases to crack concrete and rocks (as for soft fragmentation) yielding a minimum of vibration and noise.

The two latter items are available from the Nippon Kayaku Co., Ltd. of Tokyo, Japan.

References

[1] R. Gustafsson, *Swedish Blasting Technique* (Gothenburg, 1973)

[2] American National Standards Institute, A 10. 6 – 1969

[3] M. A. Perkin, "Demolition of Concrete Structures by the Use of Explosives", *Explosives Engineering*, Vol. 2, No. 1, 1986

CHAPTER 18

Blasting in Tunnels and Underground Development Headings

General

This application of blasting is confined to shaft sinking, tunnelling, drifting, crosscutting, raising, and winzing.

It is the most difficult of blasting techniques because (apart from bench cuts in shafts) no free face exists and the firing of cuts becomes necessary. For uniformly good results, burden distances are shortened and explosive usage is increased. The work of drilling, charging, and blasting demands a much higher order of skill than where free faces exist.

The hole with the least resistance is always the next to be fired. It is usually the middle hole of a row. When fired, additional free faces are then available to the remaining holes in turn. This principle is basic to the design of all round patterns. The lifters are always fired last so as to reduce the compaction of the muck pile for easier shovelling, whether by hand or machine.

Tunnels

Tunnel driving is a common type of construction project in civil engineering contract work. Depending upon the class of ground to be traversed, tunnels may be excavated in:

(a) Soft wet unconsolidated ooze, wherein tunnelling shields, with or without the use of plenum systems, are used, followed by tubbed linings (of cast iron or prefabricated concrete segments) for permanent support of the ground.

(b) Soft to medium rock in which tunnelling moles can be used to advantage. Tunnel boring machines (TBMs) have recently been developed to high degrees of sophistication.

(c) Pipe-jacking, where applicable.

(d) Hard rock, in which the conventional drill/blast/muck cycle is necessary. This is the only type that calls for the use of explosives.

Tunnels are used variously for railways and highways in mountainous terrain and under rivers; for river diversions in dam construction work; for urban underground rapid transit facilities; for hydro-electric and other aqueducts; and for many other miscellaneous applications, including mining.

Tunnels are excavated in cross-sectional dimensions ranging from 3 to 16 m in diameter and up to 82 km long. The larger sections are shaped more like a horse-shoe, with a horizontal base and an arched roof. In these large tunnel headings, sophisticated items of equipment such as drill jumbos and Conway shovels are used.

Depending chiefly on their cross-sectional dimensions, tunnels can be advanced "full face", or by pilot heading and subsequently stripping to full face dimensions (Fig. 67).

Fig. 67: Large tunnel heading excavated by pilot heading (approx. 10 X 10 ft) and by ring-drilling in a fan formation from the pilot heading

In general, the principles are the same with full face and pilot heading, although with the latter the dimensions are restricted to those of a drift or crosscut.

Various types of cuts are employed, but usually a V-cut.

Where a full face is advanced, drilling is normally done from a hydraulic jumbo. With this equipment, a large borehole (60 to 125 mm diameter) is sometimes used as the basis for a cut.

Tunnel driving, like shaft sinking, is an extremely costly operation and therefore many benefits and economies can result from the application of modern work-study principles. Well-planned operation cycles are therefore a *sine qua non* of modern tunnelling and shaft sinking operations.

Shafts

Shafts for mine development purposes are usually vertical and may be circular, elliptical, square, or rectangular in cross-section. For many reasons, the circular section is now regarded as the most effective shape. As with tunnel construction, many shafts are now being sunk by independent contractors.

Generally, irrespective of the cross-sectional shape of the shaft, centre or burn cuts are used; otherwise, bench cuts (a special case of the drag cut), used alternately on either side of the face, give good results, especially with hand-mucking in rectangular shafts.

Centre cut: This has the disadvantage that the excessive fly-rock is liable to damage the timber in rectangular shafts. Apart from this, there is the ever present risk (in wet shaft faces) of a misfire. Misfires in centre cuts usually mean the loss of the round. Misfires in wet shaft faces are usually hazardous and difficult to resolve. Shaft faces are usually wet.

Burn cut: These are to be preferred to centre cuts even though the final shape of the muck pile suits mechanical mucking in both instances.

The damaging effect of fly-rock is much less with burn cuts. With either cut the selection of a suitable short delay blasting pattern gives control of the final muck pile.

Wedge cut: These are generally not favoured because of the poor fragmentation effect of the cut itself.

Bench cut or sump cut: This method is favoured where handmucking is practised. Half the face is fired at a time in such a way that a stepped or benched effect is maintained, as in Fig. 68.

Fig. 68: Bench cut in rectangular shaft

The particular advantages of this method are:

1. A partial free face is always preserved so that drag cutting is not severe.

2. A sump is always available for drainage. This leaves the bench dry for drilling, charging, and firing.

3. It is an easier pattern to drill, and inaccuracies are less important.

4. There is better control of flyrock.

5. Charges can be kept dry with less risk of a misfire.

6. The muck is piled high against one end of the shaft. This allows gravity-aided hand-shovelling into an inclined kibble for most of the muck.

Usually a medium-high strength gelatinous explosive is preferred because of its water resistance.

If multiple fuse firing is employed, the capped fuses are always waterproofed. But because of its greater degree of safety, electric firing is more general.

Short delay detonators give better fragmentation, higher efficiency, and better control of the muck pile.

Drifts (Drives) and Crosscuts

These are headings advanced horizontally either along or across the strike of the country respectively. Because a crosscut cuts across the bedding planes, shearing of the rock by blasting is more effective than in drifts.

Holes are mostly drilled horizontally by rockdrills mounted on air-fed pusher legs. With some cuts, angled holes are necessary. Angled drilling calls for greater skill and limits the depth of hole which can be drilled because of the fouling of the equipment on the walls, floor, or roof of the drift.

Drag, wedge, centre, burn and large-hole cuts are variously used, the choice depending to some extent on local conditions.

After the cut has been fired, there follow the cut easers, side holes, knee holes, shoulder holes, back holes, and finally the lifters, each group in sequence (see Fig. 69).

The lifters point slightly downwards to ensure that the floor grade does not become excessive. Similarly, the back holes point upwards to preserve the desired headroom. Back holes are also placed so that an arched "roof" is maintained.

Where much water is to be drained away, the lifter on one side is placed lower in order that a continuous drain or ditch can be carried along with the advancing face.

Apart from purely exploratory openings (which may be smaller), and depending on their particular purpose, drifts and crosscuts in operating metalliferous mines, and pilot headings in tunnels, range variously from 1.6 x 2 to 3 x 3 m and larger in cross-section.

Fig. 69: Typical arrangement of holes in an 8 X 10 ft drift heading in very hard rock, fired with a 9-hole box-pattern burn cut.

If the centre hole of the box cut goes at zero, and the corner holes at 1, 2, 3, 4, then the four easers labelled X could be timed for 5, 6, 7, and 8 delays; or to go simultaneously at 6. The round holes would then be timed for short delay sequences as shown; or alternatively for half-second delay sequences.

Winzes

Winzes are really small shafts sunk from one level to another (but not including those sunk from the surface). Like shafts, they may be vertical or inclined.

Cross-sectional dimensions are normally 1.6 by 1.6 m, 2 by 1.3 m, 2.5 by 1.6 m, and 3 by 2 m. All types of cuts may be used; in the larger ones, if vertical, the bench method is sometimes used. This aids handmucking into the kibble.

Rises (Raises)

Raise headings are advanced upwards, in apposition to winzes. Their chief virtue lies in the fact that removal of the broken rock is, due to gravity, virtually automatic. An important disadvantage is concerned with the difficulty of adequately ventilating the heading. Some form of artificial lining is advisable in order to divide the raise so that spoil removal can be localized into one compartment whilst another can be used as an access gangway.

Raises are of a similar range of dimensions to winzes. Centre cuts are seldom used because of the resulting damage to timber. Burn cuts are more generally used.

Air-leg stoper machines are used for drilling from a staging erected 2 m from the face, or from an Alimak unit; or from a portable cage suspended by a rope through a borehole. However, raises are now commonly excavated by drilling and reaming.

CHAPTER 19

Blasting in Stoping Operations

General

Ore is extracted from orebodies in metalliferous rnines by various methods of "stoping". The ore is generally broken from the mass by drilling and blasting. A particular stope is normally delineated and prepared for ore extraction by various headings and/or timber structures appropriate to the particular stoping method selected [1, 2].

One of the important considerations in stoping is to support the walls of the country rock where necessary on either side of the vein from which the ore is being extracted. In many cases, it is necessary to fill the space resulting from the removal of the ore with waste rock or mill tailing in order to prevent the walls from caving. This filling operation normally proceeds step by step with ore extraction.

It is therefore important that the action of breaking the ore by blasting should not adversely affect the stability of the walls. Designers of stope blasting patterns must therefore bear this in mind.

Apart from this fact, and the necessity to support the back of the stope temporarily while the holes are being drilled, stope blasting is relatively simple. A free face always exists. Holes need only be spaced to suit the burden distance corresponding to the dimensions of the holes drilled. Holes fired near the walls, however, must not be allowed to break back into the walls.

Conventional Stoping

Conventional methods of stoping include horizontal cut-and-fill; inclined cut-and-fill; square-set; open; shrinkage; and combinations of these methods. They each involve the drilling of holes 1.6 to 2.7 m deep normal to the face being advanced, and parallel to the free face. Holes are normally drilled horizontally, inclined, or vertically downwards.

Horizontal (or inclined) breasts or slices about 2.7 m high are progressively advanced along the stope (see Fig. 70).

The blasting of vertical "up" holes is liable to leave a ragged unstable "back". However, when mechanized cut-and-fill stoping is employed, this problem may be overcome by using hydraulic jumbos, drilling "up" holes inclined at about 60° to the horizontal. In this way, the rock is broken mainly in tension, there is much less shearing, and the need for heavy charges is avoided.

Fig. 70:   Overhand stoping with horizontal holes

Long-Hole Sub-Level Stoping

With wide massive orebodies justifying a high rate of extraction at low unit costs, it is now the practice to drill a fan-shaped series of long holes from a sub-level drift in parallel vertical planes up to 2.7 m apart. The technique is known as "ring-drilling" and the ore is broken by "long-hole blasting" (see Fig. 71).

The average stope block may be 40 m long and 100 m high with a lode width varying from 13 to 80 m or more.

The stope block is first prepared by excavating the usual end raises and the chute raise and draw-point complex immediately above the haulage level. The next major step is to prepare a free face for ring-drill blasting. This may consist of a cut-off stope or "slot", 4 m wide, excavated by shrinkage stoping across one end of the ore block: or by excavating an opening 4 m wide from which vertical long holes can be drilled and fired to form a slot. At the same time, ring-drilling drifts are run at sublevel intervals. These serve as bases for drilling the rings of blast holes, and of course for charging operations.

Following the preparation of surveyed stope plans, ring-drilling operations may then commence. These plans indicate the orientation and depth of each hole in a fan-shaped array of holes in each vertical plane (ring) from each drill drift. Surveyors provide collar markings on the walls of the drill drifts for each drill set-up. Stope plans show the

Fig. 71: Long-hole stope blasting by ring drilling

angle of inclination of each hole, the depth to which it is to be drilled, and the depth of each charge. Plans usually provide for a burden distance of about 2 m between adjacent rings, with a maximum toe spacing of 2.7 m between the bottoms of adjacent radial holes.

Holes are drilled 6 cm in diameter with heavy percussive drifters mounted in such a way that the holes in each ring can be collared accurately by rotating the drill in its mounting.

One of the problems likely to be encountered is hole deviation. The tendency for holes to deviate increases with the depth of the hole. In some rnines, hole depths are limited to 27 m; otherwise the blast results can be prejudiced by inaccuracies in the locations of the bottoms of the holes.

Holes may be charged with AN/FO, collar-primed with a 4.5 cm diameter cartridge of ammonia gelatine 60% and electric short delay detonators; or bottom-primed with non-electric Anodet primer assemblies. Alternatively, a bulk slurry or emulsion may be used to load the holes, especially where water is a significant problem. The holes in a particular ring are fired sequentially with electric or Anodet short delay detonators, by selecting the particular delay detonator for each hole.

The firing order of rings is arranged with MS connectors between each ring in a DC trunkline, initiated with electric detonators operated by selected channels of sequential timing devices (see Chapter 9) for each set of rings in the stope, or in neighbouring stopes. In effect, each successive ring is blasted at delay intervals towards the slot, which is the free face.

In this way, full-face firing from the top to the bottom of the stope may be carried out. The ore broken in each ring with a 2.7 m burden may range from a few thousand to as much as 40,000 tons. Broken ore flows through control chutes into scram drifts above the haulage level; ore is then scraped to loading chutes and loaded into trains by gravity. Alternatively, broken ore may be arranged to flow into draw-points and to be loaded by load-haul-dump (LHD) units into ore trains.

In all such cases of primary stope blasting in wide stopes, where there is room to deploy mechanized equipment, the ore is likely to break in large blocks, resulting in poor fragmentation. But the general aim is to break ore from the solid orebody in the primary blast to a size that can be handled effectively through the later phases of the operation. This means that the ore should be reduced in size to suit ore handling activities through ore passes, chutes, chute gates. LHD shovels, into and out of haulage vehicles, and into underground crushers with a minimum of secondary blasting, and at a minimum total cost. This overall problem calls for a continuing in-depth study of all the factors involved, in respect of the characteristics of the particular orebody. The main factors concerned are those of drilling and blasting, but they should not be considered in isolation.

Vertical Crater Retreat (VCR) Stoping [3–6]

Another large scale highly mechanized stoping method for large continuous orebodies has recently been developed to offer the benefits of improved costs, safety and productivity.

The VCR method is applicable to large tabular steeply dipping orebodies at least 10 m wide. Stope blocks about 50 m high are completely undercut and prepared with the usual scram drift or draw point extraction openings at the lower level. The upper level is stripped to the full width of the orebody, and high enough to accommodate the drill.

Parallel holes about 150 mm diameter are drilled through to the undercut on a planned pattern for the full width and length of the stope block.

Each hole is blocked off at a calculated point above the back of the undercut stope. The holes are then loaded and fired. The resulting inverse crater firing delivers broken ore by gravity to the drawpoints.

At the next stage, the same holes are blocked off at a higher point, and the same loading and firing procedure follows in stages until the crown pillar is reached, and the stope block is fully extracted.

This is a simple explanation of a new method that is based upon the benefits of large scale drilling and blasting, e.g. "underground quarrying". Particular advantages are lower stope preparation cost, improved fragmentation, reduced ore dilution and wall breakage, better powder factor, less vibration, and greater safety.

This method, originally developed in Canada, is now being adopted in mines in several other countries.

References

[1] L. J. Thomas, *An Introduction to Mining* (Sydney, Hicks Smith, 1973)

[2] C. E. Gregory, *Rudiments of Mining Practice* (Clausthal, Trans Tech) 1983

[3] R. C. Lang, R. J. Roach and M. N. Osoko, "Vertical Crater Retreat an Important New Mining Method", Canadian Mining Journal, September 1977

[4] S. T. Mitchell, "Vertical Crater Retreat Mining proves Successful at Homestake Mine", *Mining Engineering*, Nov. 1980

[5] J. Muir, "Small Block VCR Mining at Homestake", *Mining Engineering*, September 1988

[6] ICI Explosives International Pte Ltd., "Loading Explosives in Large Diameter Up-holes", *Downline*, Issue No. 7, July 1988

CHAPTER 20

Blasting in Coal Mines

Restricted Choice of Explosive

The possible occurrence in underground coal mines of highly inflammable mixtures of methane and air and explosible dusts has led to special statutory requirements for explosives for use in such mines.

Permissible (permitted) explosives are designed for use in underground coal mines to avoid methane or coal dust explosions. In order to meet the exacting demands of the U.S. Mining Safety and Health Administration (MSHA) and of the Health and Safety Executive of the Department of Trade and Industry in the U.K. (and of authorities in other countries), they must be manufactured within especially close tolerances.

But it should be noted that in some countries in Central Europe, permitted explosives are rated in three levels of protection from methane and coal-dust explosions, depending on the relative risks involved. Most of these explosives are in powder (granular) form.

The main characteristics of a "permissible" explosive are that, when detonated, it must produce a flame

(a) of relatively low temperature,

(b) of small volume, and

(c) of short duration.

Permissible explosives differ then from ordinary high explosives in that they contain an appreciable proportion of one or more constituents whose function is to lower the temperature of the explosion. This has been achieved by the increased use of ammonium nitrate instead of NG; and by the addition of a cooling agent (or flame depressant), such as sodium chloride.

Brand names of currently approved explosives are shown below. The continued permissibility of specific lots of brand names in the USA are contingent upon the following requirements [1]:

(1) The explosive shall conform with the basic specifications, within limits of tolerance prescribed by MSHA; the cartridges must be of diameters that have been approved.

(2) The explosive shall be stored in surface magazines under conditions that help maintain the original product character; it must be used within 48 hours after being taken underground.

(3) The explosive shall remain in its original cartridge wrapper throughout storage and use, without admixture of other substances.

(4) The explosive shall be initiated with a copper or copper-based alloy shell commercial electric detonator (not cap and fuse) of not less than No. 6 strength.

(5) The polyethylene tubular-packaged water gel or emulsion permissible explosive shall be handled under the same requirements existing for nitroglycerine-sensitized permissible explosives regardless of the additional safety aspects. Excessive exudation of the water-gel ingredients through broken polyethylene tubes or cartridges must be treated as deteriorated explosives.

(6) In all other respects, the explosive shall be used in conformance with all the provisions of the Federal Coal Mine Health and Safety Act of 1969.

Within the ICI Explosives Group, a "permitted" explosive is one approved by the U.K. Health and Safety Executive (HSE) for use in coal mines. In Canada, permitted explosives are used in a specified manner, as set out below [3].

1. The explosive must be in good condition.

2. The size of charge detonated in any shot-hole shall be within the specific charge limit for that particular explosive.

3. The charge shall be detonated by means of EB caps only; such caps shall be not less than of No. 6 strength.

4. Shot-holes which have a burden so heavy they are obviously liable to blow out, must not be charged.

5. Shot-holes must not be fired in the presence of a dangerous concentration of combustible gas or dust.

6. Shot-holes must not be fired until they have been properly stemmed with an adequate amount of non-combustible stemming.

7. Firing must be carried out only by means of a permitted type of blasting machine of adequate capacity.

The present classification adopted for permitted explosives in the U.K. (and some other countries) is designed for maximum safety. It is set out as below [3]:

Group P1	For undercut coal or for delay firing in shafts and tunnels, remote from sources of gas. Polar Ajax or Driftex is used.
Group P2	Explosives sheathed with sodium bicarbonate. Now obsolete.
Group P3	Previously known as "Equivalent to Sheathed". For cut coal and

rock rippings by single instantaneous or delays up to six shots. Use Unigel (gelatinous) or Aquespex.
Hydropruf (gelatinous, for pulsed infusion shotfiring).
Unigex A (semigelatinous).
Unipruf (powder).

Group P4   For rock rippings with delay firing. Use Carrifrax with Carrick short delay detonators.

Group P5   For delay balsting in coal (blasting off the solid). Use Dynagex or Dynafrax or Wincoal A with Carrick short delay detonators.

Group P4/P5   For both P4 and P5 conditions. Dynobel or Seamex is used.

A list of permitted explosives available from various manufacturers is given in Table 20.

Comparative detonation velocities of permissible explosives are shown in the table below.

Type	VOD Range (m/sec)
Granular	1700 – 3500
Gelatinous	3100 – 5500
CS Slurry	3200 – 3700
CS Emulsion	5000 – 5500

Coal Blasting

There are two methods of breaking coal with explosives:

1. **Blasting "off the solid" or "grunching"**: The first stage in blasting "off the solid" is to form a free face by using explosives; a series of horizontal holes angled into the face in the form of a fan cut is generally used (see Fig. 72). Where pillars are blasted, a free face already exists.

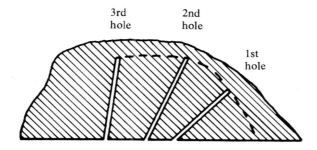

Fig. 72: Grunch blasting

Table 20: Permitted Explosives

Manufacturer (for code see Ch. 1)	Type of Explosive			
	Powder type	Gelatinous type	Slurries	Emulsions
AECI		Ajax Saxonite		
Atlas	Coalite	Gel Coalite Z		Atlas 7/D
Austin	Red Diamond	Red-D-Gel B		Coalmex 14E
BIQ			Tovex 300	
CIL	Monobel	CXL-ite		
DANTEX			Tovex 330 Tovex Dancoal	
DNAG	Wetter-Permit B	Wetter-Energit B Wetter-Carbonit C		
DNW	Wetter-Nobelit B			
DPW			Tovex 472	
DuPont			Tovex 300	
DYNO	Kullgrube-sprengstoff			Emulite 400
EBCW	Synthesit V18 Uhlometanit 26	Ostravit C		
ECP	Seamex (P4/5)	Driftex (P1) Aquespex (P3) Wincoal A (P5)		
ERT	Exp seg 12	Exp seg 9		
ETCAN			Tovex Breakrite	
ICIA	Dynobel (P4/5) Monobel Ajax	Morcol Dynagex		Super Ajax (P1)
IDL			Godyne (P1) Permadyne (P3) Pentadyne (P5) Monodyne (P1)	
IEL	Viking G	Ajax G Unisax G Alphagex Permigex Soligex Solimax		
IRECO	Collier C Red HA, HB	Irecogel A, B		Irecoal E
Nitro-Nobel				Emulite 400
NKC	AN Expl 5	TOKUUME Eq S Dynamite		Kayamite S
NOBEX	Unipruf (P3) Dynobel (P4/5) Polar Ajax (P1)	Hydropruf* Unigel (P3) Unigex A (P3) Dynagex (P5) Dynafrax*(P5) Carrifrax (P4)		
SMX				Permex 424 (P1)
TEL	Telperma 1, 5			
WASAG	Wetter-Westfalit C Roburit B Securit C Devinit A			

* for Pulsed Infusion Shotfiring, using Hydrostar detonators

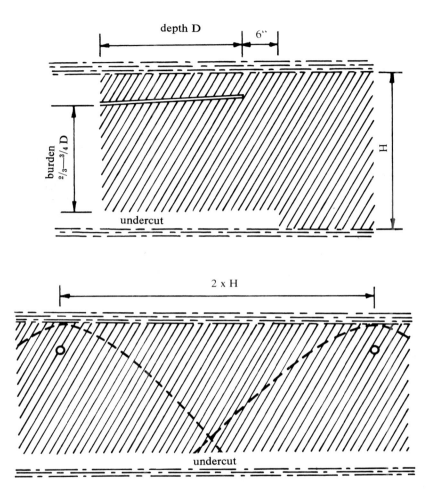

Fig. 73: Blasting a longwall face

2. **Blasting "cut coal"**: It is desirable to provide a free face for any shot; this is achieved by cutting. The normal cut or kerf is 125–150 mm wide and 1.3–3 m deep, and is placed either horizontally at floor level, or near the roof, or at some intermediate position. Vertical cuts are also used. The depth and position of the cut depend on the general mining conditions.

The position of shot-holes for blasting cut coal depends on:

(a) Thickness of the seam.

(b) Position of the cut.

(c) Presence of hard dirt bands.

(d) Type of parting with the roof.

(e) Cleat of the coal.

(f) Method of working.

Normally, seams up to 1.3 m in thickness can be blasted by one row of holes; in thicker seams, two rows may be required.

In seams containing hard bands of rock, additional holes may be necessary; these are placed near the band to fracture it without unduly shattering the coal.

Generally, two methods of working can be considered: (a) the longwall system, and (b) room-and-pillar. Examples of shot-hole placements are shown in Figs. 73–75. Fig. 73 shows the placement of holes on a longwall face in a 1.3 m thick seam, undercut to a depth of 1.6 m. In thicker seams, two rows of holes would probably be necessary. Fig. 74 shows how holes are placed in a room-and-pillar face four metres wide in a 1.6 m thick seam. In Fig. 75, the placement of holes is shown in a room-and-pillar face four metres wide, in a 1.6 m thick seam with a 10 cm "dirt" band. The centre hole is fired first, followed by the two top or two bottom holes.

Where thick coal seams (greater than about four metres) need to be mined by underground methods, as in India, difficult problems exist. Until recently, a multi-slicing room-and-pillar method was used, along with a stowage system. However, coal cannot always be fully extracted by this method.

A new semi-mechanized caving method, by drilling (with Jumbos) and blasting a fan of long holes in retreat along level galleries, is currently under test. The coal is to be loaded with LHD vehicles by remote control. Special relaxation of blasting regulations is involved [2].

Delay Firing

The advantages of delay firing in coal mining operations are now accepted. In addition to the practical advantages of better fragmentation, reduced ground vibration, and low explosive consumption, delay firing reduces the hazards from ejected fragments, from dust, and from falls of ground.

The exploitation of the advantages of delay firing in coal had been restricted due to the possibility of firing into a break or firing an open suspended shot in the presence of inflammable gas. The development of safer explosives has permitted the introduction of delay firing in coal.

Safe Charging Procedures

In breaking cut coal, several important points of procedure should be noted, whether for longwall or room-and-pillar workings, and independent of the position of the cut [3].

1. The cut (kerf) should be advantageously located.

2. Cuttings or duff should be removed from the kerf before firing.

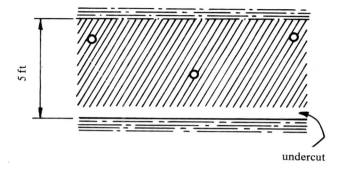

Fig. 74: Blasting in a room-and-pillar face

16″ top coal

24″ breast coal

4″ dirt band

16″ bottom coal

Fig. 75: Blasting in a room-and-pillar face with a dirt band

3. Shot holes should not extend to or beyond the rear end of the kerf, or behind the line of rib. Ample clearance should be allowed.

4. Holes should be drilled as nearly horizontal as possible.

5. Holes should be thoroughly cleaned out before charging.

6. Holes (and the face generally) should be closely examined for cracks or breaks. If noted, they should be reported to the supervisor.

7. Holes showing cracks or breaks should not be charged for firing.

8. Care should be taken not to overload nor undercharge a hole.

9. Non-incendive short delay copper shell type detonators should be used, along with a suitable type of permissible explosive charge.

10. Holes should not be charged if the methane concentration at the face exceeds one per cent.

11. Charges should be continuously loaded to the bottom of the hole with cartridge of the same type.

12. Allowable charge weights per hole should not be exceeded.

13. Adequate non-combustible stemming material should be used.

Substitutes for Explosives [4, 5, 6]

In order to avoid the potential hazard of methane/coal dust explosions, several non-explosive methods of breaking coal have been devised.

1. **High pressure gas cartridges** [5]: These depend upon the release of gas pressure from a steel tube capsule vented suddenly into a borehole.

Typical of these are Cardox and Airdox, as described in Chapter 10. Permissible models of Cardox blasting devices are listed periodically by MSHA, together with specified requirements for their employment in coal mines [1].

2. **High pressure water jet drilling** [6, 7]: This method should have wide acceptance in breaking coal, in that the coal is wetted and kept cool, dust is allayed at the source or formed as a suspension in water, and extraneous hazards are avoided (see Chapter 10).

Pulsed Infusion Shotfiring

The coal blasting technique called **pulsed infusion shotfiring** was developed in 1953. It consists of firing an explosive charge in a borehole filled with water under pressure, the water having been introduced through an infusion tube or lance, which also seals the hole. Water pressures of the order of 2800 kPa are used. The energy from the explosive is used more efficiently in pulsed infusion shotfiring than when blasting in the conventional manner.

A gelatinous explosive of high water-resistance is required [8]. There are two methods of applying pulsed infusion shotfiring:

1. Flanking holes applicable to longwall faces (both solid and undercut), and to room-and-pillar workings; and

2. Long-hole method – shot-holes up to 50 m long are drilled parallel to the face with a burden of one metre. The charge consists of a series of high velocity gelatine cartridges. Applications are in room-and-pillar workings, with holes bored from one end of a pillar to the other; and in longwall working, holes being bored parallel to the face.

Recent improvements by Schmidt, Kranz & Co. of Velbert, Germany, using both high and low pressure injection lances, provide virtually dust-free breaking of the coal [9].

References

[1] J. Ribovich, R. W. Watson and J. J. Seman, "Active List of Permissible Explosives and Blasting Devices Approved Before December 31, 1975", *Mining Enforcement and Safety Administration, I.R. 1046*, 1976

[2] "Explosives for Blasting Gallery Techniques in India", *Downline*, ICI Explosives International Pte. Ltd., Jan. 1989

[3] *Blaster's Handbook*, 6th ed. Canadian Industries Ltd., 1966

[4] B. Mohanty and P. McFarlane, "Water-jet Drilling and its Applications in Mining and Blasting", *Trans Instn Min. Metall.* (Sect. A), Vol. 95, April 1986

[5] R. E. Greenham and H. Stafford, "Recent American Developments No. 2. Shotfiring and its Alternatives in the United States of America", *Trans. I.M.E.*, Vol. 113, p. 814 (1953)

[6] D. A. Summers, "Water Jet Coal Mining Related to the Mining Environment", *University of Missouri-Rolla*, Conference on the Underground Mining Environment, October 1971

[7] "Water Jet Technology" (Exotech Inc., 1969)

[8] R. Haslam, S. H. Davidson and J. Hancock, "Development of a Combined Blasting/Water Infusion Technique for Coal Breaking", *Trans. I.M.E.*, Vol. 114, p. 87 (1954)

[9] "Pulsed Infusion Shotfiring on Coal Faces", *Mining Journal*, Nov. 26, 1982

CHAPTER 21

Explosives in Agriculture

Introduction

Explosives have a very definite place in agriculture, just as they have in mining, quarrying, and construction work. As a source of power, they enable the time-consuming and heavy work of clearing the land of trees, tree-stumps, and boulders to be done in a fraction of the time and at less cost than by hand methods. Swamp drainage, stream diversion, subsoiling, and tree planting are further operations in which explosives may be employed successfully.

In agricultural work, the quantity of explosives required for any particular operation may vary considerably according to local conditions; therefore the quantities mentioned should be regarded only as a guide, and more accurate determinations obtained by actual trials under prevailing conditions [1, 2, 3].

The chief uses of explosives in agriculture may be set out as follows:

Removal of Stumps and Trees

1. **General principles**: The method employed in the removal of stumps varies according to the age, size, and type of stump, nature of the soil, ground conditions, character of root system, and equipment available. All these factors must be taken into consideration when determining the best and most economical method of removing stumps by blasting.

The nature and condition of the soil is of considerable importance in stump blasting. The more resistance the soil offers to the force of the explosion, the greater will be the force exerted against the stump. Loose, sandy soil, which is dry, is far less efficient in this regard than firm, heavy, wet soil. Light sandy soils provide a ready escape for the explosive gases; therefore, it is always advisable to blast when the soil is wet. As a rule, charges should be placed deeper in light soils than in heavy soils.

Depending on the type of tree with its associated root system, the methods used to remove stumps may vary somewhat. However, the main requirement is to blast a conical cavity which encloses the main root system of the stump. Some trees have heavy tap roots, some lateral spreading roots, others have both. Methods of placing the explosive charge must be varied to suit the particular stump. In addition, green stumps have a large mass of fine tendril-like roots, and these normally require a heavier charge to dislodge them than dead stumps on which the tendril roots have decayed.

2. **Preparation of charges**: As a basis on which to carry out trial blasts, about one pound of ready-mixed AN/FO should be used for each 30 cm of stump diameter measured 30 cm above the ground surface where dead stumps are involved. With green stumps, it may be necessary to increase the charging ratio slightly. With standing trees, charges may have to be increased two or three times. The presence of sandy rather than clay soil also makes an increase in charge necessary (of the order of 50%).

The use of small plastic bags makes the placement of AN/FO more convenient. The required charge is placed in the plastic bag together with one-half of a cartridge of dynamite primed with a plain detonator and safety fuse, or an electric detonator. The plastic bag also serves to protect the soluble AN from any water which may be present in the hole.

Austin has prepared a special ammonia dynamite for removing stumps, subsoiling, tree planting and blasting frozen soil. It is referred to as "Stumping Powder", available in $1^1/4$ X 8 inch cartridges.

3. **Placing the charges**: A little experience on the part of the operator will soon allow rapid determination of the correct location for the charges. However, the following details will serve as a guide. Generally speaking, it is felt that the holes to accommodate the charges should be dug rather than drilled, as the charges can then be located as a whole rather than poured into place, and contamination with soil, which may cause loss of sensitivity, is avoided. A narrow spade is satisfactory as it makes digging between roots easier.

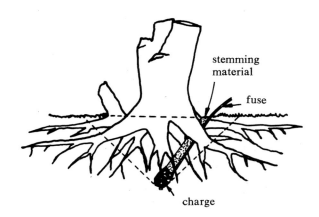

stemming material

fuse

charge

Fig. 76: Typical charge placement for small tree stumps

Small stumps up to about 60 cm in diameter with lateral spreading roots should normally be removed with one charge placed under the centre of the stump or as close to that position as possible. This is illustrated in Fig. 76.

However, it often happens that the roots are heavier on one side than the other, and in such cases the charge would be located towards the side with the heavier roots, as in Fig. 77.

Larger stumps with lateral spreading roots (Fig. 78) may require two or more charges, these normally being located under the heaviest roots.

Stumps with large tap roots may be removed by placing a large charge against the tap root at a depth of not less than 60 cm as illustrated in Fig. 79.

After the charge is in position, the soil or clay should be firmly replaced to provide maximum confinement.

Hollow stumps are dealt with as suggested in Fig. 80.

4.   **Methods of firing**: Where one charge only is to be fired under each stump, safety fuse may be used. However, if two or more charges under the stump are involved, it is

Fig. 77: Typical charge placement for tree stump with asymmetrical root pattern

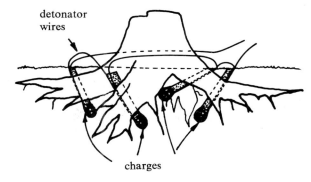

Fig. 78: Typical charge placement for large tree stumps with large lateral root system

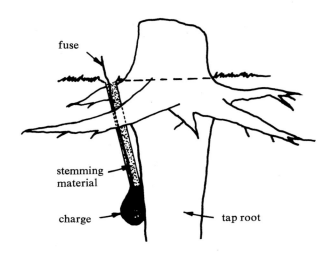

Fig. 79: Typical charge placement for tree stumps with large tap root

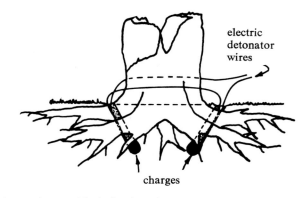

Fig. 80: Typical charge placement for hollow tree stumps

essential that they detonate simultaneously, and electric detonators or DC should be used. For electric firing, the EB caps are connected in series and fired with an exploder; while, to use DC, lines from the primer in each of the charges are connected to a main DC line by clove hitch joints. The DC main line is then initiated with a plain detonator and safety fuse. These methods are described in more detail in Chapters 7 and 8.

Breaking Boulders

Blasting is the quickest and usually the most economical method of breaking up boulders or rock ledges and reducing them to a size that can be handled more easily.

Three methods can be employed.

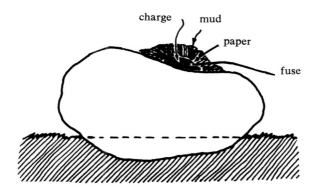

Fig. 81: Mudcapping a boulder

1. **Mudcapping** is used when no rock drilling equipment is available; it consists of placing a charge of dynamite, primed with safety fuse and detonator, in close contact with the rock and covering it completely with a liberal quantity of stiff damp clay, as illustrated in Fig. 81.

The charge should be placed at a point where it will perform most effectively, and this is usually on a flat or concave surface on the rock. It is important that the explosive is pressed down in close contact with the rock surface and all air excluded from the plaster; therefore it is often advantageous to put a thin layer of wet clay on the rock and bed the explosive in it.

Charges may vary from 0.3 to 0.6 kg/m^3 of rock, according to the type of rock to be broken.

2. **Snakeholing**: Where a boulder is almost buried beneath the surface, this method is used to lift it out of the ground and break it at the same time. It consists of making a hole under the boulder and placing a charge immediately below it, as in Fig. 82.

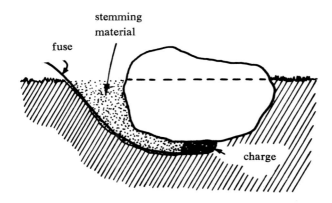

Fig. 82: Snakeholing a boulder

The charge should be calculated on a basis similar to the previous method.

3. **Blockholing** consists of drilling a hole 15 cm deep into a boulder, and charging it with 30 g of dynamite. Several holes, strategically placed, may be required with very large boulders.

Log Splitting

Probably the most economical method of splitting logs up to a metre in diameter is to use a "Log-splitting Gun", various types of which are on the market. Essentially, it consists of a solid mild steel cylinder 36–45 cm long, by 4 cm in diameter, tapering down in the last 15 cm to a diameter of slightly over 1.5 cm. At the tapered end is a 1.5 cm hole, about 20 cm long, into which, at the closed end, is drilled a touch hole for the safety fuse. The hole is filled to within 13 cm of the top with Blasting Powder (approximately 50 g); the tapered end of the gun is then driven into the end of the log for about 3–5 cm, and the charge of powder is touched off with the safety fuse. The log is split by the gases developed from the ignition of the Blasting Powder.

For logs over a metre in diameter and exceeding 1.6 m in length, it may be necessary to bore one or more holes into the side of the log and charge them with dynamite, AN/FO, or Blasting Powder. It is important that the depth of the holes should be almost two-thirds of the diameter in order to locate the charge near the centre of the log. Logs of one metre in diameter and 1.6 m long can be split in four sections with one 100 g charge, whereas a log 1.3 m in diameter and 4 m in length will require a total charge of 300 to 450 g spread over three equally spaced holes. The holes must be charged and stemmed in the usual manner.

In hard woods, the above method involves considerable labour in boring the holes unless a power drill is available.

Forestry Applications

For road building by the logging industry in forested areas, where there is a need to minimize environmental damage to plant life, CIL has designed the use of Magnafrac 1000P and 5000P.

Specially designed for blasting firebreaks in woodland terrain, with safe use in arboreal and underbrush conditions, a continuous length of a small diameter (1 to $1^1/_2$ inches) tough polylaminate water-containing slurry product is offered by IRECO. It is known as Fireline 6000, claimed to be relatively safe from accidental detonation from impact or burning.

A similar product, Tovex Firebreak, is available from ETCAN; also, Dynamite L and Logger's Choice II, for general logging applications.

Ditching and Draining

Ditches can be excavated in certain types of soil by blasting, but the practicability of this can only be determined by trial. As a general rule, it can be stated that blasting is most effective in moist or wet loam and in clay (providing it is not too sticky), whereas it is usually ineffective in sand and gravel, and in hard-packed dry earth.

There are two distinct methods of blasting ditches: by the propagation method, and by the electrical method. The former requires an explosive which is very sensitive to the propagation of a detonation wave, and can be used in wet loamy soils, while the latter can be employed in most soils except sand without the use of special explosives. Straight dynamite 50% (Ditching dynamite) is preferred for both methods.

1. **Propagation method**: In the propagation method, only one charge of explosive is primed with a detonator and safety fuse. When this is detonated, the detonation wave is transmitted through the moist soil to the adjoining charges along the line of ditch. The action takes place with great rapidity, so that the whole row of charges explodes practically simultaneously. The maximum distance through which propagation will take place between individual charges is dependent upon the characteristics of the soil and the size of the charges. In mud, a single row of 250 g charges, placed in vertical holes 45 cm deep, and spaced 45 cm apart, should provide a ditch approximately 1 m deep, and 2.5 m wide at the top. For wider ditches of the same depth, two or more rows of holes would be necessary. Where greater depth is desired, the holes must be made deeper and the charge quantity increased. For ditches over 2 m in depth, larger charges, spaced at considerable distance apart, and fired electrically, will prove more economical. Holes for the charges which are to be propagated should be made with a pinch bar or stick to a depth such that the top of the charge is not over 30 cm below the surface. The charges should be stemmed, either with water or soil, to obtain maximum efficiency. There is little hope of success for this method in a heavy, clayey soil, or in sand.

2. **Electrical method**: The electrical method of ditching must always be used when soil is insufficiently wet for the charges to propagate, and when an explosive sensitive to propagation is unavailable. With this method, each charge must be primed with an electric detonator; when charging is completed the detonators are connected in a series circuit and fired simultaneously by an exploder (see Fig. 18).

The depth of the holes, number of rows, weight of charge, and spacing will depend on the size and nature of ditch required, and should be determined by trial. For small ditches one metre in depth, holes 45 cm deep, spaced at 60 cm intervals, and charged with 250 g of dynamite should prove satisfactory.

The length of ditch that can be blasted at one time is limited by the capacity of the exploder.

Orchard Management

BIQ offers two products for the protection of orchard crops to avoid the effects of disastrous weather conditions: Anti-hail Rockets and Anti-frost Smoke.

Tree Planting

The use of explosives for tree planting has a two-fold purpose. Not only is the hole made, but the ground is loosened over an area considerably in excess of that which would have been affected by the spade. As in all soil blasting, the work must be done when the soil, especially clay soil, is dry. A vertical hole bored to a depth of one metre and charged with 100 to 250 g of explosive, well confined, should prove satisfactory.

Subsoiling

An impervious subsoil or hard pan may be treated with explosives with satisfactory results, but apart from this the practice commends itself to all agriculturists on account of its effect upon the soil at a depth many feet below that to which the plough can reach. Best results will be obtained when the ground is in a dry and friable state. When the ground is wet, the action of the explosive may cause compression of the surrounding soil, thereby aggravating its condition instead of effecting improvements.

The operation consists of boring holes to a depth of 60–90 cm at intervals of 4–7 m according to the hardness of the soil, and charging each hole with about 100 g of explosive primed with detonator and safety fuse. The stemming material should be tightly tamped to ensure the effective confinement of the charge. As in most agricultural blasting work, it is advisable to make test shots in order to determine the correct weight of charge, depth of hole, and spacing.

The procedure in detail is as follows:

Rows of holes equivalent to the number of operators are first prepared. These are then loaded and tamped, sufficient fuse being allotted to each hole to ensure the projection of several inches above the ground. When ready to fire, the operators, commencing at one end, and keeping in line, proceed along their respective rows lighting the fuses. In this way the operators are well in advance of the explosions, and in safety (Fig. 83).

Fig. 83: Subsoiling for orchard development

Digging Pole Holes

For loosening stiff clay, the surface soil is first removed and a hole punched to the desired depth with a driving bar. A light charge is then placed, stemmed and fired.

In surface rock across which fences or telephone lines or power lines are to be constructed, it is frequently necessary to blast the hole to receive the post or pole. The most difficult task is in drilling a hole to a little lower than the desired depth of the pole hole; especially where drilling equipment is unavailable. Such a hole may be charged with dynamite and well stemmed before firing with cap and fuse. The main objective is to loosen the rock for subsequent removal of the fragments by hand shovel. For deep holes, short holes are drilled and fired in stages, the rock particles being cleaned out after each stage of firing.

A new development is the Phillips PTR 101 Pole Hole Explosive which is a safe-to-handle pre-cast unit that can be fitted with a cap and set on the ground over the hole site. It acts like a simple form of shaped charge. It is more expensive than dynamite but saves considerable time and effort.

Well Sinking

The sinking of wells, for drinking water and for agricultural purposes, is practised in many countries.

For domestic water, wells are generally sunk from 2 to 6 m in diameter, up to 15 m or more deep, as necessary.

For agricultural purposes, for watering livestock or for limited irrigation of crops, they are generally twice the diameter. The depth, of course, depends on the elevation of the water table. It may vary, depending on seasonal factors.

In hard rock formations, the use of gelatinous dynamite is predicated. Generally, the cut holes are drilled (by hand) in a ring formation, inclined towards the centre. Outer rings (vertical) are drilled later. Holes are up to one metre in depth. Plain detonators and safety fuses are generally used.

A similar approach is made for the deepening of an existing well.

Note: The authorities in some countries may require that licences be obtained before mixing or using ammonium nitrate or any explosives for blasting. This should be discussed with the local Police Officer; or Inspector of Explosives or Inspector of Mines.

References

[1] *Explosives Bulletin* No. 5, Nobel (Australasia) Pty Ltd. October 1948

[2] *Blasters' Handbook*, 6th edn. Canadian Industries Ltd.

[3] "Agricultural Blasting", *Institute of Makers of Explosives*, Pub. No. 11, October 1986

CHAPTER 22

Laws Relating to Explosives

General

Persons handling and using explosive materials should realize at all times that they are not inherently absolutely safe; they are only statistically so, within broad limits of confidence. Therefore, the utmost caution should attend their use. In simple terms, explosives are dangerous but most explosives accidents could be prevented.

In handling, some types (e.g., blasting agents) are much less sensitive than dynamites. However, all are designed ideally to be relatively insensitive to handle and store when manufactured to close tolerances and inspection procedures; but to explode violently under controlled stimuli when put to use, with the release of tremendous units of energy within a mere fraction of a second.

Departures from this ideal design in the shape of substandard manufacturing performance; or with improper handling or prolonged storage under adverse conditions; or by inappropriate methods of use, can lead to various levels of calamity.

There are no specific restrictive laws governing the manufacture of explosives. With this class of product, the need for safety is paramount; manufacturers strive to preserve their reputations, and their urge to produce a reliable safe product, as members of the IME, transcends the profit motive. Any departure from a first-class standard of manufacture, inspection, distribution and service is likely to lead to expensive damage claims.

With explosives, unless mixed and incorporated properly, the mixed explosive may only be as safe as the properties of each separate ingredient.

However, some manufacturers offer no warranties and others issue disclaimers under certain conditions of use. Ethically, these policies cannot be recognized as avenues of escape from just penalties due to shortfalls from first-class standards of manufactured products.

The employment of explosives as an engineering tool has been referred to in Chapter 1; it has made a significant contribution to our standard of living by increasing the productivity of the rock breaking process, and by reducing its arduous nature.

However, if used incautiously, or with malicious intent, damage to property and personal injury (including loss of life) can readily result, either to the user, or to innocent bystanders. [Suffice it to say that any malicious use of explosives that results in personal injury or loss of human life should be regarded as a bestial offence. The perpetrator should surely forfeit all constitutional and other rights to be rated as a human being. It represents a degree of social irresponsibility that can only be expiated, in the interests of society, by capital punishment to provide a realistic deterrent].

For all the above reasons, it has become necessary to formulate laws and regulations prescribing acceptable methods of manufacture, transportation, storage, distribution and use. These will be dealt with serially, as below.

United States

1. **Manufacture**: In statutory terms, there are two aspects of manufacture of industrial explosive materials (other than sporting ammunition) in the United States:

(a) Manufacture of the complete range of explosives and accessories by established firms at their various factory sites, and

(b) the mixing of blasting agent components at or near the blast site by mining companies, quarry operators, contractors, or explosives manufacturers.

In either case, a licence is necessary under the provisions of Title XI, Regulation of Explosives, see below [1].

In order to manufacture "permissible" explosives, such products [2] must be tested and approved by MSHA.

2. **Storage**: This procedure normally occurs at several different stages between manufacture and use, e.g.:

(1) At the factory, awaiting distribution.

(2) At regional points, to give more effective local distribution.

(3) At dealers' depots.

(4) At mixing depots, in the case of contract mixing services, for blasting agents.

(5) At mines and quarries, and on contractors' premises.

(6) For underground mines, at suitable storage points.

(7) At docksides, for ocean and river transport.

Such storage depots are referred to as "magazines". Various regulations, referred to below, prescribe conditions of location, construction, maintenance, operation and surveillance. All must be licensed and/or are subject to periodic inspection. See IME Publication No. 1.

Various stages of transportation must necessarily occur between storage points.

Explosives magazines must not be located within certain prescribed distances of inhabited buildings, passenger railway stations, public highways, and of other magazines, according to the maximum weight of high explosives stored (see Appendix A).

Similarly, a facility for storing ammonium nitrate or blasting agents (or for mixing these components) must not be located within a limiting distance, as a receptor unit, of an explosive magazine (described as a donor) in case of sympathetic detonation from the latter (see Appendix B).

3. **Transportation**: Regulations covering the packaging and transportation of explosive materials by land are under the control of the Chief Inspector, Bureau of Explosives, which is a unit of the AAR U.S. Department of Transportation (DOT). Such regulations appear as CFR Title 49 [3]. (See IME Publications Nos. 14 and 17).

Similar regulations for sea transport and dockside storage are administered by the U.S. Coast Guard [4], and by the Civil Aeronautical Board, for air transport.

The DOT classifies explosive materials for transportation into:

Class A: Explosives, detonating or otherwise of maximum hazard; such as dynamite, NG, picric acid, lead azide, fulminate of mercury, black powder, blasting caps, and detonating primers.

Class B: Explosives possessing flammable hazard, such as propellant explosives.

Class C: Explosives of minimum hazard, such as detonating cord, boosters, safety fuse, fuse lighters, igniter cord.

Flammable
solids: Oxidizers, such as nitrates, AN prills, AN/FO.

However, these DOT classifications will be phased out by 1994/6 to conform with the United Nations Recommendations on the Transport of Dangerous Goods (see Appendix H):

4. **Use**: Commercial explosives are used in a variety of ways, such as in mines (surface and underground), quarries, construction jobs, farms etc. Its use in mines is governed federally by MSHA [5, 6, 7, 8] from the health and safety standpoint, and by state regulations, in many cases.

Various state and municipal authorities regulate explosive usage within the 50 states. There is no uniformity among these jurisdictions and there is insufficient space here to list their separate requirements. The particular authority holding jurisdiction within any city, county or state may be the Chief Inspector of Mines, the Chief of Police or the Chief of the Fire Department. Persons interested in using explosives should approach any of these officials (in the city concerned, or in the capital city of the state) for details and permits to use and blast.

The training, examination and certification of persons for blasting operations in surface coal mines is generally controlled by state regulations; or otherwise by the Federal Office of Surface Mining (OSM).

The National Fire Protection Association has issued a Code for the manufacture, transportation, storage, and use of explosives and blasting agents [9]. It incorporates the DOT Regulations in its chapter on transportation and the Internal Revenue Service (IRS) Regulations in its chapters on security and storage (see below). The Code is recommended for adoption as city and state regulations to promote safety and security in respect of explosive materials. The NFPA does not itself have any inspectorial or approving authority.

The Occupational Safety and Health Regulations of the Department of Labor also apply to the use of commercial explosives in the construction industry.

The Institute of Makers of Explosives (IME) issued its Publication No. 3 in 1985 [10]. Apart from a special section designed to establish close control over the unauthorized possession and use of explosives (anticipating new Federal laws for this purpose) it appears to follow closely the NFPA Code 495.

Both the above publications [9, 10] have included an appendix designed to guide legislation in state bills with the laudable aim of promoting some reasonable degree of uniformity in the control of explosive materials.

Public Law 91–452 became effective on February 12, 1971, as Title XI, Regulation of Explosives, of the "Organized Crime Control Act of 1970" [1].

Section 1101 of the U.S. Code Title 18 states that "The Congress hereby declares that the purpose of this title is to protect interstate and foreign commerce against interference and interruption by reducing the hazard to persons and property arising from misuse and unsafe or insecure storage of explosive materials."

Regulations under this Act were promulgated on January 15 and became effective on February 12, 1971 as CFR Title 26, Chapter I, Subchapter E, Part 181 "Commerce in Explosives" under the aegis of the Department of the Treasury, Bureau of Alcohol, Tobacco and Firearms (BATF).

Inter alia, the regulations are designed to cover:

The issue of licences to manufacturers, importers and dealers.

The issue of permits to users.

The conduct of business operations (relating to explosives distribution transactions).

The maintaining of records and reports (relating to explosives distribution transactions).

The location, construction, repair, control and inspection of storage facilities (magazines).

The expeditious reporting of thefts and losses.

Five different categories of magazines are set out, together with detailed specifications for the construction and operation of each.

Canada

The Canadian "Explosives Act", administered by the Department of Energy, Mines and Resources at Ottawa, through the Chief Inspector of Explosives, is a statute enacted in the interests of public safety. It controls the manufacture, authorization, sale, storage, importation and transportation by road of explosives, through a system of licences and permits. The licensing requirement for the manufacture of explosives includes on-site mixing [11].

All explosives must be submitted for authorization tests prior to manufacture or importation. Regulations specify the requirements for the transportation of explosives by road. Permits are required for road transport of quantities in excess of 2000 kg. The transport of explosives by rail is regulated by the Canadian Transport Commission in accordance with the "Regulations for the Transportation of Dangerous Commodities by Rail".

Explosives in Canada are divided into seven classes: gunpowder, nitrate mixtures, nitro-compounds, chlorate mixtures, fulminate, ammunition and fireworks, numbered from 1 to 7 in that order. However, these classes will be phased out by 1994/6 to conform with the United Nations Recommendations on the Transport of Dangerous Goods (see Appendix H).

Regulations specify the details of construction of and the licensing requirements for explosives storage magazines other than for military establishments [11, 12]. A Vendor's Magazine Licence is required for the sale of any quantity of explosives. A User's Magazine Licence is required for the storage, for private use, of 75 kg or 100 detonators. A licence is not required for the storage of lesser quantities for private use.

Detonators must be stored separately from other explosives. A detonator magazine must be at least 50 m from a dynamite magazine. Detonating cord must not be stored with detonators but in a dynamite magazine. Safety fuse is not to be stored with detonators [12]. Magazines must be located at minimum prescribed distances from railways, highways, points of public assembly, dwelling houses, shops, churches, and schools, in accordance with the Table of Safe Location Specifications (Appendix C).

Careful records should be kept of all receipts and issues of explosive materials, and of all sales transactions, including the name and address of each purchaser.

Explosives that have deteriorated are especially hazardous and must be carefully destroyed by experienced personnel according to methods laid down.

Permitted explosives only may be used in coal mines; they are tested and approved by MSHA or the U.K. Health and Safety Executive.

All members of the Royal Canadian Mounted Police are authorized to act as Deputy Inspectors of Explosives.

The actual usage of explosives is regulated by the various provincial authorities. Persons interested should contact these authorities for details.

Other Countries

(1)   Australia

In Australia, the use of explosives in mines is governed by the Mining Acts and the Mines Regulation Acts of each of the six states and the Northern Territory, under the authority of the Chief Inspector of Mines (or of Coal Mines) and/or the Chief Inspector of Explosives.

Permitted explosives as defined by the U.K. Coal Mines (Explosives) Regulations 1961 "shall be used in any coal mine that is not naturally damp and free from explosive gas".

The Standards Association of Australia has issued Australian Standard "SAA Explosives Code", Storage and Land Transport (AS 2187.1-1984) and Use of Explosives (AS 2187.2-1983), as rules governing the Use, Storage and Handling of Explosives [13].

These rules prescribe the essential requirements and precautions necessary for ensuring safety.

In an effort to improve the productivity of the Australian mining and quarrying industries through better control of blasting, the Australian Mineral Industry Research Association (AMIRA) has awarded continuing grants for Advanced Blasting Technology to the Julius Kruttschnitt Mining Research Centre (JKMRC) at the University of Queensland Experimental Mine.

(2)   New Zealand

The use of explosives in mines in New Zealand is controlled by the Mining (Safety) Regulations 1973 (sections 51-86) pursuant to the Mining Act 1971.

Similarly, the Coal Mines Regulations 1979 (as amended), under sections 219-234 (Explosives) relate to the Coal Mines Act 1925.

The Chief Inspector of Coal Mines is the responsible officer under the Mines Regulation Acts; and the Chief Inspector of Explosives under the Explosives Act 1957.

Permitted explosives, approved by the U.K. Health and Safety Executive, must be used in all coal mines where gas has been detected.

(3)   Ireland

The use of explosives in Ireland is controlled by the Quarries (Explosives) Regulations 1971 and by the Mines (Explosives) Regulations 1972.

(4)   Southern Africa

The African Explosives and Chemical Industries Ltd. (AECI) manufactures (at Modderfontein and Somerset West) and distributes blasting explosives throughout the various states constituting the southern part of Africa. Each of these different states has its own laws governing the use of explosives.

In the Republic of South Africa itself, where AECI is based, blasting certificates are granted by the Inspectors of Mines (under the Mines and Works Act), and by the Chief Inspector of Explosives under the authority of the Explosives Act and Regulations.

Purchase and transport of explosives is subject to the authority of the Chief Inspector of Explosives.

Testing of explosives and research is being conducted by the Mining Operations Laboratories of the South African Chamber of Mines.

(5)   Sweden

Swedish Regulations concerning explosives are covered by Blasting Instructions No. 3 (and other pertinent Instructions Nos. 32, 33, 56 and 67) of the Swedish Board of Occupational Safety and Health, operating under the Swedish Labour Welfare Act. Research is carried out by the Swedish Detonic Research Foundation.

(6)   Japan

Explosives research is carried out at the Nippon Kayaku Co. Ltd. laboratory at Asa.

(7)   Germany

Blasting and other aspects of mining research are carried out at the Steinkohlenberg-bauverein at Essen. There is also a French-German research partnership operating at the Deutsch-Französiches Forschungsinstitut Saint Louis.

(8)   India

The official testing authority for permitted explosives is the Central Mining Research Station (CMRS) at Dhanbad.

(9)   France

In France, explosives are approved by the Department of Industry, based on recommendations of the Explosives Substances Bureau, after testing by the National Laboratory of Mining Research (CERCHAR).

(10) United Kingdom

The law applying to the use of explosives underground in coal mines is covered by the Coal Mines (Explosives) Regulations 1961; but these are presently under review.

The relevant regulations for metalliferous mines are the Miscellaneous Mines (Explosives) Regulations 1959, also under review.

The storage, handling and use of explosives in quarries (including surface metalliferous and coal mines) is governed by the Quarries (Explosives) Regulations 1988 [14].

Otherwise, HM Mines Inspectorate (a Division of the Health and Safety Executive Organization) controls the licensing for sale and security in transport, storage, labelling and packaging of explosives, in accordance with UN requirements. It also enforces the law on manufacture, storage and conveyance of commercial explosives.

The use of permitted explosives in mines is subject to the approval of HSE, after tests at the Research and Laboratory Division at Buxton, based on recommendations by HM Inspectorate of Mines. British Standard BS5609 refers to the use of permitted explosives in the construction industry.

The disposal and destruction of explosive waste material and the decontamination of plant and buildings is controlled by the HSE.

The latest available Recommended Safe Distance from magazines containing high explosives to inhabited buildings is given in Appendix E.

(11) Venezuela

In Venezuela, the importation, storage, transport and use of explosives in mines is subject to the Law on Arms and Explosives, to the Mining Laws and Regulations, and to the Laws and Ordinances of the police.

(12) Elsewhere

Rules for safe practices in the manufacture, storage, transportation and use of explosives are prescribed by the statutory authorities in every country where explosives are customarily used.

References

[1] Department of the Treasury, "Organized Crime Control Act of 1970", Title XI – Regulation of Explosives, Public Law 91–452, October 15, 1970 (and as amended)

[2] U.S. Code of Federal Regulations, CFR Title 30, Chapter 1, Subchapter C, Part 15, sec 15–18, Lists of permissible explosives, 1980 (and as amended)

[3] U.S. Dept of Transportation Regulations, CFR Title 49, Subtitle B, Chapter 1, Subchapter C (Hazard Materials Regulations) Part 173, Subpart C, sec 173.5087; Subpart E, sec 173.150–239, 1978 (and as amended)

[4] U.S. Coast Guard Regulations, CFR Title 33, Parts 6 and 126, CFR Title 46, Subchapter N, Parts 146–147

[5] U.S. CFR Title 30 (Mandatory Safety Standards, Underground Coal Mines), Chapter 1, Subchapter 0, Part 75, Subpart N (Blasting and Explosives), sec 75.1300-1308. July 1980 (and as amended)

[6] U.S. CFR Title 30, (Health and Safety Standards, Metal and Non-metallic Open Pit Mines) Chapter 1, Part 55, sec 55.6–I to 200, July 1980 (and as amended)

[7] U.S. CFR Title 30 (Health and Safety Standards – Sand, Gravel, and Crushed Stone Operations), Chap. 1, Part 56, sec 56.6–1 to 250, July 1980 (and as amended)

[8] U.S. CFR Title 30 (Health and Safety Standards – Metal and Non-metallic Underground Mines), Chap. 1, Part 57, sec 57.6–1 to 250, July 1980 (and as amended)

[9] National Fire Protection Association, "Code for the Manufacture, Transportation, Storage and Use of Explosives and Blasting Agents", No. 495, 1985

[10] Institute of Makers of Explosives, "Suggested Code of Regulations for the Manufacture, Transportation, Storage, Possession and Use of Explosive Materials", Pub. No. 3, Jan 1985

[11] Department of Energy, Mines and Resources, Canada, "Explosives Act and Regulations (as amended)" 1980

[12] Department of Energy, Mines and Resources, Canada, "Storage, Possession, Transportation, Destruction and Sale", 1979

[13] Standards Association of Australia, "SAA Explosives Code", AS 2187.1-1984, AS 2187.2-1983, and DR91249-1991

[14] Approved Code of Practice, "Explosives at Quarries", COP 27, (ISBN 0-11-885462-3), London: HMSO

APPENDICES

Appendix A: Safe Location Specifications for Storage of Explosives (USA) (American Table of Distances for Storage of Explosives as revised and approved by the Institute of Makers of Explosives – June 1991)

Quantity of Explosive Materials [1, 2, 3, 4]		Inhabited Buildings [9]		Public Highways with Traffic Volumes of less than 3000 Vehicles/Day [11]		Passenger Railways – Public Highways with Traffic Volumes of more than 3,000 Vehicles/Day [10, 11]		Separation of Magazines [12]	
Pounds over	Pounds not over	Barricaded [6, 7, 8]	Unbarricaded	Barricaded [6, 7, 8]	Unbarricaded	Barricaded [6, 7, 8]	Unbarricaded	Barricaded [6, 7, 8]	Unbarricaded
2	5	70	140	30	60	51	102	6	12
5	10	90	180	35	70	64	128	8	16
10	20	110	220	45	90	81	162	10	20
20	30	125	250	50	100	93	186	11	22
30	40	140	280	55	110	103	206	12	24
40	50	150	300	60	120	110	220	14	28
50	75	170	340	70	140	127	254	15	30
75	100	190	380	75	150	139	278	16	32
100	125	200	400	80	160	150	300	18	36
125	150	215	430	85	170	159	318	19	38
150	200	235	470	95	190	175	350	21	42
200	250	255	510	105	210	189	378	23	46
250	300	270	540	110	220	201	402	24	48
300	400	295	590	120	240	221	442	27	54
400	500	320	640	130	260	238	476	29	58
500	600	340	680	135	270	253	506	31	62
600	700	355	710	145	290	266	532	32	64
700	800	375	750	150	300	278	556	33	66
800	900	390	780	155	310	289	578	35	70
900	1,000	400	800	160	320	300	600	36	72
1,000	1,200	425	850	165	330	318	636	39	78
1,200	1,400	450	900	170	340	336	672	41	82
1,400	1,600	470	940	175	350	351	702	43	86
1,600	1,800	490	980	180	360	366	732	44	88
1,800	2,000	505	1,010	185	370	378	756	45	90
2,000	2,500	545	1,090	190	380	408	816	49	98
2,500	3,000	580	1,160	195	390	432	864	52	104
3,000	4,000	635	1,270	210	420	474	948	58	116
4,000	5,000	685	1,370	225	450	513	1,026	61	122
5,000	6,000	730	1,460	235	470	546	1,092	65	130
6,000	7,000	770	1,540	245	490	573	1,146	68	136
7,000	8,000	800	1,600	250	500	600	1,200	72	144

Distances in feet

Quantity of Explosive Materials [1, 2, 3, 4]	Distances in feet							
8,000								
9,000	835	1,670	255	510	624	1,248	75	150
10,000	865	1,730	260	520	645	1,290	78	156
12,000	875	1,750	270	540	687	1,374	82	164
14,000	885	1,770	275	550	723	1,446	87	174
16,000	900	1,800	280	560	756	1,512	90	180
18,000	940	1,880	285	570	786	1,572	94	188
20,000	975	1,950	290	580	813	1,626	98	196
25,000	1,055	2,000	315	630	876	1,752	105	210
30,000	1,130	2,000	340	680	933	1,866	112	224
35,000	1,205	2,000	360	720	981	1,962	119	238
40,000	1,275	2,000	380	760	1,026	2,000	124	248
45,000	1,340	2,000	400	800	1,068	2,000	129	258
50,000	1,400	2,000	420	840	1,104	2,000	135	270
55,000	1,460	2,000	440	880	1,140	2,000	140	280
60,000	1,515	2,000	455	910	1,173	2,000	145	290
65,000	1,565	2,000	470	940	1,206	2,000	150	300
70,000	1,610	2,000	485	970	1,236	2,000	155	310
75,000	1,655	2,000	500	1,000	1,263	2,000	160	320
80,000	1,695	2,000	510	1,020	1,293	2,000	165	330
85,000	1,730	2,000	520	1,040	1,317	2,000	170	340
90,000	1,760	2,000	530	1,060	1,344	2,000	175	350
95,000	1,790	2,000	540	1,080	1,368	2,000	180	360
100,000	1,815	2,000	545	1,090	1,392	2,000	185	370
110,000	1,835	2,000	550	1,100	1,437	2,000	195	390
120,000	1,855	2,000	555	1,110	1,479	2,000	205	410
130,000	1,875	2,000	560	1,120	1,521	2,000	215	430
140,000	1,890	2,000	565	1,130	1,557	2,000	225	450
150,000	1,900	2,000	570	1,140	1,593	2,000	235	470
160,000	1,935	2,000	580	1,160	1,629	2,000	245	490
170,000	1,965	2,000	590	1,180	1,662	2,000	255	510
180,000	1,990	2,000	600	1,200	1,695	2,000	265	530
190,000	2,010	2,000	605	1,210	1,725	2,000	275	550
200,000	2,030	2,010	610	1,220	1,755	2,000	285	570
210,000	2,055	2,030	620	1,240	1,782	2,000	295	590
230,000	2,100	2,055	635	1,270	1,836	2,000	315	630
250,000	2,155	2,100	650	1,300	1,890	2,000	335	670
275,000	2,215	2,155	670	1,340	1,950	2,000	360	720
300,000	2,275	2,275	690	1,380	2,000	2,000	385	770

Numbers in [ ] refer to explanatory notes

Explanatory Notes Essential to the Application of the American Table of Distances for Storage of Explosives

Note 1 – "Explosive materials" means explosives, blasting agents, and detonators.

Note 2 – "Explosives" means any chemical compound, mixture, or device, the primary or common purpose of which is to function by explosion. A list of explosives determined to be within the coverage of "18 U.S.C. Chapter 40, Importation, Manufacture, Distribution and Storage of Explosive Materials" is issued at least annually by the Director of the Bureau of Alcohol, Tobacco and Firearms of the Department of Treasury.

For quantity and distance purposes, detonating cord of 50 gr/ft should be calculated as equivalent to 8 lbs of high explosives per 1000 ft. Heavier core loads should be rated proportionately.

Note 3 – "Blasting agents" means any material or mixture, consisting of fuel and oxidizer, intended for blasting, not otherwise defined as an explosive, provided that the finished product, as mixed for use or shipment, cannot be detonated by means of a number 8 test blasting cap when unconfined.

Note 4 – "Detonator" means any device containing a detonating charge used for initiating detonation. A detonator may not contain more than 10 g of total explosives by weight, excluding ignition or delay charges. The term includes, but is not limited to, electric blasting caps of instantaneous and delay types, blasting caps for use with safety fuses, detonating cord delay connectors, and non-electric instantaneous and delay blasting caps which use detonating cord, shock tube, or any other replacement for electric leg wires. All types of detonators in strengths through No. 8 cap should be rated at $1^1/2$ lbs of explosives per 1000 caps. For strengths higher than No. 8 cap, consult the manufacturer.

Note 5 – "Magazine" means any building or structure, other than an explosives manufacturing building, used for the permanent storage of explosive materials.

Note 6 – "Natural Barricade" means natural features of the ground, such as hills, or timber of sufficient density that the surrounding exposures which require protection cannot be seen from the magazine when the trees are bare of leaves.

Note 7 – "Artificial Barricade" means an artificial mound or revetted wall of earth of a minimum thickness of three feet.

Note 8 – "Barricaded" means the effective screening of a building containing explosive materials from the magazine or other building, railway, or highway by a natural or an artificial barrier. A straight line from the top of any sidewall of the building containing explosive materials to the eave line of any magazine or other building or to a point twelve feet above the centre of a railway or highway shall pass through such a barrier.

Note 9 – "Inhabited Building" means a building regularly occupied in whole or in part as a habitation for human beings, or any church, schoolhouse, railroad station, store, or other structure where people are accustomed to assemble, except any building or structure occupied in connection with the manufacture, transportation, storage or use of explosives.

Note 10 – "Railway" means any steam, electric, or other railroad or railway which carries passengers for hire.

Note 11 – "Highway" means any public street, public alley, or public road.

Note 12 – When two or more storage magazines are located on the same property, each magazine must comply with the minimum distances specified from inhabited buildings, railways, and highways, and, in addition, they should be separated from each other by not less than the distances shown for "Separation of Magazines," except that the quantity of explosives contained in cap magazines shall govern in regard to the spacing of said cap magazines from magazines containing other explosives. If any two or more magazines are separated from each other by less than the specified "Separation of Magazines" distances, then such two or more magazines, as a group, must be considered as one magazine, and the total quantity of explosives stored in such group must be treated as if stored in a single magazine located on the site of any magazine of the group, and must comply with the minimum of distances specified from other magazines, inhabited buildings, railways, and highways.

Note 13 – Storage in excess of 300,000 lbs of explosives in one magazine is generally not required for commercial enterprises.

Note 14 – This Table applies only to the manufacture and permanent storage of commercial explosives. It is not applicable to transportation of explosives or any handling or temporary storage necessary or incident thereto. It is not intended to apply to bombs, projectiles, or other heavily encased explosives.

Note 15 – When a manufacturing building on an explosive materials plant site is designed to contain explosive materials, such building shall be located from inhabited buildings, public highways and passenger railways in accordance with the American Table of Distances based on the maximum quantity of explosive materials permitted to be in the building at one time.

Appendix B: Safe Location Specifications for Storage of Blasting Agent Materials (USA) – Table of recommended Separation Distances of Ammonium Nitrate and Blasting Agents from Explosives or Blasting Agents [1, 6]

Donor Weight		Minimum Separation Distance of Acceptor when Barricaded [2] (ft)		
Pounds Over	Pounds Not Over	Ammonium Nitrate [3]	Blasting Agent [4]	Minimum Thickness of Artificial Barricades [5] (in)
	100	3	11	12
100	300	4	14	12
300	600	5	18	12
600	1,000	6	22	12
1,000	1,600	7	25	12
1,600	2,00	8˙	29	12
2,000	3,000	9	32	15
3,000	4,000	10	36	15
4,000	6,000	11	40	15
6,000	8,000	12	43	20
8,000	10,000	13	47	20
10,000	12,000	14	50	20
12,000	16,000	15	54	25
16,000	20,000	16	58	25
20,000	25,000	18	65	25
25,000	30,000	19	68	30
30,000	35,000	20	72	30
35,000	40,000	21	76	30
40,000	45,000	22	79	35
45,000	50,000	23	83	35
50,000	55,000	24	86	35
55,000	60,000	25	90	35
60,000	70,000	26	94	40
70,000	80,000	28	101	40
80,000	90,000	30	108	40
90,000	100,000	32	115	40
100,000	120,000	34	122	50
120,000	140,000	37	133	50
140,000	160,000	40	144	50
160,000	180,000	44	158	50
180,000	200,000	48	173	50
200,000	220,000	52	187	60
220,000	250,000	56	202	60
250,000	275,000	60	216	60
275,000	300,000	64	230	60

Notes to Table of Recommended Separation Distances of Ammonium Nitrate and Blasting Agents from Explosives or Blasting Agents

Note 1 – Recommended separation distances to prevent explosion of ammonium nitrate and ammonium nitrate-based blasting agents by propagation from nearby stores of high explosives or blasting agents referred to in the Table as the "donor." Ammonium nitrate, by itself, is not considered to be a donor when applying this Table. Ammonium nitrate, ammonium nitrate-fuel oil, or combinations thereof are acceptors. If stores of ammonium nitrate are located within the sympathetic detonation distance of explosives or blasting agents, one-half the mass of the ammonium nitrate should be included in the mass of the donor.

Note 2 – When the ammonium nitrate and/or blasting agent is not barricaded, the distances shown in the Table shall be multiplied by six. These distances allow for the possibility of high velocity metal fragments from mixers, hoppers, truck bodies, sheet metal structures, metal containers, and the like which may enclose the "donor." Where storage is in bullet-resistant magazines [1] recommended for explosives or where the storage is protected by a bullet-resistant wall, distances and barricade thicknesses in excess of those prescribed in the American Table of Distances are not required.

Note 3 – The distances in the Table apply to ammonium nitrate that passes the insensitivity test prescribed in the definition of ammonium nitrate fertilizer promulgated by the Fertilizer Institute [2]; and ammonium nitrate failing to pass said test shall be stored at separation distances determined by competent persons and approved by the authority having jurisdiction.

Note 4 – These distances apply to blasting agents which pass the insensitivity test prescribed in regulations of the U.S. Department of Transportation and the U.S. Department of the Treasury, Bureau of Alcohol, Tobacco and Firearms.

Note 5 – Earth, or sand dikes, or enclosures filled with the prescribed minimum thickness of earth or sand are acceptable artificial barricades. Natural barricades, such as hills or timber of sufficient density that the surrounding exposures which require protection cannot be seen from the "donor" when the trees are bare of leaves, are also acceptable.

Note 6 – For determining the distances to be maintained from inhabited buildings, passenger railways, and public highways, use the American Table of Distances for Storage of Explosives in Appendix A.

[1] For construction of bullet-resistant magazines see Bureau of Alcohol, Tobacco and Firearms, Department of the Treasury, Publication ATF P 5400.7 (6/90), *ATF Explosives Law and Regulations*

[2] Definition and Test Procedures for Ammonium Nitrate Fertilizer, Fertilizer Institute, November 1964.

Recommended Separation Distances of Ammonium Nitrate and Blasting Agents from Explosives or Blasting Agents

NFPA 495 – 1985

Chapter 1 Derivation of the Table

1–1 A test program sponsored by industry with cooperation of the Manufacturing Chemists' Association and the Institute of Makers of Explosives and conducted by the Bureau of Mines developed data on the relative sensitivity of ammonium nitrate (AN) and ammonium nitrate-fuel-oil (ANFO) to sympathetic detonation. These data were applied to the existing Table of Distances for Storage of Explosives to develop the following table of recommended separation distances for ammonium nitrate and blasting agents from stores of high explosives or blasting agents.

1–2 The American Table of Distances for barricaded storage of explosives has been proven adequate through the years, and no data were developed in the test programs that would suggest that this table should be modified for explosives. On the other hand, a factor of 2 has been suggested in the past for increasing the distances listed in the American Table of Distances when the magazines are unbarricaded. The results, employing two charge sizes of AN and one charge size of ANFO, gave ratios of unbarricaded distances of 4.2 to 7.4, for an average of about 6 which was taken as the appropriate factor, Thus, unbarricaded stores of AN or ANFO not in bullet-resistant magazines should have 6 times the separation distances as barricaded stores.

1–3 The relative sensitivity of AN and ANFO to dynamite was obtained by examining the relative K factors for 50% propagation distances when the cube root of the weight was employed in the usual equation:

$$S = KW^{1/3}$$

This equation allowed comparison of 1,600-pound dynamite acceptors with 5,400-pound AN and ANFO acceptors; results from these large charges are believed to be the most reliable available. The ratio K factors for dynamite and AN was 6.27 which was rounded to 6; the ratio for dynamite and ANFO was 1.6. These factors were applied to the American Table of Distances by thus reducing the distance for barricaded ammonium nitrate to $1/6$ the corresponding distance for explosives in the American Table of Distances and for ANFO to $6/10$.

1–4 One point should be emphasized; the distances in the table are for separation of stores only. No change should be made in the American Table of Distances with respect to inhabited buildings, passenger railways, and public highways, as the blast effect from ANFO is not importantly less than for high explosives, but the blast effect from AN is about one-half that from high explosives. The blast effect is little modified by the presence of barricades, but the American Table of Distances for the separation of stores from inhabited buildings, passenger railways, and public high ways for unbarricaded stores provides an additional safety factor and should be retained.

Appendix C: **Safe Location Specifications for Storage of Explosives (Canada)**
Quantity–Distance Table for Blasting Explosives – *Table Volume–Distance pour Explosifs Industriels*

Quantity of Blasting Explosives and Related Explosive Accessories *Volume d'explosifs industriels et accessoires explosifs*	Distance from: a) Highway, street and other road accessible to the public b) Railway c) Aerodrome and airfield d) Bank of navigable waterway including canals and recreational waters e) Park, play-ground, sportsfield and other open spaces of resort f) Work area	Distance de: a) Grande route, rue et voie publique b) Voie ferrée c) Champ d'aviation et aéroport d) Berge de voie navigable (y compris canaux et lieux de récréation) e) Parc, terrain de jeux, stade ou autre lieu public à découvert f) Lieu de travail	Distance from: a) Dwelling, living quarters b) Store, office and like buildings c) School, college or university d) Hospital and rest home e) Church and chapel f) Theatre, auditorium and other assembly buildings g) Factory, workshop, service station and garage h) Warehouse or storage area for flammable substances in bulk	Distance de: a) Demeures de habitations b) Magasin, bureau et immeuble du genre c) École, collège ou université d) Hôpital et maison de retraite e) Chapelle et église f) Théâtre, audi-torium et autres lieux publics g) Usine, atelier, stationservice et garage h) Entrepôt ou zone de stock de matières inflammables	Distance between traversed magazines Distance entre dépôts d'explosifs avec remblai ou tertre
1 Kilogr. Kilogr.	2 Metres Mètres		3 Metres Mètres		4 Metres Mètres
50	23		23		9
100	23		32		11
200	26		52		14
250	30		60		15
300	34		68		16
400	41		94		19
500	47		94		19
600	53		105		20
800	65		130		23
1,000	75		150		24
2,000	120		240		30
4,000	175		350		38
5,000	190		380		41
6,000	200		400		44
7,000	210		420		46
10,000	240		480		52
20,000	300		600		66
25,000	320		640		70
30,000	340		680		74
40,000	380		760		82
50,000	410		820		88
100,000	525		1,050		110
150,000	588		1,175		128

Appendix D: Safe Location Specifications for Storage of Explosives (Australia)
Australian Standard 2187.1–1984

Table 3.1: Minimum Safety Distance Between Explosives Storages and Minimum Mound Thickness for Ammonium Nitrate Storages

Net quantity of explosives (kg)	Minimum safety distance (m)					Minimum thickness of mound* for the separation of ammonium nitrate from explosives
	to other magazines		to process buildings	to ammonium nitrate storage		
	un-mounded	mounded	mounded	un-mounded	mounded	
50	20	10	18	7	5	0.3
100	24	12	22	7	5	0.3
200	28	14	27	9	5	0.3
300	34	17	31	11	5	0.3
400	38	19	33	12	5	0.3
500	40	20	36	13	5	0.3
1,000	50	25	57	16	5	0.4
1,500	56	28	73	18	5	0.4
2,000	62	31	86	20	5	0.4
2,500	66	33	97	22	5	0.4
3,000	70	35	107	23	5	0.5
4,000	76	38	123	25	5	0.5
5,000	82	41	135	27	5	0.5
7,500	96	48	159	31	6	0.6
10,000	104	52	177	34	6	0.6
15,000	118	59	205	39	7	0.8
20,000	132	66	226	42	7	0.9
25,000	142	71	243	45	8	0.9
30,000	150	75	260	49	9	1.0
40,000	164	82	286	54	9	1.0
50,000	178	89	308	58	10	1.2
75,000	196	101	340	73	13	1.2
100,000	214	109	375	102	17	1.5

Table 3.2:   Minimum Safety Distance Between Magazines and Protected Works

Net quantity of explosives (kg)	Minimum safety distance (m)			
	Protected work Class A mounded or unmounded	Protected work Class B		Aerodrome mounded or unmounded
		unmounded	mounded	
50	23	183	24	145
100	23	183	33	183
200	26	183	51	230
300	34	183	68	264
400	42	183	82	292
500	47	183	95	320
1,000	75	183	150	397
1,500	96	191	191	442
2,000	114	226	226	494
2,500	129	257	257	540
3,000	142	284	284	573
4,000	164	327	327	628
5,000	180	360	360	677
7,500	212	424	424	772
10,000	237	470	470	853
15,000	273	546	546	982
20,000	302	601	601	1082
25,000	321	650	650	1164
30,000	342	689	689	1235
40,000	381	762	762	1356
50,000	409	817	817	1448
75,000	470	940	940	1676
100,000	519	1034	1034	1829

Safety Distances

Distances between storages containing detonators and mounded magazines containing other blasting explosives: Storages containing detonators shall be separated from mounded magazines containing other blasting explosives by not less than the following distances as appropriate.

Maximum number of detonators	Distance to magazine (m)
2,000	2.0
5,000	3.0
10,000	3.5
20,000	4.5

Where more than 20,000 detonators are stored, the safety distance shall be determined on the basis of net explosive quantity in accordance with Table 3.1.

Where the magazine storage is unmounded, detonator storage shall be at a distance approved by the Regulatory Authority.

Distances between magazines: The minimum safety distance to be observed between magazines in the same occupancy or magazines and process buildings shall be set out in Table 3.1.

Distances between magazines and protected works: The minimum distance between a magazines and Class A or Class B protected work shall be as set out in Table 3.2.

For the purpose of this clause, the following places are included in Class A and Class B protected works:

a. **Class A:** Public street, road or thoroughfare, railway, navigable waterway, dock, wharf, pier or jetty, market place, public recreating and sports ground or other open place where the public are accustomed to assemble, open place of work in another occupancy, river-wall, seawall, reservoir, water main (above ground), radio or television transmitter, main electrical substation. Private road which is principal means of access to a church, chapel, college, school, hospital or factory.

b. **Class B:** Dwelling house, public building, church, chapel, college, school, hospital, theatre, cinema or other building or structure where the public are accustomed to assemble, shop, factory, warehouse, store, building in which any person is employed in any trade or business, depot for the keeping of flammable or dangerous goods, major dam.

Appendix E: Safe Location Specifications for Storage of Explosives (U.K.)
Abstract from Revised British Table of Distances

Amount of explosives to be allowed in the magazine (kg)	Distance from railway, public highway, canal or other navigable water, open place of resort where people may assemble (m)	Distance from railway, dwelling house, retail shop, church, school or other building where people may assemble (m)	Distance to mounded magazines containing explosives within an Enclosed Explosives Area (m)
270	34	68	17
454	48	96	20
2270	131	262	34
4540	185	370	42
9080	204	480	53
18,160	312	625	67
27,240	359	710	77
36,320	395	790	85
45,060	426	852	91
68,100	488	975	105
90,800	537	1074	115
113,500	579	1157	124
136,200	615	1229	132

Appendix F: Approximate Weight of Various Rock Materials

Material	Average Density	Solid (kg/m^3)	Broken (kg/m^3)
Andesite	2.60	2560	1830
Anorthosite	2.75	2700	1950
Basalt	3.00	3000	2100
Brucite	3.35	2300	1660
Coal-Bituminous	1.35	1360	970
Dolomite	2.85	2900	2060
Diabase	2.95	3000	2100
Diorite	2.85	2900	2060
Gabbro	2.95	3000	2100
Granite	2.65	2650	1900
Gypsum	2.80	2800	2000
Haematite	4.90	4900	3500
Limestone	2.65	2650	1900
Magnetite	5.10	5100	3660
Mica schist	2.70	2700	1950
Norite	2.85	2900	2060
Nepheline Syenite	2.60	2560	1830
Peridotite	3.20	3200	2300
Porphyry	2.55	2560	1830
Quartz	2.65	2650	1900
Quartzite	2.60	2560	1830
Rock Salt	2.35	2300	1600
Rhyolite	2.50	2500	1800
Sandstone	2.40	2400	1700
Shale	2.60	2560	1830
Siderite	3.45	3500	2500
Slate	2.65	2650	1900
Talc	2.70	2700	1950
Trap Rock	2.80	2800	2000

Appendix G: Typical Loading Density for Holes of Different Diameters
(kg of explosive per metre of blast hole)

Hole Diameter (mm)	(in)	Average Density											
		0.7	0.8	0.85	0.9	1.0	1.1	1.15	1.2	1.25	1.3	1.35	1.4
32	1¼	0.56	0.64	0.68	0.72	0.80	0.88	0.92	0.97	1.01	1.05	1.09	1.13
38	1½	0.79	0.91	0.96	1.02	1.13	1.25	1.30	1.36	1.42	1.47	1.52	1.59
45	1¾	1.11	1.27	1.35	1.43	1.59	1.75	1.83	1.91	1.99	2.07	2.15	2.23
51	2	1.43	1.63	1.74	1.84	2.04	2.25	2.35	2.45	2.55	2.66	2.76	2.86
57	2¼	1.79	2.04	2.17	2.30	2.55	2.81	2.93	3.06	3.19	3.32	3.44	3.57
64	2½	2.25	2.57	2.73	2.90	3.22	3.54	3.70	3.86	4.02	4.18	4.34	4.50
76	3	3.18	3.63	3.86	4.08	4.54	4.99	5.22	5.44	5.67	5.90	6.12	6.35
89	3½	4.35	4.98	5.29	5.60	6.22	6.84	7.15	7.47	7.78	8.09	8.40	8.71
102	4	5.72	6.54	6.95	7.35	8.17	8.99	9.40	9.81	10.21	10.62	11.03	11.44
108	4¼	6.41	7.33	7.79	8.24	9.16	10.08	10.54	10.99	11.45	11.91	12.37	12.83
114	4½	7.14	8.17	8.68	9.19	10.21	11.23	11.74	12.25	12.76	13.27	13.78	14.29
121	4¾	8.05	9.20	9.77	10.35	11.50	12.65	13.22	13.80	14.37	14.95	15.52	16.10
127	5	8.87	10.13	10.77	11.40	12.67	13.93	14.57	15.20	15.83	16.47	17.10	17.73
130	5⅛	9.29	10.62	11.28	11.95	13.27	14.60	15.26	15.93	16.59	17.26	17.92	18.58
152	6	12.70	14.52	15.42	16.33	18.15	19.96	20.87	21.78	22.68	23.59	24.50	25.40
159	6¼	13.90	15.88	16.88	17.87	19.86	21.84	22.93	23.83	24.82	25.81	26.81	27.80
165	6½	14.97	17.11	18.18	19.24	21.38	23.52	24.59	25.66	26.73	27.80	28.87	29.94
187	7⅜	19.23	21.97	23.34	24.72	27.46	30.21	31.58	32.96	34.33	35.70	37.08	38.45
203	8	22.66	25.89	27.51	29.13	32.37	35.60	37.22	38.84	40.46	42.08	43.69	45.31
210	8¼	24.25	27.71	29.44	31.17	34.64	38.10	39.83	41.56	43.30	45.03	46.76	48.49
229	9	28.83	32.95	35.01	37.07	41.19	45.31	47.37	49.42	51.48	53.54	55.60	57.66
251	9⅞	34.64	39.58	42.06	44.53	49.48	54.43	56.90	59.38	61.85	64.33	66.80	69.27
267	10½	39.19	44.79	47.59	50.39	55.99	61.59	64.39	67.19	69.99	72.79	75.59	78.39
270	10⅝	40.08	45.80	48.67	51.53	57.26	62.98	65.84	68.71	71.57	74.43	77.30	80.16
279	11	42.80	48.91	51.97	55.02	61.14	67.25	70.31	73.36	76.42	79.48	82.53	85.59
286	11¼	44.97	51.39	54.61	57.82	64.24	70.67	73.88	77.09	80.30	83.52	86.73	89.94
311	12¼	53.18	60.77	64.57	68.37	75.96	83.56	87.36	91.16	84.96	98.75	102.55	106.35
381	15	79.81	91.21	96.91	102.61	114.01	125.41	131.11	136.81	142.51	148.21	153.91	159.61
432	17	102.60	117.26	124.59	131.92	146.57	161.23	168.56	175.89	183.22	190.55	197.88	205.20

Appendix H: Comparative Classification of Commercial Explosives (as abridged), Based on Transportation Regulations

Types of Explosive Materials	USA Class	Canada Class	Classification code	United Nations Compatibility group	UN number
High Explosives *(cap sensitive)*					
Ammonium nitrate (AN)	A	3	1.1	D	0222
AN/FO blends	A	3	1.1	D	0082
Boosters	C	3	1.1	D	0042
			1.2	D	0283
CS Emulsions	A	3	1.1	D	0241
CS Slurries	A	3	1.1	D	0241
Demolition charges	A	5	1.1	D	0048
Explosive charges	A		1.1	D	0442
			1.2	D	0443
Fracturing devices, for oil wells	A		1.1	D	0099
Gelatines	A	3	1.1	D	0081
Jet perforating guns, for oil wells	A	3	1.1	D	0124
Lead azide	A	5	1.1	A	0129
Lead styphnate	A	5	1.1	A	0130
Mercury fulminate	A	5	1.1	A	0135
Nitro-cellulose (NC)	A	3	1.1	D	0340/1
Nitro-glycerine (NG)	A	3	1.1	D	0143
Nitro-starch (NS)	A	3	1.1	D	0146
Pentolite	C	3	1.1	D	0151
PETN	A	3	1.1	D	0151
Powders (NG type)	A	3	1:1	D	0081
Seismic	A	3	1.1	D	0081-3
Shaped charges	A	6	1.1	D	0059
			1.2	D	0439
Tri-nitro-toluene (TNT)	A	3	1.1	D	0209
Low Explosives					
Blasting powder	A	1	1.1	D	0027/8
Blasting Agents *(non-capsensitive)*					
AN/FO	Flamm-	2	1.5	D	0331
Emulsions	able	2	1.5	D	0332
Slurries	solids	2	1.5	D	0332
Initiating Explosives					
Detonating assemblies	A	6	1.1	B	0360
Detonating cord	C	6	1.1	D	0065
Detonating relays	A	6	1.1	B	0029
			1.4	B	0267
Detonators, non-electric	A	6	1.1	B	0029
			1.4	B	0267
			1.4	S	0455
Detonators, electric	A	6	1.1	B	0030
			1.4	B	0255
			1.4	S	0465
Fuse lighters	C	6	1.4	S	0131
Igniters	C	6	1.1	G	0121
Safety fuse	C	6	1.4	S	0105

Notes for Appendix H

(1) Five divisions of Class 1 (Explosives) are recognized

Division 1.1 covers substances and articles which have a mass explosion hazard.

Division 1.2 embraces those with a projection hazard but not a mass explosion hazard.

Division 1.3 is for those with either a fire hazard or either a minor blast hazard or minor projection hazard or both.

Division 1.4 covers those with no significant hazard.

Division 1.5 covers very insensitive substances or articles under normal conditions of transport.

Limited to the explosion of a single article.

(2) In addition to the above five divisions, according to type of hazard, there are twelve Compatibility Groupings (A to L, plus S). Only Groups A, B, D, and S are listed in Appendix H.

Among Groups A to K, packages of the same group and of the same division number may be transported together. Those of the same compatibility group but of different division numbers may be transported together, provided they are all treated as of the lowest division number.

Materials of group S may be transported with those of any other group except A.

(3) Appendix H shows a partial listing only. For full details, see UN publication "Transport of Dangerous Goods" latest edition. Class 1, Explosives. IBSN number: 92-1-139022-2.

Glossary of Terms

AN	—	Ammonium nitrate
AN/FO	—	A blasting agent consisting of AN and fuel oil
AN slurry	—	*See* Slurry
Aluminized	—	*See* Metallized
Back-break	—	Ground broken beyond the limits of the last or outer row of holes
Binary explosive	—	A 2-component explosive based on safe-to-handle compounds such as hydrazine or nitromethane, shipped separately and united at the site to form a high-energy explosive
Blasthole	—	*See* Borehole
Blasting agent	—	Any material or mixture consisting of a fuel (combustible) and oxidizer, intended for blasting, not otherwise classified as an explosive provided that the finished product, as mixed and packaged for shipment, cannot be detonated by a No. 8 test blasting cap
Blasting pattern	—	*See* Pattern
Blasting Powder	—	A low explosive consisting of potassium or sodium nitrate, charcoal and sulphur
Blistering	—	*See* Mud-capping
Blockholing	—	A method of breaking a boulder with explosives placed in a small borehole
Booster	—	An explosive of special character, generally used in small quantities to improve the performance of another explosive, the latter constituting the major portion of the charge. When it is armed with a detonator, it becomes a primer.
Borehole	—	A hole drilled into rock to accommodate an explosives charge for blasting (breaking) the rock

Bottom priming	—	A method in which the primer is placed near the bottom of the charge or hole
Brisance	—	The ability of an explosive to break (or shatter) rock by shock or impact, as distinct from gas pressure
Bulled hole	—	A shot-hole which has been bulled or chambered by exploding a light charge of high explosive in the bottom; a hole with a chamber at the bottom to accommodate a large quantity of explosive
Burden	—	The volume of rock which lies within the zone of influence of a charge of explosive; the volume of rock to be broken by any one hole or charge
Burden distance	—	The distance between the main body of a charge and the nearest free face
Butt	—	The remaining part of a hole after the charge has been fired; a hole which was not fully blown out; a bootleg. It is a likely place to find an unexploded charge and it is therefore dangerous to try to extend it by further drilling.
Cap	—	Detonator
Capped fuse	—	Safety fuse to which a plain detonator has been crimped
Cartridge	—	A preformed unit of high explosive wrapped to a predetermined diameter and length; a plug; stick of dynamite; a soft plastic stick of AN/FO, slurry or emulsion
Chapman-Jouget plane	—	The C-J plane may be described simply as that "point" along a confined cylindrical column of explosives at which the detonation shock wave reaction is complete; and from which point onwards a permanent steadystate reaction continues
Collar priming	—	A method in which the primer is placed near the top, or at the collar end of the charge
Cooling salt	—	Either sodium chloride or sodium carbonate incorporated in a high explosive to reduce the heat of the explosion as in permitted (permissible) explosives. A flame-depressant
Cordeau detonant	—	*See* Detonating cord
Coupling, degree of	—	The extent to which an explosives charge is in direct contact with the rock wall of the hole

Critical mass	—	Combustion, or burning, is a term usually employed to describe a reaction between a fuel and atmospheric air. This typically occurs when a small quantity of explosives burns.
		When a considerable quantity of explosives is burning, an adiabatic reaction may develop between the ingredients, reinforced by heat transferred from the gaseous products of the reaction.
		The threshold quantity of explosives so required to produce this second class of reaction is known as the "critical mass", which has a characteristic value for each explosive substance. In quantities above the critical mass, therefore, quiescently burning explosives may suddenly spontaneously explode.
		This propensity is particularly important to be aware of when destroying deteriorated or unwanted explosives by burning (see Chapter 11).
Cut	—	An artificial opening made in a face to provide a free face for blasting. It may be made mechanically as in coal mining or by explosives. *See also* Kerf
Demolition	—	The breaking up of artificial (man-made) structures by blasting.
Detonating cord (DC)	—	A strong flexible cord containing a core of detonating explosive, used primarily for initiating a series of charges. It explodes practically instantaneously throughout its length, when initiated with a detonator.
Detonating wave	—	The shock wave set up when a detonator is ignited
Detonator	—	A cap or capsule of sensitive explosive material used to initiate a charge of high explosives
"Dirt"	—	A band of stone or shale in a coal face
Emulsion	—	A blasting agent in which the AN is encapsulated by the fuel in an emulsion of water in oil
Fragmentation	—	The extent to which rock is broken up into small pieces by (primary) blasting
Gelatinous	—	Plastic. A property of those types of high explosive that can be pressed into different shapes, e.g., blasting gelatine, gelatine dynamite, etc. Gelatinous explosives are much more readily

		and efficiently placed or tamped in a hole without including pockets of air
Gunpowder	—	*See* Blasting Powder
HE	—	High explosive (cap-sensitive)
Hole	—	*See* Borehole
Ignite, to	—	The act of lighting; to set alight. A safety fuse is ignited by a flame. A plain detonator is ignited by safety fuse. An electric detonator is ignited by a current that fuses a fusible bridgehead embedded in a flashing mixture. Black powder is ignited by safety fuse.
Igniter cord (IC)	—	A cord filled with thermite for readily igniting a multiplicity of safety fuses in sequence
Initiate, to	—	The act of detonating a high explosive by means of a detonator or by detonating cord
Jumbo	—	A highly integrated, mobile drilling rig on which the drills are mounted on booms manoeuvred (usually) by hydraulic controls
Kerf	—	A cut made in a coal face by a hand pick or by a mechanical coal cutter to provide a free face for blasting
Kibble	—	Bucket in which broken ore or rock is hoisted from a winze
Leg (lead) wires	—	The wires connecting the electrodes of an electric detonator; the wires which are permanently attached to the electric detonator
Lifter	—	The bottom holes of a round pattern for a drift or tunnel heading
Metallized	—	In respect of blasting agents, sensitized or boostered with metal powders or granules (usually aluminium or ferrosilicon), to yield more energy
Misfire	—	A charge or part of a charge which for one of any number of reasons has not exploded. They are usually difficult and dangerous to resolve. Misfires must be treated with respect.
Mud-capping	—	A method of breaking a boulder with explosives without drilling a hole. The charge is set in a depression on the boulder and covered with a thick plaster of wet clay to confine it.
Muck	—	The broken ore or rock resulting from the firing of one or more charges

NG	—	Nitroglycerine
Overbreak control	—	A method of firing perimeter holes in such a way as to avoid intensive fracturing of a wall with the aim of preserving a regular outline (cushion blasting; pre-splitting)
Pattern	—	A dimensioned plan of holes to be drilled for blasting a face.
Permitted (Permissible)	—	A term signifying that a particular explosive has been approved as suitable for use in coal mines
Plastering	—	*See* Mud-capping
Plug	—	*See* Cartridge
Powder	—	A general term designating any commercial explosive, irrespective of type
Prills	—	Cellular sub-globular particles of AN formed by spraying concentrated AN solution against a stream of air
Primer	—	A cartridge of HE (or a prefabricated pre-cast "booster") incorporating a detonating device. This is the key element of a charge of explosives.
Pull, pulled	—	The quantity of rock excavated in a unit of advance in a heading, as by drilling and blasting a round
Ring drilling	—	A method of drilling a fan-shaped pattern of holes in a single plane from one drill rig position.
Round	—	The series of blastholes required to produce a unit of advance in a development heading or other face
Scram drift	—	An underground drift in which ore is transported (transferred) by drag scraper
Sequential firing	—	A system of firing in which the holes with least resistance are detonated progressively, thus reducing the burden on each subsequent hole in turn
Shot-hole	—	See Borehole
Slurry	—	An aqueous solution of AN sensitized with a combustible fuel (and thickened with a gelling agent at the point of charging).
SN	—	Sodium nitrate
Spacing	—	The linear distance between collars of shotholes bored approximately parallel to a free face

Standard AN/FO	—	A mixture of prilled AN (having a 1% inert coating) and 5.7% diesel fuel, resulting in a product whose density is 0.84 and which has an oxygen balance of –0.5%. The RWS and RBS value is deemed to be 100.
Stemming	—	Sandy clay material prepared and wrapped in cartridge form and used for sealing a blasthole after the charge has been placed
Stick	—	"Stick of powder"; plug, cartridge
Stope	—	The chamber or excavation from which ore is extracted underground
Strength	—	The explosive strength of unit weight (or volume) of a high explosive when compared with that of Blasting Gelatine in a ballistic mortar. In another sense, strength is expressed relative to that of "Standard AN/FO".
Strike	—	The direction along which a lode or vein intersects the surface
Tamping	—	The act of charging or tamping a charge into a hole, with the aid of a tamping stick. Sometimes used loosely for "stemming" (*q.v.*)
TNT	—	Trinitrotoluene
Top priming	—	*See* Collar priming
Toe	—	A remnant of rock left unbroken at the foot of a quarry face by an unsatisfactory blast (see Fig. 43).
USSS	—	United States Standard Sieve
VOD	—	Velocity of detonation, a measure of the rate at which the detonating wave travels through an explosive charge; the speed of detonation of a particular explosive

For additional items, see "Glossary of Commercial Explosives Industry Terms", IME Safety Publication No. 12 February 1991

Index

Sampling
in the Non-Ferrous Metals Industry
Concentrates and Recycled Commodities

by G. Kraft, Editor

1993, 248 pp, ISBN 0-78849-085-X,
sFr. 125.00 (worldwide); US$ 95.00 (USA & Canada only)

Contents:

Trans Tech Publications
Trans Tech House • CH-4714 Aedermannsdorf • Switzerland
Fax: +41 62 74 10 58